Mitchell®

AUTOMATIC TRANSMISSIONS AND TRANSAXLES

Fundamentals and Systems

THE MITCHELL AUTOMOTIVE TECHNOLOGY SERIES

Mitchell Automotive Electrical Systems

Mitchell Automotive Heating and Air Conditioning Systems

Mitchell Automotive Engines

Mitchell Automatic Transmissions and Transaxles

FORTHCOMING TITLES

Mitchell Autobody

Mitchell Automotive Braking Systems

Mitchell Automotive Fuel and Emission Systems

Mitchell Automotive Wheel, Steering, and Suspension Systems

OTHER TITLES FROM MITCHELL

Mitchell Automechanics

Orientation to the Auto Shop

Mitchell Automotive Technology Today

AUTOMATIC TRANSMISSIONS AND TRANSAXLES

Fundamentals and Systems

Mitchell International, Inc.

PRENTICE HALL, Englewood Cliffs, New Jersey 07632

Library of Congress Cataloging-in-Publication Data
Mitchell automatic transmissions and transaxles: fundamentals and
    systems / Mitchell International, Inc.
        p. cm. — (The Mitchell automotive technology series)
    Includes index.
    ISBN 0-13-587015-1
        1. Automobiles—Transmission devices, Automatic. 2. Automobiles—
Transmission devices, Automatic—Maintenance and repair.
    I. Mitchell International. II. Series.
    TL263.M57   1989
    629,2'446—dc19   88-38652
                                                                  CIP

Editorial/production supervision
    and page layout: PATRICK WALSH
Manufacturing Buyer: ROBERT ANDERSON

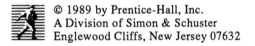 © 1989 by Prentice-Hall, Inc.
A Division of Simon & Schuster
Englewood Cliffs, New Jersey 07632

Printed in the United States of America

10 9 8 7 6 5 4 3 2 1

ISBN 0-13-587015-1

Prentice-Hall International (UK) Limited, *London*
Prentice-Hall of Australia Pty. Limited, *Sydney*
Prentice-Hall Canada, Inc., *Toronto*
Prentice-Hall Hispanoamericana, S.A., *Mexico*
Prentice-Hall of India Private Limited, *New Delhi*
Prentice-Hall of Japan, Inc., *Tokyo*
Simon & Schuster of Asia Pte. Ltd., *Singapore*
Editora Prentice-Hall do Brasil, Ltda., *Rio de Janeiro*

Contents

13 Chrysler Corporation

220

14 Foreign Manufacturers

234

15 Modification for Heavy-Duty Operation

256

16 Technical Manuals and Information

263

Preface

This volume in the *Mitchell Automotive Technology Series*, entitled *Automatic Transmissions and Transaxles: Fundamentals and Systems*, is designed for the beginning technical student in a community college. It covers both theory and application.

Automatic shifting, from the driver's point of view, has changed little since the late 1940s. However, since the inception of the early automatic transmission systems there have been many changes in the *Design*, *Application*, and *Location* of the various elements which make up the system.

This text is designed to be used in the classroom. A counterpart, *Automatic Transmissions and Transaxles: Student Training Manual*, exists for the shop portion of the course. The textbook tells how the automatic transmissions and transaxles work. The *Student Training Manual* shows how to repair specific transmission and transaxle makes and models.

This is a modern book using the latest technical information and employing the systems approach. The student should study the objectives for each chapter and when finished should review those objectives to check his or her knowledge.

Even if the student has some working familiarity with transmissions it is highly desirable that the material be studied in sequence to eliminate "holes" in his or her base of knowledge.

The text contains exercises and problems at the end of each chapter which are directly related to the material covered in the text.

Mitchell International, Inc., the publisher of the leading automotive reference material, the classic *Mitchell Manuals*, wishes you well in your study of automotive systems and welcomes your comments on its textbook material.

Acknowledgments

The following individuals and companies have worked together to complete this project:

Editor-in-Chief and Technical Writer

Curt Cowan

Contributing Mitchell Editors

Eric G. Back
David L. Skora

Art and Information Sources

Mitchell International, Inc., would like to thank the domestic and import automobile manufacturers and the aftermarket industry for their generous cooperation and assistance. This textbook would not be possible without their help.

Allied Aftermarket Division
American Motors Corporation
Buick Motor Division

Chrysler Motors Corporation
Ford Motor Company
General Motors Corporation
America Honda Motor Company, Inc.
Nissan Motor Corporation in USA
Oldsmobile Division
Subaru of America
Toyota Motor Sales, USA
Transgo
Volkswagen of America

Art was also provided by:

Mitchell International, Inc., *Mitchell Automechanics*, 1986, pp. 413, 419, 420, 421, 432, 438, 480, 481, 483, 490, 491, 493, 495. Reprinted by permission of Prentice Hall, Inc., Englewood Cliffs, New Jersey.

Brejcha, *Automatic Transmissions*, 1982, 2nd ed., pp. 150, 156, 157, 196, 215, 327. Reprinted by permission of Prentice Hall, Inc., Englewood Cliffs, New Jersey.

1

Introduction

POWER TRAIN

A **vehicle** is a self-propelled conveyance. Whether it is a sailboat, airplane, locomotive, or other surface conveyance, it has a power train.

A **power train** begins with a source of power and ends with delivery of power. The route that the power takes may be very simple, as it is with the sailboat—from sail to mast to hull and rudder—or it may be more complex. For example, a motor vehicle (Figure 1-1) requires an assembly in the power train that allows the source (engine) to deliver power (wheels) that most effectively meets various driving conditions, such as acceleration,

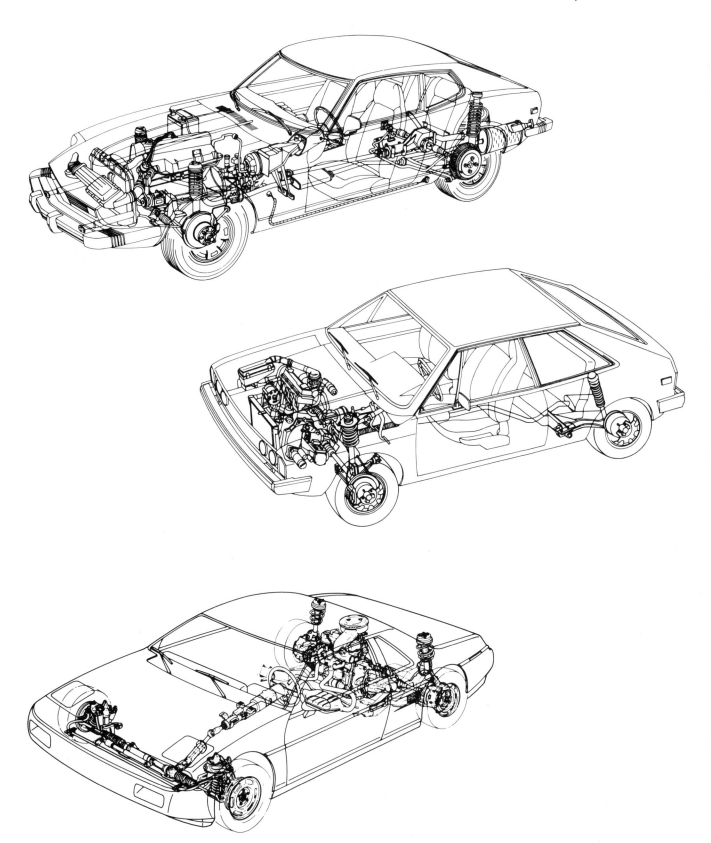

hill climbing, cruising, and change in direction of power delivery. This assembly—called a **transmission**—can affect the comparative speed of the engine and drive wheels as well as the amount of turning force (called *torque*) and the direction of rotation. It can be a manual transmission, which is completely controlled by the vehicle's driver, or it can be an automatic transmission, which requires virtually no driver control.

Also part of the power train is the *final drive*—a **gearset** (two or more gears working together) that reduces the speed of output rotation between the transmission and drive axles. Most automobiles cruise at 2000 to 3000 engine revolutions per minute (rpm), so if it were not for the speed reduction of the final drive, rear wheels would be turning well over 100 miles an hour at cruising speeds. Also, because of this speed difference, the amount of torque to the drive axles is increased by the final drive.

Transmission

A transmission assembly includes various rotating parts, such as gears and shafts, to carry the turning force of the engine. In an automatic transmission, these parts are connected together mechanically by levers, bands, and clutches that are controlled by direct mechanical linkage and hydraulic, electrical, or vacuum-operated devices. The entire transmission mechanism is contained in a case, or housing, that is bolted to the vehicle frame. The turning motion of the gears and shafts bear against the housing through bearings, bushings, and thrust washers to transmit engine power through the rest of the power train to the drive wheels.

Drive Wheels

Traditionally, motor vehicles—especially passenger cars and light trucks—have been driven by the rear wheels. And with a few exceptions, these **rear-wheel drive (RWD)** vehicles located the engine at the front, transmitting power through a transmission drive shaft and final drive gears to the rear wheels (Figure 1-2a).

Although not nearly as popular until recently, **front-wheel-drive (FWD)** vehicles have a long history, appearing in early race cars and passenger cars, both domestic (Oldsmobile Toronado, Cadillac El Dorado) and foreign (Saab, Renault, Subaru). In most cases, their transmissions were convention-

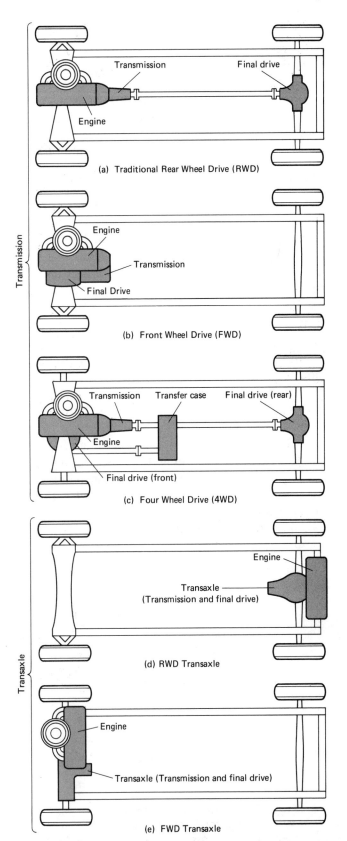

FIGURE 1-2 Power train configurations: (a) traditional rear-wheel drive; (b) front wheel drive (FWD); (c) four-wheel drive (4WD); (d) RWD transaxle; (e) FWD transaxle.

ally located behind the engine, with a change in output direction to reach front-wheel-drive gears accomplished by sprocket and chain or gears (Figure 1-2b).

Now, **four-wheel-drive (4WD)** passenger cars and light trucks, made popular by the World War II Jeep, also share the market. Most of these are part-time 4WD with full-time RWD, although there are now both domestic and foreign models with full-time 4WD (Figure 1-2c).

The **transaxle**, appearing in such foreign makes as Volkswagen (Figure 1-2d) and Morris, offer the best solution to the need for lightweight, fuel-efficient vehicles of various power train configurations. It combines the transmission and the final drive gears for the drive axles into a common housing, hence the name. Its most efficient configuration is with **transverse-mounted engines** (engines mounted sideways) because its rotating axis is then parallel to that of the drive axles and engine crankshaft (Figure 1-2e). Compared to other drive train configurations, this one requires less bulk and no change in direction of rotation, so it uses less power.

Some early automatics were two-speed units, but the three-speed automatic was dominant for many years. Now there are more and more four-speed transmissions and transaxles. Whether a transmission is two-, three-, or four-speed is determined by the number of *forward* speeds it has. A

quick look at the selector indicator (Figure 1-3) is all that is needed.

HISTORY AND DEVELOPMENT OF AUTOMATIC TRANSMISSIONS

Development of the automatic transmission dates back to the early 1930s, although the first true automatic (requiring no clutch) did not appear in production until 1939. But its history is rooted in the Ford Model T whose foot operated planetary gear (Chapter 3) transmission helped move over 15 million copies off the assembly line between 1908 and 1927. Other companies' developments also contributed: Chrysler's work with fluid drive (Chapter 4) and General Motor's development of the hydraulic control system and the torque converter (Chapter 6) are the most significant.

It was General Motor's Hydra-Matic Division, formerly the Detroit Transmission Division, that completed the first fully automatic production transmission in October 1939—six months after the division was formed. These transmissions were built for Oldsmobile. A year later Hydra-Matic was producing an average of 220 transmissions a day, and shipments to Cadillac began. Automatics were used in some military vehicles during the war years, and continued development led to the torque converter—an ingenious fluid drive coupling that transmitted negligible engine torque at low vehicle speeds, and produced a highly efficient hydraulic coupling at cruising speeds.

By 1950, all the major automobile manufacturers offered automatic transmissions, and it was not long thereafter that many models included automatics as standard equipment.

So we can say that the major elements of the automatic transmission—the *fluid coupling*, *planetary gears*, and *hydraulic control systems*—were established by the late 1940s. Since that time, engineers have made changes in the *design*, *application*, and *location* of these elements but no major changes or additions to them. There have been peripheral developments, such as computer-controlled shifting that appeared in the early 1980s, but automatic shifting, from the driver's point of view, has changed little since 1948.

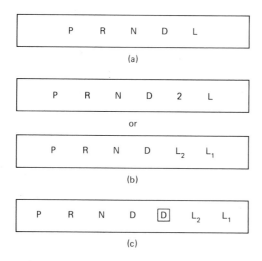

FIGURE 1-3 Automatic transmission gear selector indicators: (a) two speed; (b) three speed; (c) four speed.

LEARNING ABOUT AUTOMATIC TRANSMISSIONS

This book, *Automatic Transmissions and Transaxles: Fundamentals and Systems*, is designed for use in the classroom. Its counterpart, the *Automatic Transmissions and Transaxles: Training Manual*, is for the shop portion of the course. The fundamentals and systems book tells how the automatic transmission works, and the training manual shows how to repair specific transmission and transaxle makes and models. It presents much of the same information in the same manner as a professional shop manual does.

Automatic transmission courses are organized and taught differently from one school to another. Some may be two-semester courses; others only one. Some are limited to classroom sessions only; others hold shop sessions as well. Your school may use both books at the same time, the books may be used separately, or you may be asked to read chapters out of sequence. There are many ways to use textbooks and training materials. You will have no trouble adapting to the manner in which your instructor chooses to use these books and makes assignments as long as you become familiar with the books themselves.

Getting to Know This Book

You may already know something about automatic transmissions and transaxles through direct experience. If you do, it can be to your advantage only if you do not skip any parts of this book. Learning on a catch-as-catch-can basis is a long and uncertain process—it leaves "holes" in your knowledge. A textbook, such as this one, and a formal course of study and training are designed to cover the subject thoroughly so that one's knowledge can be as complete as possible.

Familiarize yourself with this book by thumbing through its pages. The more familiar you become with it, the better you will learn from it:

- Look at the table of contents. Read the chapter titles to see what and how information is presented. Read the major heads to get a better idea of what is in each chapter.

- Glance at the glossary and index at the back of the book; note how they are presented and think about how you can use them.
- Note the words in the text that are set in **boldface type**. They are important terms. They are set in bold type to indicate that their meaning is defined there or in the Glossary. They are also listed at the end of each chapter.
- Notice that the illustrations, charts, and tables are numbered. These are referenced by number in the text where they are discussed. Learn to use these numbers: In reading the text, look at the referenced illustration, chart, or table. Or, if you are looking first at the illustration, chart, or table, refer also to the text discussion where it is referenced; either way will give you the best and most complete information.
- Read through the objectives for each chapter to see what kinds of things you will be learning, and look at the end of each chapter for review.
- Glance at the Chapter Activities suggested at the end of most chapters; these will give you practical exposure to some of the points taken up in the chapter.

Do this now, before you read any further; then return to the following section.

An Approach to Study

There are lots of different study methods, and each person has to develop his or her own approach. Here is a general one you might draw on to refine your method of study using this book:

- In preparing to read a chapter, read the title, thumb through the chapter to read the heads, and glance at the illustrations.
- Read the objectives and relate them to what you know about the chapter from thumbing through it.
- Read the chapter. Remember the boldface words and their meanings. Study the illustra-

tions, charts, and tables. After reading each section (text following each head), briefly summarize it in your own words (10 to 20 words should be enough).

• After reading the chapter, examine the part or assembly discussed, and recall to yourself what the chapter said about it. (You can find external parts easily by looking at any number of vehicles; internal parts can be checked in your school shop transmissions and subassemblies.)

• Answer the review questions. Restudy the text for any questions you answered wrong. (It is okay to jump around; there is no need to read from beginning to end again.) Also review the chapter objectives and see if you think you can meet them.

• If there is anything that you still do not understand, discuss it with one or more of your classmates. See if they understand it and can help you; if not, ask your instructor to review it in class.

A NOTE ABOUT SHOP PRACTICE

Good shop practice includes a clean, organized work area, safe use of tools and equipment, and above all, a resourceful, deliberate person who thinks before acting. Slam-banging your way through a job is unsafe and unproductive. Most shops and technical manuals list cautionary measures to ensure safe and efficient practices; among them:

JACKS FOR EFFICIENCY AND SAFETY

Here are three types of hydraulic jack used for transmission removal and installation. The one to the left is for use with vehicles that are on a lift, and the one in the center is used when you have supported the vehicle a couple of feet off the floor on jack stands. Both are fitted with a cradle that securely holds the transmission so that it cannot slip off.

You sometimes see a shop using a standard floor jack, but this is both dangerous and inefficient. It usually takes two people—one to hold the trans-

mission on the jack and the other to operate the jack—and both have to joggle the transmission into place at the same time. Beside minimizing the possibility of injury, a good transmission jack soon pays for itself by helping to make transmission removal and installation more efficient.

The jack at the right is called a joggle jack. It is used in conjunction with a lift when an adjustable support is needed, such as when removing and installing gas tanks, shock absorbers, exhaust systems, and transmissions. In

the latter case, it is used together with a transmission lift jack to help adjust and support interfacing systems, such as the engine. There are also special tools or fixtures that are designed especially to support the engine when the transmission is removed, but these are usually not adjustable. Both the joggle jack and the lift jack have foot-operated levers so that you can use both hands in other removal and installation tasks.

Lift jack

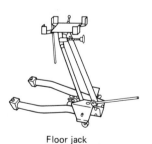

Floor jack

Joggle jack

- Protect your eyes with safety glasses.
- Protect your back. Use jacks, levers, and hoists.
- Protect the vehicle. Use fender blankets, seat blankets, and paper floor mats.
- Wipe up lube, fuel, and other liquid spills immediately and deposit soaked rags in the proper container. This avoids personal injury from slipping and reduces the chances of fire.
- Whenever possible, clean the exterior of the assembly or assemblies you are going to work on *before* removal or disassembly. Also work only with clean tools. Again, this helps avoid personal injury by minimizing slippery surfaces, it helps avoid internal parts contamination, and it expedites the job's quality completion.
- Think through the job and review the appropriate shop manual before you start so that you can prepare the work area, layout the right tools, assemble the right equipment, and generally plan for the safest and most efficient approach.
- Route electrical cords for drop lights and electrical tools to avoid entanglement in rotating parts.
- When raising a vehicle with a jack, make sure it is placed to support the vehicle without damage. Always place jack stands or some other rigid support beneath the vehicle before going under it.
- Disconnect the battery if other electrical wires are to be disconnected or parts adjacent to electrical terminals (such as under dashboards) are to be worked on.
- Avoid injury in disconnecting springs by relieving spring tension beforehand, if possible, or by securing the spring with special holding tools before disassembly.
- During removal or disassembly, think ahead; don't do one thing without looking ahead to see the effect it will have on the next thing to be done. Also, layout subassemblies and group parts in an organized fashion to help expedite cleaning, inspection, and reassembly.

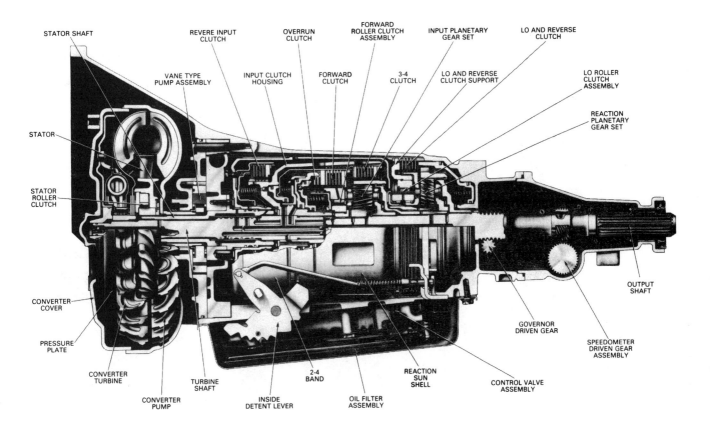

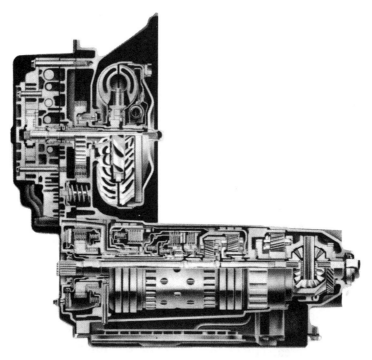

• Following major installations (e.g., engines, transmissions, etc.) but before operating the vehicle, take time to review the job to make *sure* that you have completed it (especially adding oil, ATF, coolant). A good idea is to put away hand tools and equipment and generally clean up while you are doing this.

When you complete this book, you will be able to describe the parts and assemblies that make up an automatic transmission, how each works, and how each contributes to the entire assembly; you will be able to read and understand hydraulic control diagrams and diagnostic charts, and you will be familiar with the majority of both domestic and

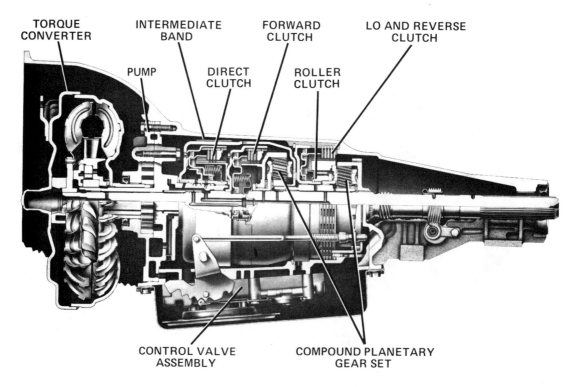

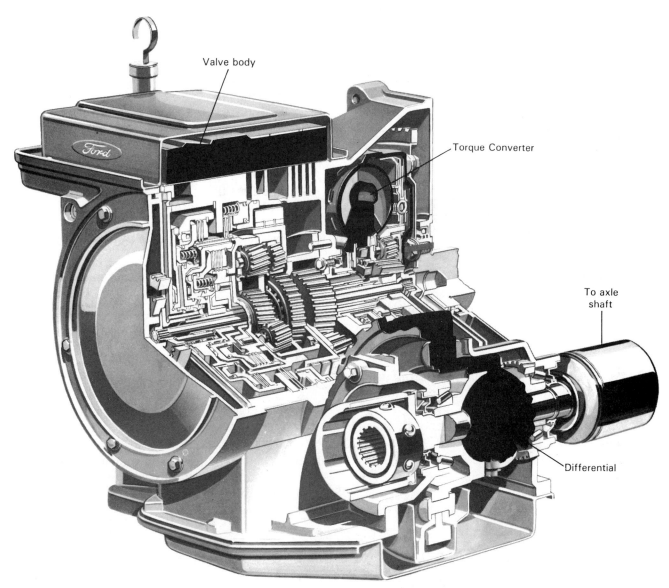

foreign automatic transmissions and automatic transaxle designs.

※ The shop course, along with the *Automatic Transmissions and Transaxles Training Manual*, will give you a practical knowledge in the testing, diagnosis, removal, disassembly, cleaning, inspection, reassembly, and installation of specific transmission makes and models.

Your successful completion of the automatic transmission course and these two books will provide you with the knowledge and practical skills to begin your career in automatic transmission and transaxle rebuilding and repair.

TRADE TERMS

Four-wheel drive (4WD)	**Power train**	**Transmission**
Front-wheel drive (FWD)	**Rear-wheel drive (RWD)**	**Transverse-mounted engine**
Gearset	**Transaxle**	**Vehicle**

REVIEW QUESTIONS

1-1. The major elements of an automatic power train are _____, _____, and _____.

1-2. The three types of drive used with passenger cars and light trucks are _____ _____ __ ___ (RWD), _____ _____ _____ (FWD), and _____ _____ _____ (4WD).

1-3. All FWD cars use transaxles.   T   F

1-4. The major elements of an automatic transmission are _____ _____, _____ ___ __, and _____ _____ _____.

1-5. Chapter 2 of this book includes details about different transmission makes and models.   T   F

1-6. Four of the chapters toward the end of this book cover certain models from specific transmission makes. Name the sources (or manufacturers) discussed in each of the four chapters. _____, _____, _____, _____

1-7. Two sources for the meaning of terms used in this book are words set in _____ and the _____.

1-8. Which among the following is not included in this book?
   (a) Table of contents.
   (b) Glossary.
   (c) Index.
   (d) Illustrations.
   (e) Charts.
   (f) Objectives.
   (g) Tables.
   (h) Frontispiece.
   (i) Text.
   (j) Activities.

1-9. The first thing to do after raising a vehicle with a jack is to put a _____ _____ underneath it.

1-10. The best way to protect your eyes is to wear _____ _____.

1-11. A transaxle includes the transmission and __ ___ _____ within the same housing.

1-12. Make sure that you route electrical cords for tools, drop lights, and electrical testing equipment to clear _____ parts.

1-13. A final drive _____ the speed of rotation between the transmission and drive axles and _____ the _____, or turning force.

1-14. The crankshaft of a transverse-mounted engine points in the same direction as the drive axles.   T   F

1-15. Technical bulletins and shop manuals are for use mostly by those inexperienced in automotive technology.   T   F

ESSAY QUESTIONS

1-1. Choose a specific vehicle make, model, and year (you may choose your own, if you have one) and describe the major elements of its power train, including the type of drive it has.

1-2. Prepare an approach-to-study for yourself. Include: how you will *prepare* to read a chapter, how you will go about reading it, and what you will do after you have read it.

CHAPTER ACTIVITIES

1-1. Examine the following vehicles and identify (a) whether they use a transmission or a transaxle, and (b) whether they are FWD, RWD, or 4WD: Toyota Tercel, American Motors Eagle, Renault Alliance, Chrysler Newport, Diplomat, or Fifth Avenue or General Motor's Chevrolet El Camino or Cadillac El Dorado and Seville, Ford Tempo and Thunderbird (you may select other makes and models at random).

1-2 Prepare a preliminary approach to study for yourself. Refine it as you proceed through this course.

1-3. Go on an inspection tour of your automotive shop; as you inspect each area and piece of equipment, list at least one major safety hazard you think might be associated with it. Make a second list of safety signs and notices that you see—or check off any that you listed during your inspection. How many safety hazards did you list? Were there any that you listed that were not already posted or given to you on a separate sheet of paper? If so, mention them to your shop instructor.

2

Some Principles Involved in Automatic Transmissions

OBJECTIVES

When you have completed this chapter, you should be able to:

- Discuss the concept of matter, citing everyday examples.
- Identify the three physical states of matter and give examples.
- Discuss the concept of energy and in what basic forms it exists.
- Perform calculations in work and mechanical advantage in both mechanical and hydraulic systems.
- Explain how force is transmitted through a fluid in a closed system.

WHAT IS A PRINCIPLE?

Think back to when you were very young. Remember how easy it was to take something apart and, often, how difficult it was to put it back together?

We all learned from that experience—some learned to forget the whole thing! They figured that they could best stay out of trouble by not getting into it in the first place and simply stopped taking things apart. Others, including those of us reading this book, learned to take things apart very slowly and carefully, trying to determine at each step the purpose of the part or subassembly. In doing this, we observed some facts or basic *principles*, and learned how they related to the gadget we were disassembling.

As our observations improved, we recognized these principles more readily. We began to take apart gadgets that did not work properly because we recognized that they needed to be fixed—we could detect that something fundamental was wrong. We knew the principles involved in the gadget's operation, and we knew that one or more parts involving that principle were not working.

One of the benefits of learning about a principle is that it can apply to many different things. So once we understand a principle, it broadens our knowledge tremendously. Knowing the key principles involved in automatic transmissions helps develop and sharpen diagnostic and repair skills.

ELEMENTS AND MATTER

In learning some of the principles that apply to automatic transmissions, we need to understand that all substances are made up of one or more very basic things called **elements**. There are well over 100 elements, but not all of them are in all substances. *Gold*, *silver*, *iron*, and *aluminum*, for instance, are each separate elements in themselves. Their symbols are Au, Ag, Fe, and Al, respectively. Water, ice, and steam are made up of the same two elements: hydrogen (H) and oxygen (O). Crude oil includes the elements *carbon* (C) along with *hydrogen* (H), *sulfur* (S), *nitrogen* (N), *oxygen* (O), and others in very small amounts. These and all other substances are considered to be matter. Examples of matter are: water, air, sand, and oil, but there are many others. **Matter** includes anything that occupies space and has weight.

Physical States of Matter

Each substance , or type of matter, occurs in nature, or we say exists *naturally*, in one of three forms: solid, liquid, or gas. A substance can be changed from one form, or **physical state**, to another as it is affected by temperature or pressure.

Standard Temperature and Pressure. Many substances occur in their *natural physical states* at standard temperature and pressure. Science has determined that **standard temperature** is the melting point of ice 32°F (0°C), and **standard pressure** is 1 atmosphere, or 14.7 lb/ in.^{2} (1 N/M^2). The *natural physical state* of transmission fluid is **liquid**; air is a **gas**; and iron is a **solid**. Water occurs in its natural physical state at *standard* temperature and pressure. Even though ice and steam occur in nature, they only exist at temperatures and pressures *other* than what has been defined as standard.

Changing Physical States of Matter. Water, ice, and steam are substances made up of two parts hydrogen and one part oxygen (H_2O). At 1 atmosphere of pressure, the physical state of H_2O is a solid when it is below 32°F (ice). It is a gas when it is above 212°F (steam) and it is a liquid (water) between 32 and 212°F. Many metals can be turned to liquid by applying a great amount of heat, as in soldering or welding, but their more natural state is solid.

Example of Automotive Application. Ethylene glycol is a substance that is common to automotive brake fluid and engine coolant. It does not boil until 355°F (197°C), which allows it to withstand heat generated by braking, and it does not turn solid (freeze) until about –22°F (–12°C), allowing a vehicle to be parked in subfreezing temperatures without freezing. The fact that its liquid state is stable over such a wide temperature range makes it particularly suitable for both high-temperature and low-temperature automotive applications.

ENERGY

One way to think about pure energy is that it is always around us, in us, affecting us; it is everywhere. Practically speaking, *energy* is the source of all movement. We think of heat, light, and magnetism as different kinds of energy, but they are really the *effects* of energy. And they, in turn, exert affects. We see the effect of magnetism, or gravity, in the tremendous force of a large waterfall. The force to lift a hot-air balloon is created by energy through the heating effect of a blowtorch-like fire. The effect of energy through light hitting this book page and reflecting (bouncing) back to the eyes in letters and illustrations is also a force, or movement.

A very important thing about energy is that it cannot be created or destroyed. As an automobile engine burns a gallon of gasoline–air mixture, only some of the available energy is used to move the car. Part of the energy creates heat—heat generated by friction and heat from combustion of the gasoline–

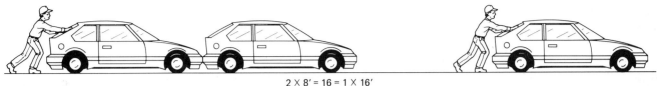

$$2 \times 8' = 16 = 1 \times 16'$$

Force × Distance = Work = Force × Distance

air mixture. So the total energy expended in moving the automobile, overcoming friction, and creating heat is equal to the total energy available from the gallon of gasoline–air mixture. This illustrates a scientific fact referred to as **conservation of energy**—energy cannot be created or destroyed.

MECHANICAL PRINCIPLES

Force

Movement is controlled or changed by force. **Force** is *directed* energy. We know from the study of physics that a moving object tends to keep moving in the same direction *unless* it is subjected to a force that is equal to it and in a direction opposite to its direction of movement (Figure 2-1). When an object is acted on by equal forces from all opposed directions, it remains stationary. From this we can say that for every action there is a reaction.

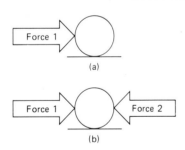

FIGURE 2-1 Force moving an object (a) and holding it stationary (b). (a) Ball moving by direct energy, force 1; (b) ball stationary by force 1 and force 2 equal and opposite directed energies

The design and function of an engine flywheel and a centrifugal clutch are derived from these principles. If a flywheel spins too fast, it can fly apart because the force trying to move the metal of which it is made away from center (*centrifugal force*) exceeds the force holding the metal together (*centripetal force*). The design of the centrifugal

clutch (Chapter 4) makes direct use of these same principles.

Work

We move things by directing energy, or by applying force. The amount of force we apply and the distance over which we apply it is called work. So **work** is equal to force multiplied by distance:

$$work = force \times distance$$

The same amount of work is done by simultaneously pushing *two* identical vehicles over a distance of *8 ft* as there is pushing *one* of these vehicles over a distance of *16 ft*.

In physics and chemistry, **force** is expressed in units called newtons (N) and distance in meters (m), and a unit of work is the newton-meter, or joule. In applied mechanics, other units are used, such as the pound-foot, or the more common expression **foot-pound** (ft-lb). But the important part about the concept of work is that it is the product of force multiplied by distance.

Mechanical Advantage

A **machine** in its simplest definition is a device to transmit energy. One of the oldest "machine" concepts is the **lever**—it ranks right up there with the roller, the precursor to the wheel. It probably developed from the use of sticks for prying while digging. It allows us to transmit energy through a path that makes it seem as though we get more energy out than we are putting in. But we know that energy cannot be created or destroyed, and in the following paragraphs we see how the concepts of *force* and *work* can give us a **mechanical advantage**. Look at Figure 2-2.

(a)   A uniform beam weighing 10 lb is held stationary by an equal and opposite force shared by two sup-

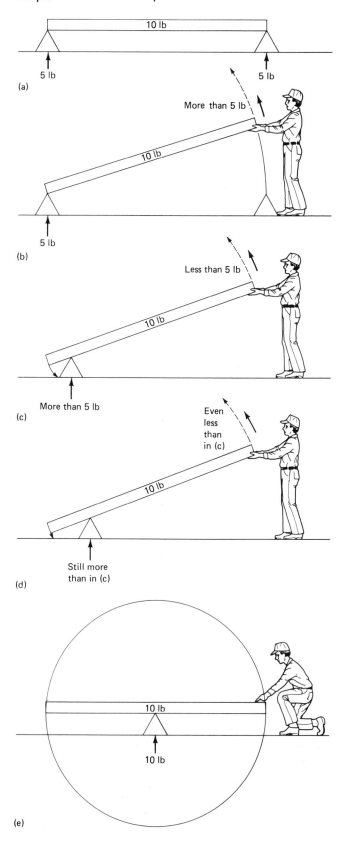

FIGURE 2-2   Beam and support.

ports. That is, each support is exerting a 5-lb force against the 10-lb pull of gravity on the beam.

(b) A man has lifted the beam. He had to lift with a force slightly greater than 5 lb to make that end of the beam move. The opposite end still rests on the other support because no additional (lifting) force has been applied there. Suppose the beam were attached to that point by a hinge and the man kept lifting or moving the beam. The man's end of the beam would circle the other end of the beam at the center.

(c) If the stationary support is placed a little to the right, it will carry a greater part of the 10-lb beam load than the man carries. Also, the *center* around which the beam can *rotate* is now located a little to the right.

(d) Here the stationary support has been moved still farther to the right. It now carries even more of the beam's 10-lb weight, and the man carries even less. As before, the *center of rotation* has moved with the stationary support.

(e) If the stationary support is moved again and again to the right, it carries more and more weight and the man carries less and less. At the center of the beam, the stationary support carries all the weight—that is, the equal and opposite force to the pull of gravity on the beam is all concentrated at the center of the beam. It is balanced.

Now look at Figure 2-3. For this illustration, disregard the weight of the beam itself.

(a) It is 20-ft long and balanced on a support located at its center (10 ft).

(b) A 20-lb force is added at each end, so the force at the center support is 40 lb. Observe that the product of the force, or weight, and its distance from center on one side equals the product of the weight and distance on the other side.

(c) Here the support has been moved 1 ft to the right. Now the force, or weight, must be distributed differently to keep the beam stationary. Again, multiplying the weight and distance on one side produces the same answer as multiplying the weight and distance on the other side.

(d) The same thing happens when the support has been moved 2 ft to the right of center. The weight must be distributed so that the product of weight and dis-

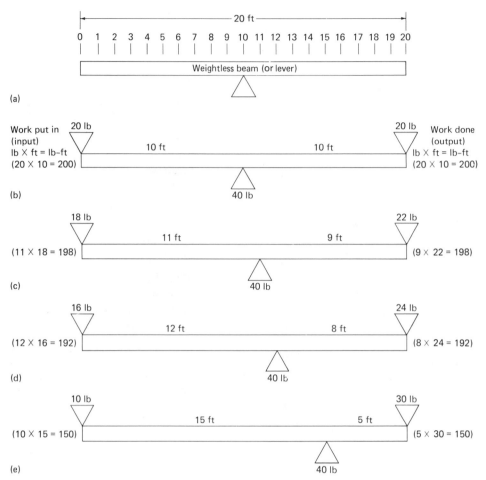

FIGURE 2-3 Balanced lever.

tance on both sides is equal and the beam remains stationary, or balanced.

(e) Moving the support still farther to the right requires the same redistribution of weight so that the products of weight and distance on both sides are equal and the beam remains balanced.

Notice that in Figure 2-3, c through e, it takes less and less weight, or force, to **counterbalance** the weight, or load, on the opposite end. This is because the distance between the small weight and the support is increasing and the distance between the support and the large weight is decreasing.

Leverage.   Suppose that a small, additional force is added to the left side of Figure 2-3e. This causes the beam to become unbalanced and it turns counter clockwise (CCW) about the support, or **fulcrum**, as in Figure 2-4a. If a certain force is applied at the long end of a beam, or **lever**, as in Figure

2-4b, it will move an even greater opposing force at the other end as long as its force–distance product is greater than the force–distance product at the other end:

$$10 \ 1/2 \ \text{lb} \times 15 \ \text{ft} = 157 \ 1/2 \ \text{lb-ft} \qquad 30 \ \text{lb} \times 5 \ \text{ft} = 150 \ \text{lb-ft}$$

unbalanced condition
causes lever to rotate about
fulcrum or axis

To balance the load in Figure 2-4b, the same amount of work is being done at both ends of the lever, but because of the force–distance principle of work, a greater amount of the force is carried by this simple machine called a lever—that is, the *smaller force* over a greater distance equals the *greater force* over a smaller distance. Notice that the *value of the length of the lever* from each load to the fulcrum is what allows a smaller load (10 1/2 lb) to

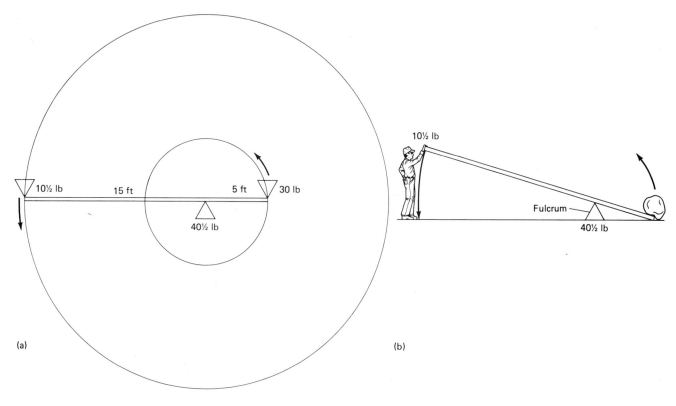

FIGURE 2-4   Leverage.

---

    work = force x distance
leverage = force x distance from fulcrum
   torque = force perpendicular to radius x radius distance

---

move a larger load (30 lb). This is the lever principle.

Leverage is used extensively in automotive devices. The principle is used in cranks, gears, cams, and in the pure lever form itself.

The balance beam in Figure 2-3 illustrates forces in **equilibrium**—there is no motion. This is **static** force. When the forces on the beam become unbalanced, as in Figure 2-4, there is motion exhibiting **dynamic** force.

Torque.   Closely related to leverage is **torque.** It is a rotating or twisting motion about a center point or axis. It is measured as a force–distance unit, where the force is in a right-angle (**perpendicular**) direction to the **radius** (distance from the center of a circle to its edge). Figure 2-5 illustrates the measurement of torque. For example, if a force of 10 lb is applied at a radius of 3 ft, the torque at the center is 30 ft-lb. Torque is a twisting force derived from the lever, so we measure it by determining the force–radial distance combination required to stop it. All the following measure a 30 ft-lb torque:

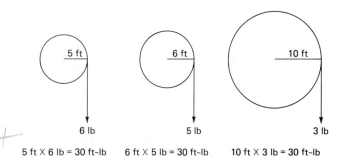

5 ft × 6 lb = 30 ft-lb   6 ft × 5 lb = 30 ft-lb   10 ft × 3 lb = 30 ft-lb

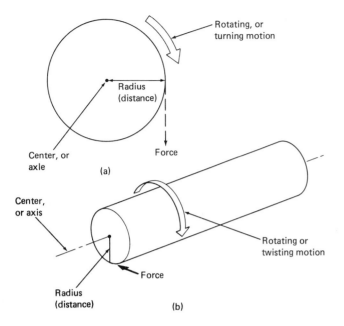

HYDRAULIC PRINCIPLES

Hydraulics is an area of knowledge that concerns liquids in motion. Automatic transmission operation draws heavily on an important aspect of hydraulics: fluid power. Fluid power controls and transmits energy through fluids.

How Fluids Transmit Force

Over 300 years ago a man named Pascal determined that force is transmitted through fluids *equally* in all directions. Figure 2-6 illustrates how a force is transmitted through a solid (a) only one way, but in

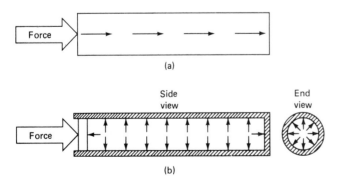

FIGURE 2-6   Force on one end of a solid (a) is transmitted straight through, whereas force (pressure) against a liquid (b) is transmitted equally in every direction.

a liquid (b), it is transmitted in every direction—all along the container and at each end (side view), as well as all around the container (end view). Also, the container can be *any* shape—the force will always be perpendicular to the container walls.

Force applied to liquid creates **pressure**, or the transmission of force through the liquid. Pressure is expressed in pounds per square inch (psi). Also keep in mind that the term **fluids** includes both gas and liquids and that the biggest practical difference between the two is that a gas can be compressed and a liquid cannot.

Hydraulic System

The fluid principles embodied in Pascal's law are used extensively in automobile technology and in automatic transmissions. Figure 2-7 shows a simple hydraulic system: liquid contained in a tube, or **cylinder**, with a disc or cylindrical-shaped **piston** at each end. The pistons seal against the walls of the cylinder only enough to allow them to move while preventing the liquid from escaping or air to enter. (Air, or gas of any kind, in a hydraulic system renders it ineffective because air is compressible.)

By attaching mechanical links to the pistons of a simple hydraulic system, the force applied at one end creates pressure in the system that exerts equal pressure at the other end of the piston. The distance between the two pistons can be small or very large

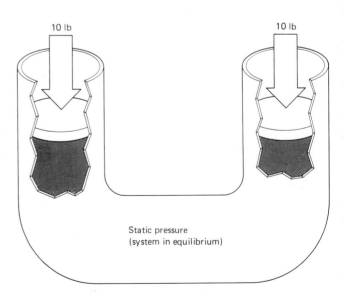

FIGURE 2-7   Simple hydraulic system in equilibrium.

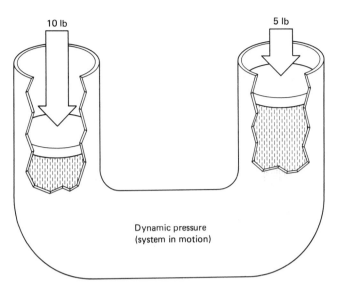

FIGURE 2-8   Simple hydraulic system in motion.

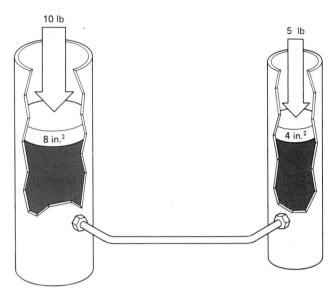

FIGURE 2-9   Hydraulic system with pistons of unequal areas under unequal loads, but static.

and the path taken by the liquid can follow any course. The path can even be flexible by connecting the two pistons with a hose of reinforced flexible material.

Static Pressure and Dynamic Pressure. The system in Figure 2-7 is in equilibrium (balanced, as the levers are in Figure 2-3) because the same amount of force, or load, is applied at each piston *and* each piston is of *equal area.* The pressure in this balanced system is called **static** pressure because there is no motion.

In Figure 2-8 the same simple hydraulic system is no longer balanced because there is less force at one of the two pistons of equal area. The pressure in this system is called **dynamic** pressure because there *is* motion.

Calculating Pressure and Force. Now look at the system in Figure 2-9. The area of one piston is twice that of the other, so it takes twice the amount of force on the larger piston than on the smaller to balance the system. Suppose that you wanted to prove that the system is in balance. You might want to multiply the force and area on one side to show that it equals the force multiplied by the area on the other side, but that does not work. That is 5×4 does not equal 10×8. But what does work is to multiply the *force on one side by the area on the other*—that will equal the remaining force multiplied by the remaining area:

$$\text{Force}_1 \times \text{Area}_2 = \text{Force}_2 \times \text{Area}_1$$
$$10 \times 4 = 5 \times 8$$
$$40 = 40$$

Mathematically, this says that area and force are directly proportional, and it is best to express the formula this way:

$$\frac{F_1}{F_2} = \frac{A_1}{A_2}$$

Remember that hydraulic pressure is in *pounds per square inch* (psi or $lb/in.^2$), so the area against which hydraulic pressure is applied must be known in order to determine the resulting force. For example, the pressure in the system in Figure 2-9 is 1.25 psi:

$$\frac{5\,lb}{4\,in^2} = 1.25\,psi \quad \text{and} \quad \frac{10\,lb}{8\,in^2} = 1.25\,psi$$

Calculating Work. The principle of work also applies to hydraulic systems. Suppose that an additional pound of force were added to the smaller cylinder of Figure 2-9. The highest pressure would now come from the smaller cylinder:

$$6 \text{ lb} \;\div\; 4 \text{ in}^2 \;=\; 1.5 \text{ psi}$$

$$10 \text{ lb} \;\div\; 8 \text{ in}^2 \;=\; 1.25 \text{ psi}$$

That changes the pressure from static to dynamic as shown in Figure 2-10.

Work, remember, is force × distance. And input work always equals output work. In Figure 2-10, if we move the small piston 2.5 in., we can calculate how far the large piston moves by using the work formula:

$$\text{Force}_1 \;\times\; \underline{\text{Distance}_1} \;=\; \text{Force}_2 \;\times\; \text{Distance}_2$$

$$10 \;\times\; \underline{1.5} \;=\; 6 \;\times\; 2.5$$

$$15 \;=\; 15$$

or to express it better algebraically;

$$10 \;\times\; D_1 \;=\; 6 \;\times\; 2.5$$

$$D_1 \;=\; \frac{6 \times 2.5}{10}$$

$$=\; 1.5$$

Mechanical Advantage. You have probably noticed the mechanical advantage gained with the system in Figure 2-10: only a 6-lb force is required to lift a 10-lb load. A great many devices made use of that force advantage in the relationship of input work to output work. The indispensable hydraulic jack is one, of course. The automobile hydraulic brake system is another. Calculations can be made to design hydraulic systems that will produce a specific mechanical advantage for any particular cylinder.

Applications. Look at Figure 2-11. The principles that Pascal discovered serve us well in understanding that to keep this system in balance, the force from the larger cylinder (a) remains the same, *no matter how many* cylinders of equal size (b) and (c) there are in the system. This is because the forces applied to them are equal. It is the pressure in the system that is important. If this seems questionable to you, calculate the system's pressure at any one of the cylinders by dividing force by area—all answers will be the same, because pressure is in pounds *per square inch.* If we were to add two more cylinders, (d) and (e), identical to (b) and (c), we would have the basics of an automotive brake hydraulic system. Cylinder (a) would serve as a **master cylinder** (system input) and cylinders (b) through (e) would be **slave cylinders**, or wheel

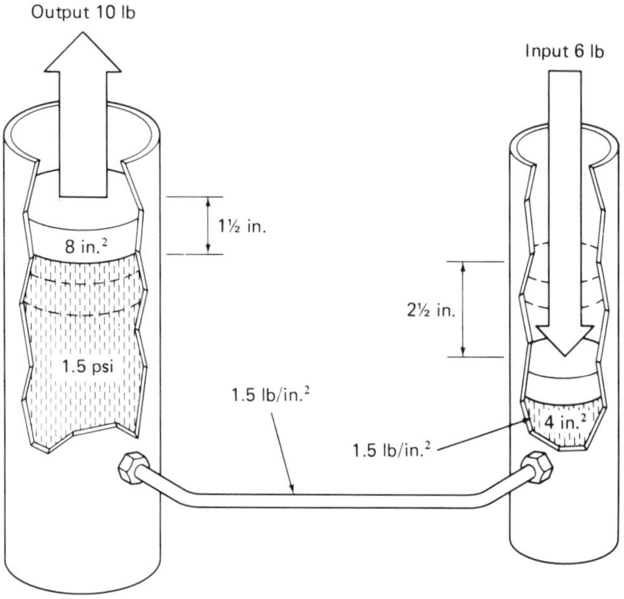

FIGURE 2-10 Hydraulic system with pistons of unequal areas under unequal loads, but dynamic.

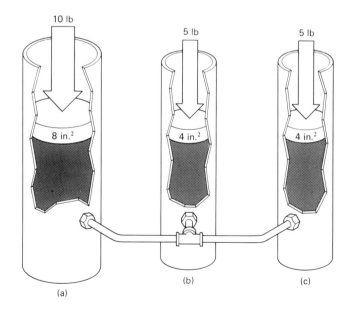

FIGURE 2-11 Hydraulic system with more than two cylinders.

cylinders in automotive terms. Of course, engineering designs combine mechanical leverage with the hydraulic system to make automotive brake systems suitable to the input source (humans) and output device (wheels). Automatic transmissions make extensive use of this combination, as we show in Chapters 4, 6, and 7. It is also possible to have a master cylinder with slave cylinders of various sizes, and the role of the master cylinder (input) can be taken over by any of the other cylinders—it all depends on the purpose of the hydraulic system.

Pressure Control

In any hydraulic system, **dynamic** pressure is affected as the liquid moves from one chamber to another through a **restriction**, such as a connecting line. The flow is slowed down, which results in higher pressure on the inlet side (and in the restricted area, itself) than there is on the outlet side. Transmission design takes this into account; in fact, devices called **orifices** are purposely built into hydraulic systems to control dynamic pressure at selected points. An orifice does not work under static pressure. Figure 2-12 depicts this effect.

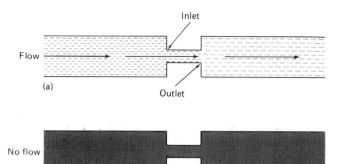

FIGURE 2-12 An orifice works only under dynamic pressure conditions: (a) dynamic pressure (lower pressure in right cylinder); (b) static pressure (equal throughout).

The size of the orifice (restriction) can be calculated to produce a required pressure reduction.

There are other pressure control devices in automatic transmissions that are covered in Chapter 6. The orifice—which can take other forms, such as connecting lines and passages—is basic and is incorporated in conjunction with other pressure control devices to achieve specific pressure control requirements.

TRADE TERMS

Axis	Fulcrum	Physical State
Conservation of	Gas	Piston
energy	Lever	Pressure
Counterbalance	Liquid	Radius
Cylinder	Machine	Slave cylinder
Dynamic	Master cylinder	Solid
Element	Matter	Standard pressure
Equilibrium	Mechanical	Standard temperature
Fluids	advantage	Static
Foot-pound	Orifice	Torque
Force	Perpendicular	Work

REVIEW QUESTIONS

2–1. Which of the following is not matter?
  (a) Sand.
  (b) Oil.
  (c) Force.
  (d) Gold.

2–2. The physical state of a substance can be:
  (a) Liquid.
  (b) Solid.
  (c) Gas.
  (d) All of the above.

2–3. Physical states of many substances can be changed by temperature and:

(a) Hydrogen.

(b) Humidity.

(c) Pressure.

(d) None of the above.

2–4. 32°F (0°C) at standard pressure is:

(a) The temperature between solid and liquid states.

(b) 14.7 lb/in.^{2}.

(c) The natural physical state.

(d) The melting point of ice.

2–5. All liquid is fluid, but not all fluid is liquid.
T   F

2–6. Match the terms in the first column with those in the second.

(a) Gas.   (1) Gold.

(b) Liquid.   (2) Air.

(c) Solid.   (3) Gasoline.

2–7. Standard temperature and pressure change with the weather.   T   F

2–8. Which of the following terms does not belong?

(a) Heat.

(b) Light.

(c) Friction.

(d) Magnetism.

2–9. Energy can be created, but not destroyed.
T   F

2–10. Centripetal and centrifugal forces oppose each other.   T   F

2-11. Which of the following requires the greatest amount of work?

(a) Moving a 50-lb tool box 100 ft.

(b) Lifting a 250-lb rock with a 20-ft lever.

(c) Pushing a 2500-lb vehicle 2 ft.

(d) Coasting a bike and rider weighing 200 lb for 1 mile downhill.

2–12. Which of the terms is not similar to the others?

(a) Center of rotation.

(b) Axis.

(c) Fulcrum.

(d) Balance.

2–13. Counterbalance means:

(a) To lose equilibrium.

(b) Equal and opposite force.

(c) To add balancing distances.

(d) Equal force × distance product.

2–14. The lever principle is used in:

(a) Gears.

(b) Crankshafts.

(c) Hydraulic jacks.

(d) All of the above.

2–15. Static pressure is:

(a) Working pressure.

(b) Stationary.

(c) Opposing pressure.

(d) All of the above.

2–16. Three of the following measure the fourth. What is being measured?

(a) Torque.

(b) Radius.

(c) Perpendicular.

(d) Force.

2–17. What forces are required to produce 28 ft-lb torque at the center of pulleys of the following radius measurements?

(a) 7 ft = _____ lb.

(b) 8 ft = _____ lb.

(c) 2 ft = _____ lb.

(d) 28 ft = _____ lb.

2–18. Force is transmitted through a liquid in a closed system:

(a) In all directions.

(b) Without loss.

(c) Both of the above.

(d) Neither of the above.

2–19. A pressure of 5 psi against a piston of 10-in.^{2} area creates a force of:

(a) 5 lb.

(b) 2 lb.

(c) 50 lb.

(d) 25 lb.

2–20. What is the pressure in a hydraulic system with four cylinders of 5-in.^{2} area and a force of 15 lb each and one cylinder of 3-in.^{2} area and a force of 30 lb?

(a) 12 psi.

(b) 50 psi.

(c) 3 psi.

(d) 10 psi.

2–21. The system in Question 2–20 is:

(a) Static.

(b) Dynamic.

2–22. An orifice is:
  (a) A leverage support.
  (b) A hydraulic line.
  (c) A restriction to flow.
  (d) A door with a number.

ESSAY QUESTIONS

2–1. Identify the three physical states of matter and give examples of each that relate to automobiles.

2–2. Explain how force is transmitted through fluid in a closed system.

CHAPTER ACTIVITIES

2–1. Find examples of each of the three physical states of a common substance in your kitchen.

2–2. Fill a medicine dropper, turkey baster, or battery hydrometer with water, then squeeze the bulb to expel the water. Describe how the forces in one direction (your hand) change direction (the drops or stream of water).

3

Gears, Shafts, Bearings, and Seals

OBJECTIVES

When you have completed this chapter, you should be able to:

- Recognize five common gearsets and describe the significance of each.
- Follow the direction of gear rotation through a gearset or system from input to output.
- Calculate gear ratios given a means of circumferential measurement.
- Describe the key differences in the design of the Simpson gearset and the Ravigneaux gearset with respect to a simple planetary gearset.
- Understand how gear teeth mesh and apply this knowledge during inspection of gear teeth for wear.
- Recognize the various machined surfaces on a shaft and generally describe the purpose of each.
- Identify the directions of radial and axial forces and name the types of bearings associated with them.
- Compare the two types of seals most often used to seal rotating surfaces in automatic transmissions.

Gears and shafts are very important parts of any transmission, whether automatic or manual. To reduce friction, gears and shafts run on bearings, and gears bear against thrust bearings and washers. Seals are required to keep lubricant in and dirt out.

As you begin to learn about the operation of gears and gearsets in this chapter, follow the diagrams closely, tracing the force (torque) from one element to the next as you read the text. This may seem tedious at first, but just be patient and follow it through.

It helps, too, if you have an open transmission or a gearset subassembly that you can study while slowly turning the gears, but you cannot always see every part. With diagrams, we can "see through" some parts to others and thereby see the entire operation demonstrated. So it is important to you to follow through each illustration as the text describes it.

GEARS

Having only one gear is like trying to clap with one hand. For a gear to work, it must **mesh** with another gear. Two or more gears meshing together is called a **gearset**. Figure 3-1a shows two gears of the same size meshing—notice that they turn in *opposite* directions. In Figure 3-1b a third gear has been put between to make input and output direction the same. It is called an **idler gear** because its only purpose is to change direction. It could be the same size, or even bigger than the other gears, but it is usually smaller to save space and materials. Figure 3-2 shows an **external gear** (teeth on the outside) meshing with an **internal gear** (teeth on the inside). When an internal gear meshes with an external gear, *both turn in the same direction.*

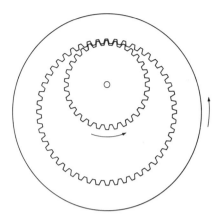

FIGURE 3-2 Internal gear running with an external gear.

Gearsets

Examples of all the basic gearsets are shown in Figure 3-3. **Spur gears** have teeth that are parallel to the gear axis as in (a) and (b), whereas the teeth on **helical gears** (c) are at an angle to the axis. The gearset in (d) is used in many steering systems. Although this is a combination of a rack gear (flat "box-gear") and a spur gear, the term **pinion** is used instead of spur. A **pinion gear** is any gear considerably smaller than the one with which it is meshing. The small gears in (b), (c), (d), the right view of (e) and (g), are all pinions. The **rack and pinion** gearset changes rotary motion to linear travel perpendicular to the axis of rotation. **Bevel gearsets** connect two shafts rotating at an angle to each other. The right view at (e) is a ring and pinion. A **ring gear** is a gear that resembles a ring rather than a disc. It can be an internal ring gear (sometimes called an **annulus**) or an external ring gear. External ring gears usually mount around some other part. For example, a starter ring gear mounts on a flywheel, flexplate, or torque converter; a third-member ring gear mounts on the differential case. The **worm and worm gear** (f) consists of a coiled, or cylindrical-shaped, worm whose diameter is usually only slightly larger than its shaft and a circular spur gear. It is used in certain cases to drive elements whose axes are at right angles. A popular use of the worm gear is to drive the speedometer cable off a transmission output shaft. Shown at (g) is a simple planetary gearset. Variations are used extensively in most automatic transmission designs. Obviously, it gets its name from the planets (pinion

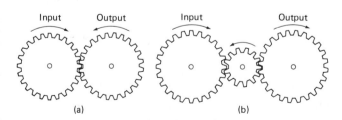

FIGURE 3-1 Effect of idler gear on input–output gear rotation: (a) opposite turning; (b) idler gear in center.

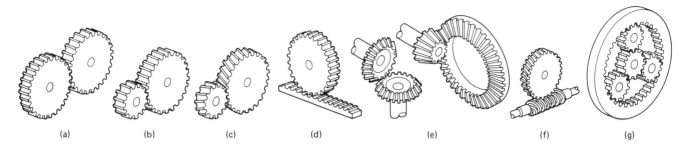

FIGURE 3-3   Gear sets: (a) and (b) spur gears; (c) helical gears; (d) rack and pinion gears; (e) bevel gears; (f) worm (and helical or spur) gear; (g) internal gear with sun gear in center and three planetary pinions.

gears) revolving around the sun (center gear). We look at planetary gearsets in detail later in this chapter.

Gears and Torque

Gears, like levers, can produce a mechanical advantage. The two spur gears in Figure 3-3a are the same size and they produce the same torque—the only difference is that they turn in opposite directions.

$$R_1 \times F = F \times R_2$$

same size = same torque

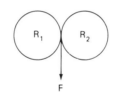

But what happens when we have a gearset of two different-sized gears? Look at Figure 3-4. Each gear produces a different torque and revolves at a different number of revolutions per minute (rpm) (see Chapter 2 for torque explanation).

- Gear *A* torque is $R_A \times F$ or 2 in. × 100 lb = 200 in.-lb
- Gear *B* torque is $R_B \times F$ or 4 in. × 100 lb = 400 in.-lb

Here we are making gear *A* drive gear *B* and a torque of 200 in.-lb is producing a torque of 400 in.-lb! The mechanical advantage is 2:1. Because the force is the same for both gears (where they mesh) it is easy to calculate the mechanical advantage by determining the ratio of the gear circumferences. This can be done by counting the number of teeth in each gear and dividing the output number by the input number:

$$\frac{\text{output}}{\text{input}} \rightarrow \frac{24 \text{ teeth}}{12 \text{ teeth}} \rightarrow \frac{2 \times \text{larger}}{1} \rightarrow \text{ratio 2:1}$$

This calculation gives us the **gear ratio**, and it is expressed in terms of how much bigger the output gear is than the input gear. *Gear ratio is not an expression of the number of times the output gear turns with respect to the input gear.* The *distance* is what produces the mechanical advantage. The small gear, *A*, must revolve twice to every revolution of the large gear, *B*. It has twice as far to go per revolution as the big gear does. The *work* done is the same (see Chapter 2 for work explanation):

$$\text{work} = \text{force} \times \text{distance}$$

$$\text{input work} = \text{output work}$$

$$F_B \times D_B = F_A \times D_A$$

$$100 \text{ lb} \times 24 \text{ teeth} \times 1 \text{ rev.} = 100 \text{ lb} \times 12 \text{ teeth} \times 2 \text{ rev.}$$

$$100 \times 24 \times 1 = 100 \times 12 \times 2$$

$$2400 = 2400$$

Reduction and Overdrive. When input is produced by the smaller gear, the input–output relationship is referred to as gear **reduction**. It takes more than one turn of the smaller, input gear to turn the larger, output gear once—a reduction in revolutions from input to output. But when the larger gear is the input gear, the smaller output gear turns more than one revolution to every one of the larger. Then the input–output relationship is called **overdrive**. The large gear "overdrives" the smaller; that is, it drives it more than one revolu-

The distance a point on a circle travels in one revolution is equal to the *circumference* of (*distance around*) the circle. We could measure the distance in any kind of units—inches, feet, millimeters, thumbnail widths, any-thing—as long as we used the same kind of unit for both gears. We could use inches, but that would mean formulas for the circumference of a circle, and so on. Since both gears have the same-size teeth, we can use the teeth as units. One gear has 24 teeth (distance around—circumference—is equal to 24) and the other has 12 teeth, meaning that the circumference, or distance around, is 12.

---

tion. Note also that the resulting torque in overdrive is lower at output than at input.

Simple Planetary Gearset

Earlier in this chapter (Figure 3-3) we identified three of the parts of a simple planetary gearset: internal gear, sun gear, and three planetary pinion gears. Another part, called the **planet carrier**, holds the shafts on which the planetary gears turn. The carrier itself turns on the same center that the ring and sun gears do. When referring to input and output of the planetary pinion gears, we speak in terms of the planet carrier, or just *carrier*.

Planetary gearsets are in **constant mesh**. They do not engage or disengage by sliding into or out of mesh as do many gears in a manual transmission. The sun gear meshes with the planetary gears and the planetary gears mesh with the internal gear.

Also, all three are splined, or otherwise connected, to other rotating transmission parts.

Figure 3-5 shows the three major parts of a simple planetary gearset (a) and the same unit assembled (b). There may be only three planetary gears in some designs, and the gears themselves may be different sizes than the ones shown here. But they are always smaller than the sun or ring gears in automotive applications. We cover other more complex designs, too, in this chapter.

FIGURE 3-5   Simple planetary gearset: (a) disassembled; (b) assembled.

Gear B (output)   Gear A (input)

FIGURE 3-4   Different sized gears, different torque, different speed. Gear *A*: radius, R_A = 2 in.; circumference, D_A = 12 teeth; Gear *B*: radius R_B = 4 in.; circumference, E_B = 24 teeth. Force, F = 100 lb.

Through the use of holding devices, discussed in Chapter 5, a planetary gearset can produce reduction or overdrive in forward and reverse. This is achieved by using one gear for input, another for output, and the remaining one as a **reaction member** by holding it stationary. Unless one of the gears is held stationary, no torque will be transmitted (**neutral**). If *any two* of the gears are *held together*, input torque equals output torque (**direct drive**).

Table 3-1 lists all the gear combinations possible for a simple planetary gearset together with the calculations for each gear ratio, using the number of teeth as a measure (Figure 3-6). Notice that the number of teeth for the carrier is *not* the number of teeth in the planetary gears. They are merely idler gears. The number of teeth for the carrier equals the total of the sun gear and ring gear teeth; because when the sun gear or ring gear is held while the other turns, the carrier's rotation is affected by *both* the ring and sun gears. The effect is like taking two steps forward and one step backward. So, in effect, the carrier's circumference is equal to the sum of the circumference of the ring gear *and* the sun gear.

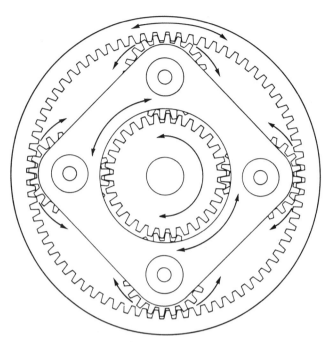

FIGURE 3-6 Simple planetary gearset—neutral. Ring gear, 72 teeth; sun gear, 30 teeth; carrier, 72 + 30 = 102 teeth.

Table 3–1

Gear combinations available for a simple planetary gearset

Sun (30 teeth)	Carrier (102 teeth[a])	Ring (72 teeth)	$\dfrac{Output}{Input}$	Ratio	Drive
Held	Output	Input	$\dfrac{102}{72} = \dfrac{1.43}{1}$	1.43:1	Second[b] (Figure 3-10)
Held	Input	Output	$\dfrac{72}{102} = \dfrac{0.71}{1}$	0.71:1	Overdrive (Figure 3-11)
Input	Held	Output	$\dfrac{72}{30} = \dfrac{2.40}{1}$	2.40:1	Reverse (Figure 3-12)
Held	Output	Held	—	1:1	Direct
Held	Held	Output	—	1:1	Direct
Output	Held	Held	—	1:1	[c]
Input	Output	Held	$\dfrac{102}{30} = \dfrac{3.34}{1}$	3.34:1	[c]
Output	Input	Held	$\dfrac{30}{102} = \dfrac{0.29}{1}$	0.29:1	[c]
Output	Held	Input	$\dfrac{30}{72} = \dfrac{0.42}{1}$	0.42:1	[c]

[a]30 + 72 = 102.
[b] The low ratio of first gear (over 2:1) requires the use of a second planetary gearset.
[c] Not used in automobile transmissions.

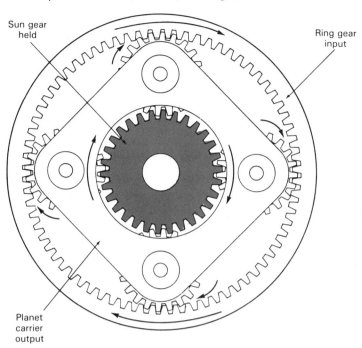

FIGURE 3-7   Gear reduction (second gear). 102/72 = 1.42 : 1.

The first three gear combinations listed in Table 3-1 are illustrated in Figure 3-7 through 3-9. These and direct drive are the only simple gearset combinations used in automobile transmissions. The rest of the gear combinations, listed in the bottom part of Table 3-1, are not used in automobile

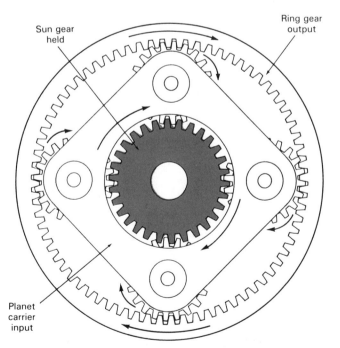

FIGURE 3-8   Overdrive. 72/102 = 0.71 : 1.

transmissions for one or both of the following reasons: (1) resulting gear ratios are too high or too low to fit the rest of the drive train requirement, and (2) the combination of input, output, and stationary gear requirements would be impossible, or inefficient, to work into the overall design of the transmission.

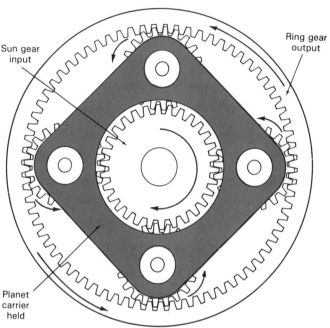

FIGURE 3-9   Reverse gear. 72/30 = 2.40 : 1.

Compound Planetary Gearsets

A simple planetary gearset provides only two forward speeds that are of practical use in automobile transmissions, but three, even four, are needed—and five, for those with overdrive. So rather than using two simple planetary gearsets, engineers have developed combined, or **compound**, **planetary gearsets**. In some designs, both a compound and simple planetary gearset are used.

There are two compound planetary gearset designs used in automobile transmissions: the **Simpson** and the **Ravigneaux** (pronounced *rav-in-yo*). Of these two, the Simpson is more popular. It is used in all the Ford C series and JATCO transmissions, General Motors 125 and 200-400 series, Chrysler and American Motors, BMW, Volkswagen, Mazda, Nissan transaxle, and Toyota. The Ravigneaux is used in some of the Borg Warner designs, Renault, Mitsubishi, Mercedes, and the Ford and General Motors transaxles.

Simpson Planetary Gearset. Figure 3-10 depicts a Simpson planetary gearset. In an automatic transmission, one half is referred to as the front planetary and the other the rear planetary. This is really two simple planetary gearsets with the sun gears made from one piece. The gears may be sized the same or differently.

In one design, both parts of the compound gearset are used in first gear, but second and reverse use different halves of the gearset. Direct drive requires lock-up of any two parts of any one side of the compound gearset. There are different ways of combining input, output, and lock-up depending on design requirements.

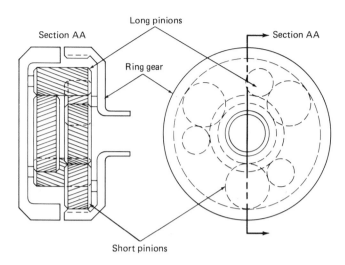

FIGURE 3-11   Ravigneaux planetary gearset.

meshing of a spur gear set. Notice the point of contact between teeth *A* and *B*, *B* and *A'*, and *A'* and *B'*. It follows a line made by a fixed angle to the centerline of the two gears. Design engineers call this the **pressure line**. As the gears turn, the shape of the teeth is such that contact begins at the tip of one tooth, *A'*, by the base of another, *B'*. Contact

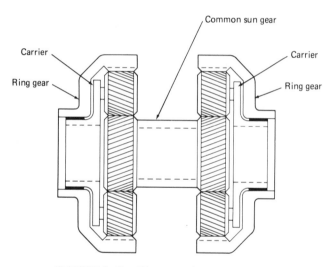

FIGURE 3-10   Simpson planetary gearset.

Ravigneaux Planetary Gearset. Figure 3-11 represents a Ravigneaux planetary gearset. It is more complex than the Simpson. It has only one ring gear, but there are two sun gears. The carrier is fitted with two sets of pinion gears—one set is longer than the other. The short set mates with the ring gear and one sun gear. The long set mates with the other sun gear and with the short pinions. So both sun and carrier "sets" use the same ring gear.

Gear Wear

Gear teeth are machined to very close tolerances, and their design is precise. Figure 3-12 shows the

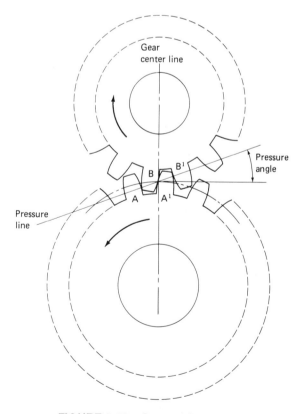

FIGURE 3-12   Gear tooth meshing.

FIGURE 3-13 Worm gear teeth.

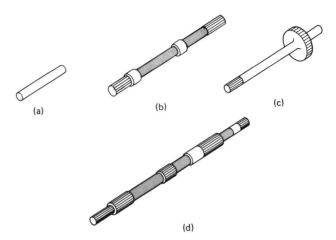

FIGURE 3-14 Simple non-rotating shaft; (b) rotating shaft with splines at each end and machined bearing or seal surfaces; (c) shaft with spline and gear machined from one piece of steel; (d) two shafts, one rotating inside the other (notice also, the spline machined into the middle of the hollow shaft.

remains, but it also moves all along the tooth flank with gear rotation until it ends at the tip for one, as at *B*, and at the base, as at *A*, for the other. Helical cut and hypoid (a spiral or twisted helical cut) gear meshing occurs similarly. Through such design, the load is always shared by at least two teeth. Gearsets are assembled with a specified clearance between teeth called **backlash**. Part of this clearance is taken up by expansion as the gears reach operating temperature, and the remaining clearance is for lubrication.

Worn bearing surfaces cause misalignment of tooth surfaces, or **tooth flanks**, resulting in tooth wear. Figure 3-13 shows badly worn helical gear teeth. The profile of the tooth shows a flattened pressure side, and a definite wear line left by the tooth tips is evident across the flank. Gear bearing-surface wear is discussed later in this chapter.

SHAFTS

The simplest transmission shaft is a stationary length of steel of uniform diameter that serves as a supporting axis for a gear or other rotating device. A simple stationary shaft is shown in Figure 3-14a. Many shafts are more complex. They are of different lengths and sizes and can have machined circumferential surfaces for gears to turn on, oil holes and passages to transmit oil under pressure to various parts on the shaft, and grooves to hold seals and snap-ring retainers. Rotating shafts have a set of long teeth called a **spline** machined at one or both

ends (Figure 3-14b) and sometimes at other locations (Figure 3-14d).

Splines

The male spline on a shaft is a clearance fit to a female spline in another part that must rotate with the shaft. Often the male spline is longer than the female spline, so the latter can operate at different locations along the shaft, and these splines can have spiral teeth rather than straight ones.

Spline and Shaft Wear

A spline does not mesh with another like a gear does. Its wear occurs from sliding friction and clockwise and counterclockwise torque forces. Visual inspection is usually sufficient to detect a damaged or worn spline, but if there is a sloppy fit when the splines are mated, consider replacement.

Wear on smooth machined surfaces of a shaft should be determined by measurement with a micrometer. It will be easy to identify the areas of the surface that are not used. Measure and record the diameter of the unused area. Follow this with at least two measurements—one near each end—for taper of the wearing surface. Then take at least two measurements 90° apart to determine whether the surface is out-of-round.

BEARINGS

When a machine part slides over or rotates around another, the surfaces that contact, or bear upon, each other are called **bearing surfaces**. A gear turning on a fixed shaft can have more than one bearing surface. It is supported and held in place by the shaft in a **radial** direction, that is, by forces "radiating" out from the center of the shaft. Also, the gear tends to move along the shaft in an *axial* direction as it rotates, so it is held in place by other gear parts. The surfaces between the sides of the gear and the other parts are also bearing surfaces (Figure 3-15).

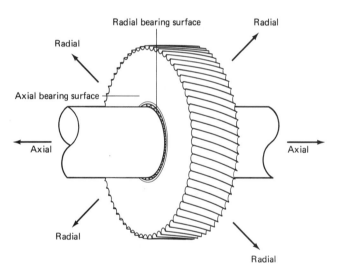

FIGURE 3-15 Bearing surfaces on rotating parts.

A **bearing** is a device placed between two bearing surfaces to reduce friction and wear. Most bearings have surfaces that either slide or roll against each other. In automatic transmissions, sliding bearings are used where one or more of the following conditions prevail: low rotating speed, very large bearing surfaces compared to the forces present, and low use. Rolling bearings (roller or ball bearings) are used in high-speed, high load/small bearing surfaces, and high-use conditions.

Sliding Bearings

Automatic transmissions use sliding bearings that are composed of a relatively soft bronze alloy. Many are made from steel with the bearing surface bonded, or fused, to the steel. Those that take radial loads are called **bushings** and the ones that take axial loads are **thrust washers** (Figure 3-16a and b, respectively). The bearing's surface usually runs against a harder surface such as steel to produce minimum friction and heat wear characteristics.

Bushings. Bushings are cylindrically shaped and usually held in place by a **press fit**; that is, their outside diameter is a few thousandths of an inch larger than the inside diameter of the hole, and the bushing is pressed into place. The press fit actually changes the inside diameter, but this is allowed for during bushing design so that the bushing is compressed to the required size during installation.

Thrust Washers. Often serving both as a bearing and a spacer, thrust washers are made in various thicknesses. They may have one or more tangs or slots on the inside or outside circumferences that mate with the shaft hole to keep them from turning. Some thrust washers are made of nylon or Teflon. These are used where loads are small.

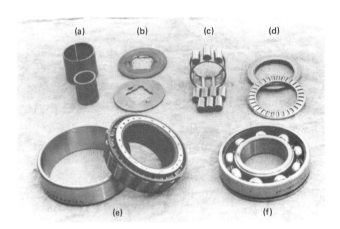

FIGURE 3-16 Bearings: (a) bushing; (b) thrust washer; (c) roller bearing; (d) needle bearing; (e) tapered roller bearing and outer race (cup); (f) ball bearing.

Lubrication and Wear. Some sliding bearings have holes drilled in them to match oil passages so they can be lubricated under pressure. Others simply operate in a bath of oil. Often, the bearing surface is grooved to help the flow of lubricant.

A pattern of wear on both bushings and thrust washers is often evident. Both are inexpensive, replaceable items. Thrust washer clearance specifications should always be checked, even after installing new ones. Excessive axial clearances can cause heavy wear on major parts.

Roller Bearings

The bearing surface is greatly reduced through the use of roller bearings. The simplest roller bearing design leaves enough clearance between the bearing surfaces of two sliding or rotating parts to accept a half dozen or more rollers. Each roller's two points of contact between the bearing surfaces are so small that friction is greatly reduced. The bearing surface is more like a *line* than an area.

If the roller length to diameter is about 5:1, or more, the roller is called a **needle** and such a bearing a **needle bearing**. Sometimes the needles are loose, as in the simple roller bearing just described, or they can be held in place by a steel cylinder or by rings at each end. Often the latter are drilled to accept pins at the ends of each needle that act as an axle. These small assemblies help save the agony of losing one out of a dozen or so loose needles and the resulting delay in finding it or having to buy a new bearing.

Many other roller bearings are designed as assemblies (Figure 3-16c and d). The assembly consists of (1) an inner and outer steel, ring-shaped track, each called a **race**; (2) rollers; and (3) a piece called a **cage** to help hold the rollers in place and keep them separated. There are roller bearings designed for radial loads and others designed for axial loads. Both are used extensively in automatic transmissions. Although roller bearings are more expensive than bushings and thrust washers, they cost less than the parts to which they are fitted (shafts, gears, housings, etc.), so one of their advantages is that they can be replaced at a relatively low cost.

There is a roller bearing design that accepts both radial *and* axial loads. It is the **tapered roller bearing** (Figure 3-16e). Its rollers turn on an angle to the bearing assembly's axis rather than parallel to it. And, of course, the rollers themselves are slightly tapered to fit the angle of the inner and outer races.

The bearing assembly consists of two parts: (1) the inside race, rollers and cage, and (2) the outside race, or **cup**. Because the outside race is separate, bearing clearance or preload can be adjusted during assembly to meet both axial and radial specifications simultaneously. **Preload** is simply a tightening process accomplished by using shims, or by tightening a shaft nut to a specified torque which allows no end-play.

Tapered roller bearings are usually used in pairs. Although rarely used in transmissions, tapered bearings are almost always used in transaxles, such as for the differential case ring gear, and for the drive pinion, and other applications where preload is required.

Ball Bearings

The heaviest radial loads in automatic transmissions are carried by either roller or ball bearings. Ball bearings are constructed similarly to roller bearings except that the races are grooved to accept the balls. The groove radius is *slightly* larger than the ball radius, which reduces the bearing surface area more than the roller does. Another advantage of the ball bearing is that like the tapered roller bearing, it can handle radial and thrust loads simultaneously; however, it cannot take the heavy preloads that a tapered roller bearing can.

Figure 3-17 summarizes the key differences in construction of the three designs of rolling bearings used in automatic transmissions.

Lubrication and Wear in Rolling Bearings. Bearing rollers, balls, and races are made from ultrahigh-quality steel, and they are finished to tolerances of less than 0.00005 (5/100,000) of an inch (0.0013 mm). They are lubricated by packing with a solid lubricant in some applications, but in

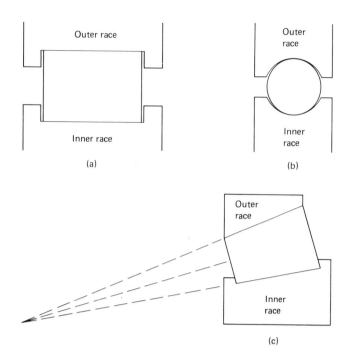

FIGURE 3-17 Bearing surface cross sections:
(a) roller; (b) ball; (c) tapered roller.

automatic transmissions and transaxles, they run in a bath of oil.

Heat damage from lack of sufficient lubricants is probably the most common cause for bearing replacement. Wear from insufficient or dirty lubricant is next. Bearing surfaces that have gotten too hot show an irregular, or mottled, blue-black discoloration.

Bearings that have been well lubricated during their lifetime will eventually fail or begin to pit from fatigue. Pitting of the race, roller, or ball surfaces results from tiny stress cracks caused by many, many rotations under heavy loads.

The easiest test for wear in rolling bearings is to grasp the bearing before cleaning, and rotate it, applying a little pressure. It should be *velvety smooth.* If any roughness is felt, or any "hang-ups" or "flat" spots, the bearing should be replaced. If the bearing passes this test, give it a quick cleaning in solvent, but do not dry it. Test it again. Then look for discoloration and wear marks. Many bearings wear so much that they make noise when spun by hand.

SEALS

Shafts and other rotating parts in automatic transmissions operate in fluid contained in the transmission housing. Some have drilled passages to direct fluid flow under pressure. Seals encircle these rotating parts at certain points and confine the fluid to specific locations.

Although rarely used in automatic transmissions, another device that helps retain fluid is called a **hydrodynamic seal**. It is really more of a pump than a seal. It consists of spiral grooves cut into a shaft so that a large amount of the fluid is moved away from a sealed surface when the shaft is rotating. Also, O-rings are used occasionally for dynamic application (seals), but they are most often used in static applications (gaskets).

Lip Seals

Lp seals (Figure 3-18) are used around input and output shafts to keep fluid *in* the housing and dirt *out*. Lip seals and others are sometimes built into ball bearings to retain lubricant. The flexible part of the seal is usually made of synthetic rubber, such as neoprene and silicone, shaped and sized so that it is flexed when installed to apply pressure at the sharp edge of the lip. Some seals are double-lipped. A toroidal spring (garter spring) is enclosed in many lip seals to help maintain the sealing pressure. The seal pressure and sealing surfaces are designed to allow an oil film of about 0.0001 (1/10,000) of an inch (0.0025 mm). More than this amount allows leakage; less creates too much heat damage to the seal. Lip seals should always be replaced. Heat eventually destroys rubber, making it hard and in-

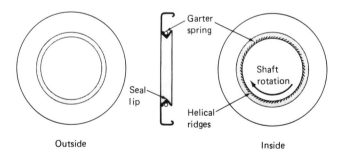

FIGURE 3-18 Lip seal.

flexible. Always check the surface that runs against the seal. Dirty lubricant can wear grooves in steel shafts, bosses, and sleeves. Sometimes a new seal can be positioned to run over an unworn part of the surface. If it cannot, then replace the part, or expect leaks—new seal or not.

Ring Seals

Sealing inside the transmission at points where some leakage is acceptable is done by **ring seals**.

Similar to piston rings, ring seals fit into a groove on a shaft and the outside circumference slides against the bore of the mating piece. But ring seals in an automatic transmission seal against rotary motion rather than reciprocating motion. They are placed near pressurized fluid outlets on shafts to help retain pressure. Some are made of cast iron, others of nylon or Teflon. As with other types of seals, ring seals should be replaced during reassembly.

TRADE TERMS

Annulus	Helical gear	Rack and pinion
Axial	Hydrodynamic seal	Radial
Backlash	Idler gear	Ravigneaux gearset
Bearing	Internal gear	Reaction member
Bearing surface	Lip seal	Reduction
Bevel gear	Mesh	Ring gear
Bushing	Needle	Ring seal
Cage	Needle bearing	Simpson gearset
Compound planetary	Neutral	Spline
gearset	Overdrive	Spur gear
Constant mesh	Pinion gear	Tapered roller bearing
Cup	Planet carrier	Thrust washer
Direct drive	Preload	Tooth flank
External gear	Press fit	Worm
Gear ratio	Pressure line	Worm gear
Gearset	Race	

REVIEW QUESTIONS

3–1. Force transmitted by gears is called:
   (a) Meshing.
   (b) Mechanical advantage.
   (c) Torque.
   (d) Rotation.

3–2. The direction of rotation for both gears in the following gearsets is opposite except for:
   (a) External spur-to-external spur.
   (b) Planetary pinion-to-sun.
   (c) External helical-to-external helical.
   (d) Internal spur-to-external spur.

3–3. Idler gears are used to:
   (a) Change torque.
   (b) Change gear ratio.
   (c) Change direction.
   (d) Change speed.

3–4. Gearsets consist of two or more gears.   T   F

3–5. Which of the following does not belong?
   (a) Internal gear.
   (b) Annulus gear.
   (c) Ring gear.
   (d) Planetary gear.

3–6. Match the terms in the first column with those in the second.

  (a) Pinion.   **(1)** Flat.
  (b) Idler.   **(2)** Angle.
  (c) Bevel.   **(3)** Small.
  (d) Rack.   **(4)** Direction.

3–7. Spur gears are always the same size and always produce the same torque.   T F

3–8. On a reduction gearset, the input gear:

  (a) Turns faster than the output gear.
  (b) Turns in a different direction than the output gear.
  (c) Turns with less torque than the output gear.
  (d) All of the above.

3–9. In an overdrive gearset, the force on the teeth of the large gear is:

  (a) Greater than on the small gear.
  (b) Less than on the small gear.
  (c) Equal to that on the small gear.
  (d) Greater than the torque.

3–10. Expressions of mechanical advantage and gear ratio are similar.   T F

3–11. Except for one, all the following rotate on the same axis.

  (a) Ring gear.
  (b) Sun gear.
  (c) Planetary gear.
  (d) Carrier.

3–12. The reaction element for reverse in a planetary gearset is:

  (a) Sun gear.
  (b) Planet gear.
  (c) Carrier.
  (d) Any of the above.

3–13. Gear ratio is calculated by dividing:

  (a) Input by output.
  (b) Output by input.
  (c) Neither of the above.
  (d) Both of the above.

3–14. In neutral, the following element of a planetary gearset is held.

  (a) Sun gear.
  (b) Ring gear.
  (c) None.
  (d) Carrier.

3-15. If any two planetary elements are held together, the result is:

  (a) Overdrive.
  (b) Neutral.
  (c) Park.
  (d) Direct drive.

3–16. The number of planetary gears in a simple planetary gearset can be:

  (a) Two.
  (b) Three.
  (c) Four.
  (d) Any of the above.

3–17. The effective circumference of the carrier is:

  (a) The number of teeth in one pinion.
  (b) The number of teeth in all pinions.
  (c) The total of the number of teeth in the sun gear and one pinion gear.
  (d) The total of the number of teeth in the ring gear and sun gear.

3–18. Some planetary gear ratios are not used in automatic transmission design because:

  (a) They are not needed.
  (b) They are overdrive ratios.
  (c) They turn in the wrong direction.
  (d) They are too high or too low.

3–19. Which term below is common to both Simpson and Ravigneaux gears?

  (a) Spur gears.
  (b) Compound.
  (c) Off-center.
  (d) None of the above.

3–20. Which of the following is characteristic of a Simpson planetary gearset?

  (a) One ring gear, two sun gears, one carrier.
  (b) Two carriers, one sun gear, two ring gears.
  (c) Short and long planetary pinions, one ring gear, two sun gears.
  (d) Short and long planetary pinions, two ring gears, one sun gear.

3–21. Which of the following is characteristic of a Ravigneaux planetary gearset?

  (a) One ring gear, two sun gears, one carrier.
  (b) Two carriers, one sun gear, two ring gears.
  (c) Short and long planetary pinions, one ring gear, two sun gears.

(d) Short and long planetary pinions, two ring gears, one sun gear.

3–22. Which statement is true?
  (a) As gears turn, the teeth mesh at two points only: the base and the tip.
  (b) The flanks of gear teeth are rounded so that they remain in contact throughout the meshing cycle.

3–23. Splines mesh with gears.   T   F

3–24. Match the terms in the first column with those in the second.
  (a) Bearing surface.   (1) Thrust.
  (b) Cup.   (2) Bushing
  (c) Axial.   (3) Race
  (d) Sliding bearing.   (4) Tapered roller.

3–25. The hydrodynamic seal concept is incorporated in some lip seals.   T   F

ESSAY QUESTIONS

3–1. Describe the key differences in the design of the Simpson gearset and the Ravigneaux gearset with respect to a simple planetary gearset. (*Hint*: Describe the simple planetary gearset first.)

3–2. Describe how to determine the ratio of a particular gearset; give an example, identify which is output, and which of the two types of gear ratio it is.

CHAPTER ACTIVITIES

3–1. If your shop has a planetary gearset, examine its operation. Assign your own input/output/reaction member combinations, and observe the results. Now assign only those combinations used in automatic transmissions for each gear (Table 3-1).

3–2. Calculate the gear ratios that actually will be used in this gearset.

3–3. Examine an automatic transmission input, output, or mainshaft. Identify the splines, bearing surfaces, oil passages, and seal grooves.

3–4. Examine roller bearings, tapered roller bearings, and ball bearings. Name the parts of each.

4

Drive Links

OBJECTIVES

When you have completed this chapter, you should be able to

- Recognize the major transmission drive links: bands, clutches, and torque converters.
- State the purpose of clutches and bands in automatic transmissions.
- Describe the "self-energizing" effect associated with bands.
- Name and describe the function of major parts of the roller clutch and the sprag clutch.
- Explain the primary reasons for grooves in band and clutch linings.
- Explain the most significant differences in the design and operation of one-way clutches and disc clutches.
- Name the most common reasons for clutch and band wear.
- Describe the two primary functions of the torque converter.
- Name and describe the function of major parts of torque converters.
- Describe the four types of lock-up torque converters.
- Describe the purpose, function, and operation of the mechanical damper.

Drive links are the means by which a transmission picks up the circular motion of engine torque and routes it through various shafts and gear combinations for forward or backward motion. There are two kinds of drive links: one involves fluid resistance, and the other uses friction.

The mechanisms that depend on friction to link one rotating body with another are **bands** and

clutches. The mechanism that utilizes fluid resistance derives from windmills and water wheels (both driven by *fluids*) and is called a **fluid coupling**. The modern automatic transmission application of the fluid coupling is called a **torque converter**.

In this chapter we present the design and function of bands, clutches, torque converters, the drive links in automatic transmissions, and a summary of representative transmission powerflow.

BANDS AND CLUTCHES

Bands and clutches both use friction, but in automatic transmissions, clutches rotate while they are applied or released, and bands do not. Bands are connected to the transmission housing and are used only to stop rotating drums or cylindrical shells. This is why a band is sometimes referred to as a reaction element.

Bands have been around for a long time. Although they were used as rotating clutches in some of the very early flatbelt-driven machinery, one of the earliest vehicular uses was the external drum brake. For many years, Chrysler used an external brake band and drum on the end of the transmission output shaft as a parking brake. In fact, some automatic transmission manufacturers refer to transmission bands as brakes. Bands and clutches are used together in automatic transmissions to change gear ratios—and even direction.

Band Design

Bands are applied by anchoring one end and moving the other toward it. The band can be mounted so that the applying force moves against the direction of rotation or with it. More force is required to apply against the direction of rotation because the friction between that end of the band and the drum opposes it. If the band is mounted so that the force is applied in the same direction as the drum is rotating, the drum now adds to the applying force rather than opposing it. This is known as the **self-energizing** effect and is shown in Figure 4-1.

Other factors that are considered in band design are:

- The surface area (width and circumference) and configuration (grooving)

- Drum material and surface finish
- Band material or band lining material
- Transmission fluid

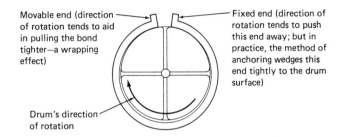

FIGURE 4-1   Simple band and drum illustrating the "self-energizing" effect that occurs when band tightening is initiated in the direction of rotation.

Single-Wrap Bands.   There are two types of **single-wrap**, or one-piece, band designs: one is light, flexible steel, and the other is a heavy cast-iron piece with more limited flexibility but still enough to allow it to self-release when clamping pressure is removed (Figure 4-2). The heavy bands are used where there is greater need for static torque, such as reverse gear. They are made with a metallic lining material that can withstand large gripping pressures, but such material is more abrasive than others. The light bands are used where dynamic torque is predominant, as in shifting from one forward gear to the next, and they are lined with a less abrasive material that helps hold down drum wear.

Double-Wrap Bands.   Known also as a split-band or dual-band, the **double-wrap band** is a more expensive design, but it has a distinct advantage over the single wrap: It has a smoother,

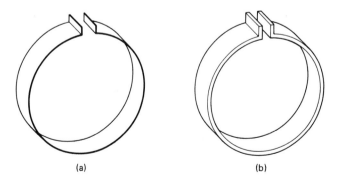

FIGURE 4-2   Single-wrap bands: (a) light; (b) heavy.

more uniform grip and it is more sensitive to self-energizing—it requires less pressure to exert the same amount of braking action as a single band. This can be demonstrated by pulling on a piece of cotton string or ribbon that has been wrapped once around your wrist. It does not grip as tightly as when you wrap it twice around your wrist, and this is comparable to the difference between single- and double-wrap bands.

Figure 4-3 shows the fundamental design of a double-wrap band. The diameter and overall width are much the same as a single-wrap, except that the double-wrap is really three bands acting as one. Pressure is applied at the leading end of the center band, and the trailing end of that band is connected to the leading end of the two outside bands by a metal block, or lug. So the center band acts much the same way that single-wrap does, except that as it wraps, its trailing end pulls the leading ends of the two outside bands, causing them also to wrap. The trailing ends of the two outside bands are anchored to the transmission case.

Band Wear

As you might expect, the greatest point of wear is at the band lining, although the drum surface is subject to wear, too. Both the band lining and drum surface must be checked. Some bands are self-adjusting; others require an adjustment check at each service period. Any good service manual will provide the necessary adjustment instructions and

Center segment of band pulls attaching lug in direction of rotation causing two outside segments to wrap and pull against case

Reacts against case

Rotation

Pressure applied here in direction of rotation

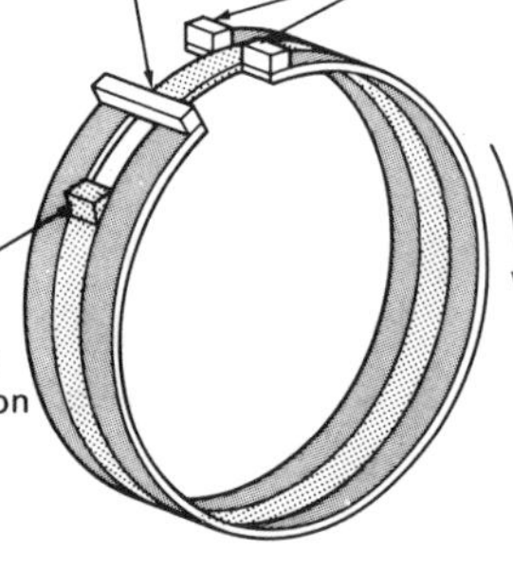

FIGURE 4-3 Double-wrap band requires less pressure than one-piece band to achieve same squeezing or braking force.

specifications. Most band linings have one or more grooves cut into them (Figure 4-4). This helps to ensure that there is enough transmission fluid to help soften the braking action and cool the band-to-drum interface. If even a part of the band grooving is worn completely away, the band should be replaced.

FIGURE 4-4 Single-wrap steel band with two lining grooves to permit good fluid distribution.

Clutch Design

There are three types of clutches used in automatic transmissions: (1) disc, (2) one-way, and (3) centrifugal. Within any transmission model, there can be several of these, especially the first two.

You will note that manufacturers use different terms for the various disc clutch applications: for example, the clutch that functions for high-reverse is called the front clutch by Chrysler, the rear clutch by Ford, and the direct clutch by General Motors. And what General Motors calls the forward clutch is called the rear clutch by Chrysler and the front clutch by Ford. In practice, someone who perhaps works mostly on Ford transmissions might tend to use the Ford terminology—"rear clutch"—even when working on a Chrysler "front clutch." It is best to think in terms of the function of the clutch (high-reverse, forward, low-reverse, intermediate); then you will avoid confusion.

Disc Clutch. The simple **disc clutch** consists of (1) a lined disc that is splined to one drive train member through a hub, and (2) two plates—one on each side of the disc—that are connected to another member of the drive train. The two drive train members turn independently of each other until pressure is applied, forcing the plates to squeeze tightly against the clutch disc, thereby con-

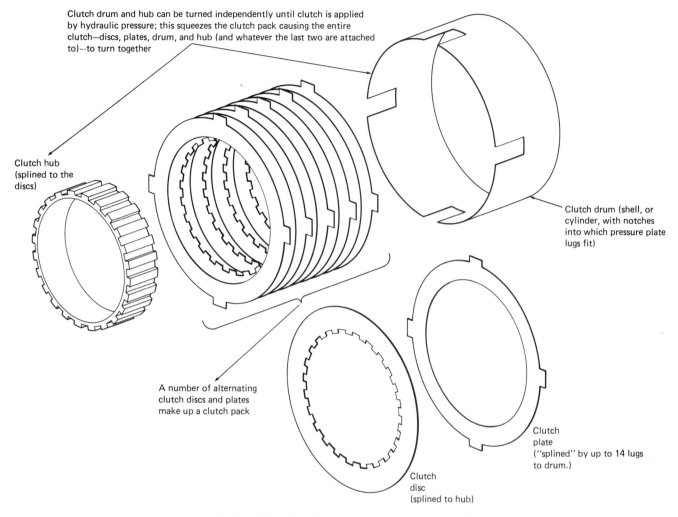

Clutch drum and hub can be turned independently until clutch is applied by hydraulic pressure; this squeezes the clutch pack causing the entire clutch—discs, plates, drum, and hub (and whatever the last two are attached to)--to turn together

Clutch hub
(splined to the
discs)

Clutch drum (shell, or
cylinder, with notches
into which pressure plate
lugs fit)

A number of alternating
clutch discs and plates
make up a clutch pack

Clutch
plate
("splined" by up to 14 lugs
to drum.)

Clutch
disc
(splined to hub)

FIGURE 4-5   Simplified view of multiple disc clutch.

necting the two drive train members so that they turn as one. You will recognize this as the same principle used in passenger car and light truck manual transmissions. The main difference between those applications and the single-disc applications in automatic transmissions is that the latter is a **"wet" clutch**, that is, it operates in transmission fluid, whereas light-duty manual transmission clutches are designed for dry operation.

In automatic transmissions, even greater use is made of **mutiple-disc clutches**. They incorporate the same plate–disc–plate arrangement, except—as the name implies—there are a number of plates and discs alternating to create a "clutch pack" of typically two to five pairs or more. In principle, the greater the number of plate–disc pairs there are, the smaller the diameter need be to achieve the same holding power. This principle is used widely in

linking together rotating members of planetary gear sets. Multiple disc clutches are also used in some automatic transmission applications to stop a rotating planetary member by locking, or **grounding**, it to the case—the same application for which bands are used. Figure 4-5 shows the hub, disc, plate, and drum arrangement in simplified form. In some applications, the drum is eliminated and the plate lugs slide directly into grooves machined on the inside of the transmission case.

The lining on most clutch discs carries a groove pattern (Figure 4-6)—often more complex than band grooves. It is also made of either metallic- or paper-based material, depending on the application. The pattern and amount of grooving is carefully worked out for the lining material that is used. It helps effect smooth shifts and improves fluid circulation for cooling.

FIGURE 4-6   One of several groove patterns used in clutch discs.

There is more to a multiple-disc clutch than hub, drum, discs, and plates. The mechanism for clutch application and release involves the use of the hydraulic system and springs of various types. The hydraulic application system is covered in Chapter 6.

Disc wear: Excessive heat and dirt are the most significant causes of disc wear damage. *If a vehicle's transmission fluid and cooling system fluid were faithfully changed periodically according to manufacturer's specifications, significant wear would not be expected before 100,000 miles under midrange operating conditions.* With very few exceptions, of course, this is not the case. So we find worn and burned discs and plates (Figure 4-7), as well as cone-shaped ones (Figure 4-8), all of which must be replaced. Those discs and plates shown in Figure 4-9 are acceptable.

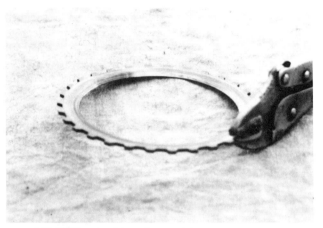

FIGURE 4-8   Disc distorted into a cone shape from excessive heat.

Other than building-in specified clearances during assembly, there is no adjustment for multiple disc clutches. Clearance is achieved primarily by selecting various thicknesses of **pressure plates** and/or snap rings.

Not all manufacturers provide clearance specifications. A correctly reassembled clutch should have sufficient clearance to allow the discs and plates to turn without a heavy drag against each other, but if there is more than a 1/8-in. clearance, the assembly is too loose.

One-Way Clutch.   This is a descriptive name for a mechanism also known as an **overrunning clutch**, a **roller clutch**, or a **sprag clutch**; it is designed so that it will turn only one way.

The **one-way clutch** is a very simple, rugged, and dependable design. It consists of an inner and outer race separated by rollers (Figure 4-10) or by bone-shaped sprags (Figure 4-11). The inside circumference of the outer "race" of the roller clutch

FIGURE 4-7   Clutch disc and plate wear.

FIGURE 4-9   Acceptable discs and plates.

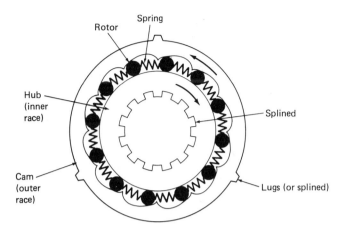

FIGURE 4-10   One-way or roller clutch.

has wedge-shaped grooves called **cams**, one for each roller. The spring behind each roller applies just enough pressure to keep the roller at the narrow end of the cam. The inner race can turn in the direction toward the larger part of the cam because it tends to move the roller with it—*away* from the wedge end of the cam. As soon as it tries to turn in the opposite direction, the roller, which is at the small end of the cam (assisted by the spring), is wedged tightly between the inner and outer race, which locks the two together. The same thing happens with the sprag clutch, except that the wedge, or *cam*, is the sprag itself—the outer race is smooth. When the clutch is turned one way, the sprag tends to lie down—it drags, allowing the races to turn in opposite directions. But as soon as it tries to turn in the other direction, the sprags stand up, binding the inner and outer races together. Both the inner and outer race of the sprag clutch have smooth, circular surfaces that bear against the sprags, whereas only the inner race of the roller clutch is smooth.

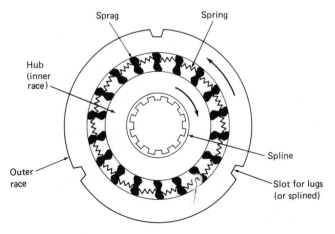

FIGURE 4-11   One-way or sprag clutch.

One-way clutches are used in combination with multiple-disc clutches to hold members of the planetary gear set, and they are used to allow the torque converter stator to turn after the coupling phase has been reached. (The torque converter is discussed later in this chapter.)

Some one-way clutches can be assembled for either clockwise (CW) or counterclockwise (CCW) rotation simply by flopping them during assembly. Notice that if you hold a one-way clutch so that its hub will turn only CW, flopping it to the other side allows you to turn it only CCW. Keep this in mind during assembly; some clutches can be installed either way.

One-way clutch wear: Springs and spring retainers are the parts that show the greatest damage and/or wear. Although the roller, sprags, and races should be inspected, they are not subject to the extent of wear or damage that you might expect from the similarity in appearance of a one-way clutch to a roller bearing, because one-way clutches carry no significant rolling loads. Acid pitting or other damage from fluid breakdown and electrolysis can occur, however.

Centrifugal Clutch. Taking advantage of centrifugal force (see Chapter 2), the **centrifugal clutch** design incorporates two or more segments (called weights or shoes) fastened to a hub, and a cylinder (or drum) against which the weights are forced when the hub reaches a particular speed. The centrifugal force is in direct proportion to the speed of the turning hub, so the shoe moves from no drum contact through a sliding contact at low hub speeds to a fixed contact at a higher speed (Figure 4-12). In addition to hub speed, the weight of the shoes—and even the design—as well as the load on the drum affect the speed at which fixed contact occurs.

Although the centrifugal clutch has many applications, it is not used extensively in current automatic transmissions. In one of its few applications, it serves as a lock-up device in lock-up converters (e.g., Ford C-5), but even in this application it is not used as widely as other torque converter lock-up devices discussed later in this chapter.

Centrifugal clutch wear: The friction material, or lining, is subject to the greatest wear. But the only current application of the centrifugal clutch design is in the torque converter, which is a sealed unit, so wear will not be discussed further in

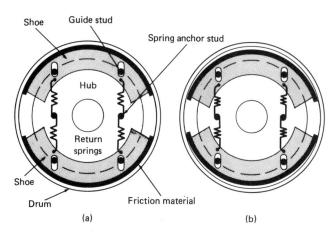

FIGURE 4-12 Simple centrifugal clutch: (a) applied (hub spinning fast enough to allow centrifugal force to overcome retracting springs); (b) released (hub speed slow enough to allow springs to overcome centrifugal force.

this chapter. Refer to Chapter 10 for ways to check for lock-up in torque converters that use the centrifugal clutch design.

FLUID COUPLING

Fluids include liquids and gases, as mentioned in Chapter 2. Both behave similarly, but they are not without their significant differences. The **fluid coupling**, which might better be called the liquid coupling, uses liquid ("transmission fluid") rather than gas because liquids are noncompressible and heavier than gases, but they have the same properties of flow and the ability to assume any shape that is characteristic of gases.

Origins of the Fluid Coupling. Just as the planetary gearset was in popular use long before development of the automatic transmission, so was the fluid coupling. Its use began in the early 1900s in steamship propulsion and was later used to help dampen the vibrations of large diesel engines. Interest in its application in automobiles was generated initially by the desire to eliminate shifting gears and depressing the clutch pedal. There had to be some automatic means to allow the engine to run while the vehicle was standing still, and the fluid coupling offered the best prospect. Just before World War II, Chrysler was the first to use it in the United States, by adding it to the standard power train—it allowed the engine to idle in gear—but the

foot-operated clutch was still used when shifting gears. Since then, the fluid coupling concept has been developed through a series of designs—many quite elaborate—to the highly refined torque converter units in use today.

Structure. A simple fluid coupling contains three basic members: a housing, an impeller, and a turbine. The **impeller** and the **turbine** are shaped like two halves of a donut, or **torus**. Visible from the cut sides are vanes—like the membranes between sections of a breakfast grapefruit (Figure 4-13).

Operation. With the two halves of the housing sealed together and filled with fluid, the impeller, which is connected directly to the housing, is driven by an input source (engine) and acts as a pump, moving the fluid (liquid) in its direction of rotation. The moving fluid flows against the vanes of the turbine, which turns independently of the housing and is connected to an output device (transmission).

The efficiency of the fluid coupling ranges from essentially zero (engine idle, car at rest) to about 90%, depending on several factors, among which are fluid type, impeller and turbine **vane** or **blade** design, vehicle load, and engine torque. It is this spread of efficiency that makes the fluid coupling so useful in the automotive power train. At engine idle, the impeller turns so slowly that it cannot move the fluid fast enough to overcome the turbine load or stall the engine. But as engine speed increases, the impeller increases the force of the fluid flow to the turbine, which overcomes the load inertia.

The low efficiency that allows the engine to idle while the transmission is in gear also allows too much slippage (inefficiency) at high turbine loads (acceleration). It was this problem that lead to the development of the torque converter.

Fluid flow: One of the first steps in this development was to identify exactly how the fluid was flowing inside the housing. One of the most obvious types of flow—especially at low efficiency— was **turbulent flow,** which is best described by a mixing or agitating action—misdirected fluid running into itself and producing little useful force. Turbulent flow was greatly reduced by the addition of a hollow torus, or guide ring, in the center of the

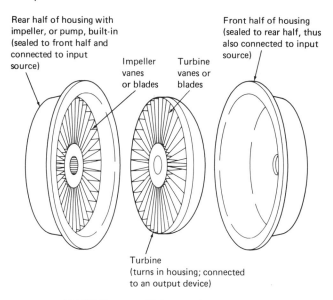

Rear half of housing with impeller, or pump, built-in (sealed to front half and connected to input source)

Impeller vanes or blades

Turbine vanes or blades

Front half of housing (sealed to rear half, thus also connected to input source)

Turbine (turns in housing; connected to an output device)

FIGURE 4-13   Fluid coupling members.

two torus halves making up the impeller and turbine (Figure 4-14). Since that center portion of neither the impeller vanes nor the turbine vanes contributed much to the coupling, overall efficiency was significantly improved.

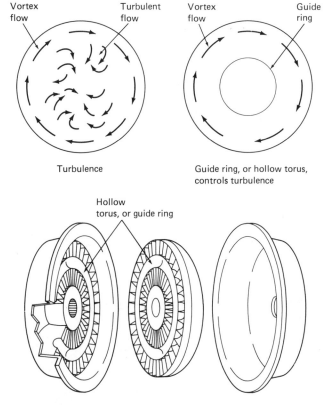

Vortex flow

Turbulent flow

Vortex flow

Guide ring

Turbulence

Guide ring, or hollow torus, controls turbulence

Hollow torus, or guide ring

FIGURE 4-14   Addition of hollow torus in center of the impeller/turbine torus.

Two other types of fluid flow were identified: rotary and vortex. These complement each other, depending on the difference in speed between the impeller and turbine. At high impeller-low turbine speeds (acceleration), vortex flow predominates, but as turbine speed approaches impeller speed, rotary flow takes over. **Rotary flow** is in the direction of impeller rotation and is the result of the "paddle" action of the impeller vanes against the fluid (Figure 4-15). **Vortex flow** results from the combined effect of centrifugal force, the curve of the outside torus cross section, and the pitch of the impeller vanes (Figure 4-16).

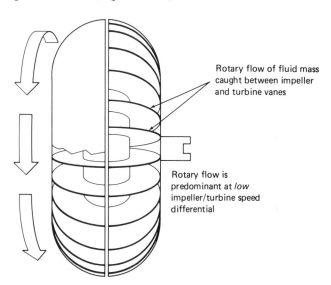

Rotary flow of fluid mass caught between impeller and turbine vanes

Rotary flow is predominant at *low* impeller/turbine speed differential

FIGURE 4-15   Rotary flow caused by impeller vanes and increased as turbine vanes approach same speed.

Torque Converter

Consider the effect of vortex flow in the fluid coupling. Starting at the impeller, the fluid flows to the turbine blades and back to the impeller. But when it returns to the impeller, its direction has been changed by the turbine blades so that it tends to work *against* the impeller (Figure 4-17). The addition of stationary, or reaction, vanes to redirect the flow (Figure 4-18)—so that it not only works with the impeller but doubles the torque effect—was the simple step of development that created the **torque converter**.

Stator.   The basic torque converter has three elements: impeller, turbine, and **stator** (Figure 4-19). The stator holds the reaction vanes, and it is

INNOVATIVE THEN—COMMON TODAY

At about the same time that the first automatic transmission appeared, there were other "breakthroughs" such as sealed beam headlights, speed warning lights in speedometers, safety-rim wheels, all-coil-spring suspension, pushbutton radios, inside hood locks, air-conditioning, and batteries mounted in the engine compartment, to name a few.

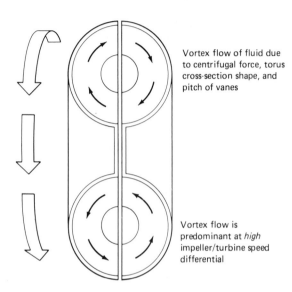

FIGURE 4-16 Vortex flow caused by centrifugal force, torus shape, and vane pitch.

Vortex flow of fluid due to centrifugal force, torus cross-section shape, and pitch of vanes

Vortex flow is predominant at *high* impeller/turbine speed differential

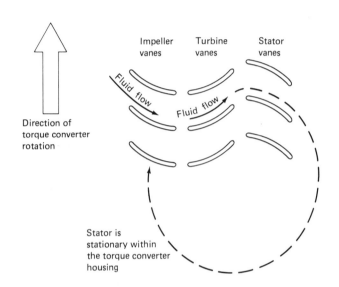

FIGURE 4-18 Addition of stator changes direction of vortex flow so that it assists pump.

Impeller vanes   Turbine vanes   Stator vanes

Direction of torque converter rotation

Fluid flow

Fluid flow

Stator is stationary within the torque converter housing

mounted on a one-way clutch so that as turbine speed approaches impeller speed, and rotary flow becomes predominant (**coupling phase**), the stator can turn with the flow instead of obstructing it. The coupling phase is very near a 1:1 torque ratio in-

stead of the 2:1 ratio that can occur when turbine speed is sufficiently exceeded by impeller speed.

So it is the fluid coupling and the stator mounted on a one-way clutch that produce the unique charac-

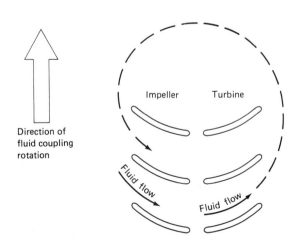

Direction of fluid coupling rotation

Impeller   Turbine

Fluid flow

Fluid flow

FIGURE 4-17 Vortex flow returning from turbine tends to work against impeller.

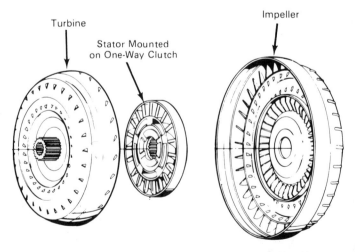

Turbine

Stator Mounted on One-Way Clutch

Impeller

FIGURE 4-19 Three elements of a basic torque converter.

teristics of a torque converter: (1) a *continuous coupling* through fluid that allows the engine to idle while the vehicle is stopped but in gear, and (2) a *conversion of torque* from as high as 2:1 when impeller speed exceeds turbine speed to nearly 1:1 when impeller and turbine approach the same speed.

Complex variations of the basic three-element torque converter have been used in automobiles, beginning with Buick, which in 1948 developed the Dynaflow that had two impellers, two stators, and one turbine, and in 1953 the Twin-Turbine Dynaflow, with two turbines, one impeller, and one stator. In 1956, Buick also introduced multiple-turbine torque converters with variable-pitch stators to optimize fluid flow for maximum torque efficiency. But these multiple-element variations were phased out of passenger car and light truck applications in the late 1960s.

Lock-Up Torque Converters. Growing concern over fuel economy renewed the development and application of torque converters, which have little or no slippage under cruising conditions. These include torque converters with clutch coupling devices and torque converters that combine hydraulic and clutch coupling. Some lock-up only in high gear (direct drive), others operate in other gears as well.

One of these employs a centrifugal clutch, and its most popular application is in the torque converter for the Ford C-5 automatic transmission (Figure 4-20).

Another type, used in the Ford automatic transaxle (ATX), incorporates a planetary gear set called a **splitter gear** (Figure 4-21). It is so named because it splits the transfer of torque between mechanical and hydraulic. It also works in both second and third gear. In second gear it transmits 62% of the torque mechanically, and in third gear it transmits 93% of the torque mechanically. The planetary ring gear is connected to the torque converter housing cover through a damper (dampers are discussed later in the chapter). The carrier is splined to the intermediate shaft for mechanical transfer, and the sun gear is splined to the turbine for hydraulic transfer. The ratio between the sun gear and the carrier is what determines the percentage split.

Perhaps one of the simplest concepts in the lock-up devices is the direct-drive shaft. The Ford Automatic Overdrive Transmission (AOT) can drive the transmission output shaft by a shaft running directly from the turbine down the center of the turbine shaft, or input shaft. In overdrive, it connects the two by application of the direct clutch at the rear of the transmission (Figure 4-22). In third gear, it also "splits" torque in a manner similar to the splitter gear torque converter, except that it is using the transmission planetary gear set with the forward and direct clutch.

Finally, the broadest application is the single-disc Torque Converter Clutch (TCC), which is mounted on the turbine and applies against the in-

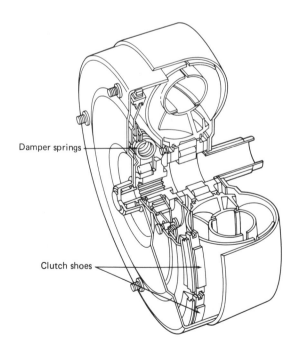

FIGURE 4-20   Lock-up converter using centrifugal clutch.

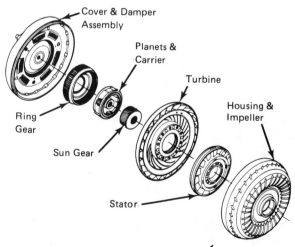

FIGURE 4-21   Splitter gear lock-up torque converter.

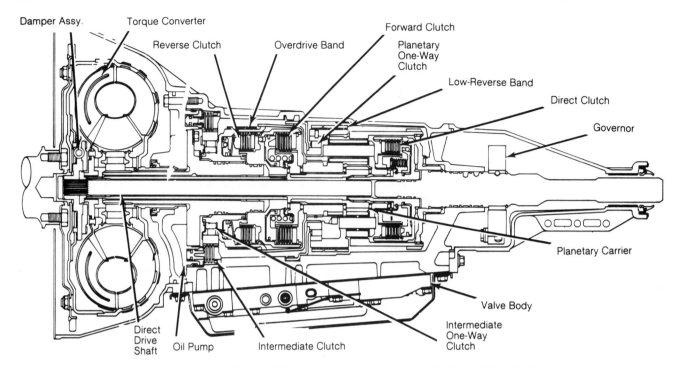

FIGURE 4-22   Ford AOT showing lock-up converter with direct drive shaft.

side of the torque converter housing cover—much the same way as does a manual transmission clutch (Figure 4-23). It is narrower, "wet," and applied/released directly by hydraulic fluid, however. This concept allows a complete mechanical link to be made at any speed and in any gear called for in an automatic transmission design. The "pressure plate" serves also as the clutch disc, having friction material bonded to its front face (many designs have friction material bonded to the cover as well).

The pressure plate is applied and released by directing the flow of mainline pressure into the housing. Normally, mainline pressure enters through the input shaft to the front chamber of the housing, which is formed by the cover and pressure plate. This keeps the pressure plate released. The pressure plate is applied by exhausting (releasing pressure) from this chamber and redirecting mainline pressure to the back of the pressure plate—between it and the turbine.

A variation on this is the viscous converter clutch (VCC). It is mechanically similar to the TCC, and it is also applied hydraulically. What makes it different is the use of a viscous silicone fluid that can be chemically formulated for numerous applications: adhesives, compressible fluids, damping media, heat transfer media, and

lubricants—to name a few. The viscous silicone fluid in the VCC is sealed in the chamber formed by the torque converter housing cover and the clutch "pressure plate" mounted on the turbine. It remains

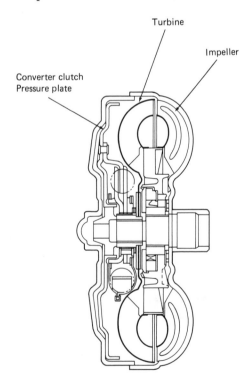

FIGURE 4-23   Torque converter clutch.

viscous (resistant to flow) when heated or subjected to high shear. As it is forced between the cover and plate surface during clutch application, it is displaced, and it expands, creating shear friction and increased resistance to shear between the two surfaces. It also helps to "dampen" (see the next section) and smooth out torque converter lock-up. It is also employed in full-time four-wheel-drive transfer case designs (see Chapter 8).

Dampers. All lock-up torque converters use dampers in the mechanical link. Manual clutch discs are also designed with built-in dampers. They look like those used in lock-up torque converters (Figure 4-24).

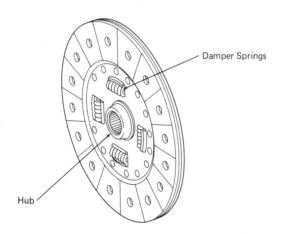

FIGURE 4-24 Manual clutch disc with built-in damper.

The splined hub of the **damper** has arms (usually four) radiating out like the spokes of a wheel. A heavy spring is placed between each arm and this whole assembly is sandwiched between two steel plates and riveted together. The plates have a hole in the center that fits shoulders on each side of the hub, and they have slots sized to the width and nearly expanded length of the springs. The hub is attached to one member on the drive train, and the plates to the other. The sudden application of torque to one member is absorbed by the springs as they compress and start the other member turning.

The damper is a simple, but important device. It acts as a shock absorber to the pulse of engine vibration, and it softens clutch engagement. During the fluid drive phase of torque converter operation, these torsional shocks and vibrations are absorbed by fluid resistance, so a mechanical dampener is not required until the mechanical link mechanisms are actuated.

Torque Converter Wear. The torque converter is a major assembly. It is considered as part of the transmission, but it has other functions as well. In addition to dampening engine vibration and torsional shock, it serves as a flywheel; it drives the transmission oil pump and, in some designs, serves as a mount for the starter ring gear. These last two items are easily inspected and exhibit a greater instance of damage from meshing rather than wear.

Internally, there are several areas subject to wear, damage, and outright failure. But virtually all torque converters are welded units that require machine-shop capabilities for disassembly and reassembly. Rebuilt units are readily available, and if wear, damage, or failure can be detected, replacement is the solution (Figure 4-25).

Chapter 10 includes tests and checks that can be performed on torque converters, but some wear, damage, and failure is difficult, often impossible, to detect even after a conscientious checking and testing effort. Experience suggests that a torque converter be replaced if it has clocked 40,000 or 50,000 miles, especially under "normal" use (erratic servicing). Certainly, if you have rebuilt the transmission, that cost alone should justify replacing the torque converter. But if the vehicle is of low mileage and has been well maintained, and you have removed the transmission for a premature or isolated part failure, then passing the tests of Chapter 10 should produce sufficient assurance that the torque converter is serviceable.

FIGURE 4-25 There are independent shops in most areas that rebuild torque converters.

Transmission Power Flow

The flow of power from engine through transmission involves complex combinations of clutch and band application (1) to *hold* planetary gear elements and spinning multiple disc clutches, (2) to *connect* one revolving element with another, and (3) even to combine these two functions. Chapters 12 through 17 present specific clutch and band applications for representative domestic and foreign transmissions.

TRADE TERMS _____

Band
Blade
Cam
Centrifugal clutch
Clutch
Coupling phase
Damper
Disc clutch
Double-wrap band
Fluid coupling
Grounding

Impeller
Multiple-disc
  clutch
One-way clutch
Overrunning clutch
Pressure plate
Roller clutch
Rotary flow
Self-energizing
Single-wrap band

Splitter gear
Sprag clutch
Stator
Torque converter
Torus
Turbine
Turbulent flow
Vane
Vortex flow
"Wet" clutch

REVIEW QUESTIONS

4-1. Transmission bands:
  (a) Help stop a vehicle. .
  (b) Drive transmission members.
  (c) Hold clutch or planetary members.
  (d) All the above.

4-2. All bands are adjustable.   T   F

4-3. Only double-wrap bands self-energize.
  T   F

4-4. Band linings are either:
  (a) Plastic or metal based.
  (b) Metal or paper based.
  (c) Paper or plastic based.
  (d) None of the above.

4-5. Drive links consist of:
  (a) Bands.
  (b) Clutches.
  (c) Fluid coupling.
  (d) All of the above.

4-6. Which of the terms does not belong?
  (a) Groove.
  (b) Band.
  (c) Sleeve.
  (d) Lining.

4-7. Match the terms in the first column with those in the second.
  (a) Sprag.   **(1)** Vortex.
  (b) Rotary.   **(2)** Disc.
  (c) Clutch.   **(3)** One-way clutch.
  (d) Turbine.   **(4)** Gas.
  (e) Liquid.   **(5)** Impeller.

4-8. The difference between static torque and dynamic torque depends on temperature.
  T   F

4-9. Identify the part or parts not common to both torque converters and fluid couplings.
  (a) One-way clutch.
  (b) Impeller.
  (c) Turbine.
  (d) Fluid.
  (e) Stator.
  (f) Housing.

4-10. Match the terms in the first column with those in the second.
  (a) Splitter gear.   **(1)** Guide ring.
  (b) Rotary flow.   **(2)** One-way clutch.
  (c) Turbulent flow. **(3)** Lock-up converter.
  (d) Torus.   **(4)** Coupling phase.
  (e) Stator.   **(5)** Donut.

4-11. The greatest torque multiplication occurs under:
   (a) Turbulent flow.
   (b) Rotary flow.
   (c) Rotary and vortex flow.
   (d) Vortex flow.

4-12. All torque converters contain mechanical dampers.   T   F

4-13 Hydrodynamic drive is another name for:
   (a) Torque splitting.
   (b) Fluid coupling.
   (c) Automatic four-wheel drive.
   (d) Gas drive.

4-14. Vanes, or blades, are used in:
   (a) Stators.
   (b) Turbines.
   (c) Impellers.
   (d) All of the above.

4-15. A "wet" clutch:
   (a) Is used only on torque converters.
   (b) Operates in transmission fluid.
   (c) Must be replaced.
   (d) Holds in only one direction.

4-16. Torque converters are sealed units and cannot be rebuilt.   T   F

4-17. Under ideal conditions, automatic transmissions can give:
   (a) Lifetime service.
   (b) 30,000-mile service.
   (c) 60,000-mile service.
   (d) 100,000- mile service.

4-18. One-way clutch hubs always turn:
   (a) CW.
   (b) CCW.
   (c) Either of the above.
   (d) Depends on whether it is a sprag or roller type.

4-19. Which term does not belong?
   (a) Drum.
   (b) Cylinder.
   (c) Band.
   (d) Shell.

4-20. The path of power flow through the automatic transmission depends on:
   (a) Stators.
   (b) Clutches and bands.
   (c) Dampers.
   (d) Torque converter housing.

ESSAY QUESTIONS

4-1. Describe the major parts of a torque converter and the function of each.

4-2. Describe the differences between a sprag clutch and a roller clutch.

CHAPTER ACTIVITIES

4-1. If your shop has a roller clutch or sprag clutch available, investigate what happens to CW input. Holding the outside race of the clutch with your left hand, turn the inside race CW with your right hand. Does the clutch turn or lock? Now flop the clutch, still holding it with your right hand. Does the clutch turn or lock when you turn the inside race CW with your right hand? What conclusion can you reach from this experiment?

4-2. If your shop has a cutaway model of a torque converter, examine the relationship of the impeller, stator, and turbine vanes with respect to vortex flow. (If your shop does not have such a model, ask your instructor to help you make one from an old, discarded torque converter.)

5

Control Devices

OBJECTIVES

When you have completed this chapter, you should be able to:

- Recognize orifices and the orificing effect of lines and valves.
- Compare the operation of check valves and spool valves.
- Explain the differences between servos and accumulators, and describe how the two are sometimes combined.
- State the main differences in at least three governor designs.
- State the purpose of a vacuum modulator.
- Name the four basic characteristics of a computer.
- Discuss the developing role of computers in automotive technology and, specifically, in automatic transmission operation.
- Recognize examples of the four types of control links.

The backbone of a machine is its **power train**—the means by which it contains and directs energy to perform work. The automotive power train, like any other, requires control of the major subassemblies—engine, transmission, and final drive—so that they operate together. This is achieved by mechanical or electrical control devices which act singly, or with others, through mechanical, electri-cal, vacuum, or hydraulic linkages to control power, speed, and heat. Some also serve as safety controls.

Some automatic transmission control devices are operated directly by mechanical linkage; others are operated by vacuum or hydraulic linkage. All these are mechanical devices, it is just that some are designed to be actuated by either vacuum or hydraulic pressure.

Devices that are actuated by electricity are **electromechanical**; that is, they are mechanical devices whose design and function include electrical components such as coils, resistors, magnets, and switches.

Electronic components are also part of the control system, but they do no direct work because they are **solid-state**—they have no moving parts. Instead, they receive and send signals. In the case of computers, the electronic system is receiving, *processing*, and sending signals.

Representative control devices are presented in this chapter to help you become more familiar with the fundamental design operation of each type.

ORIFICES AND VALVES

Orifices restrict the rate of fluid flow; whereas valves can start and stop fluid flow as well as control its rate and direction. Orifices are very simple; valves can be much more complex.

FIGURE 5-1 Transmission case, valve body, and separator plate.

An **orifice** is simply a passage in a hydraulic circuit or device that has been made smaller to slow down, or restrict, fluid flow. The size of the restriction is calculated (metered) to effect a specific pressure drop (Chapter 2). An orifice is a fixed opening and is effective only under dynamic, not static, pressure. Orifices can be line "plugs" with metered holes, or they can be cast into oil passages in the valve body or transmission case (Figure 5-1). Any valve that can be held partially open—that is, any position between fully open or fully closed—also has an orifice effect. The easiest place to see orifices is in the valve body **separator plate**. The smaller holes are orifices. The rectangular holes are usually not orifices; they are made in that shape to be of equal or greater cross section than the oil passage itself so that they do not act as orifices. Many separator plates look the same at first glance, but they may have different-sized orifices, additional holes, or fewer holes for different applications or valve bodies.

Check Valves

The direction of fluid flow is what operates a **check valve**. The ball-type check valve is a popular means of redirecting fluid, as shown in Figure 5-2, or stopping it from **back-flow**. In an automatic transmission, some of the holes in the valve body separator

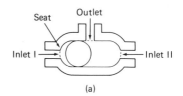

(a)

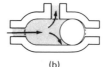

(b)

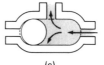

(c)

FIGURE 5-2 Redirecting fluid flow with ball-type check valve.

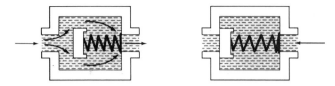

FIGURE 5-3   Stopping back-flow with poppet-type check valve.

plate are seats for ball-type check valves. Back-flow can also be stopped by a poppet-type check valve (Figure 5-3). The poppet valve return spring totally prevents back-flow because it seats the valve just before forward flow stops—when spring pressure exceeds hydraulic pressure. Ball valves with no return springs require a small amount of back-flow to seat. A ball or poppet valve with a heavier spring that is designed to compress at a specific pressure is called a **pressure relief valve**. Its purpose is to protect the system from high-pressure damage. When the pressure exceeds specifications, it opens the valve, releasing pressure and allowing the spring to close the valve.

Spool Valves

Many of the valves used in hydraulic systems are variations of the spool valve design. A simple **spool valve** is shown in Figure 5-4.

More complex spool valves have bodies with more inlets and/or outlets and spools with more

lands, which increases the valve capability from a simple "on/off" as in Figure 5-4 to a relay or switching valve as in Figure 5-5. The manual valve, or selector valve, is a good example of a complex relay valve (Figure 5-6). Many spool valves are hydraulically actuated, and these may have lands of more than one size on the same spool to direct its action (Figure 5-7).

A **pressure regulating valve** uses principles of both pressure relief valve and the spool valve. It

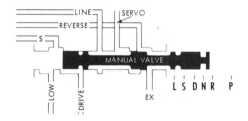

FIGURE 5-5   Spool valve that can switch back and forth from Outlet I to Outlet II or shut off com-

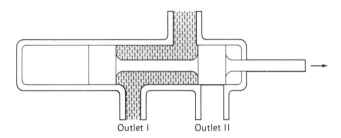

FIGURE 5-6   Manual relay valve. Multiple lands open or close ports in the valve body to route hydraulic pressure to clutch and band servos according to the position the valve is placed in by the selector lever. (Courtesy of Oldsmobile Division, General Motors Corporation.)

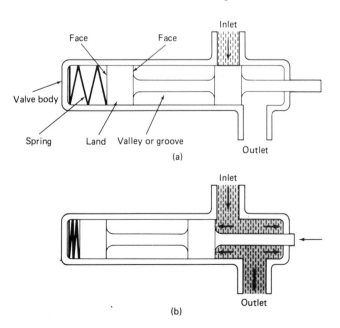

FIGURE 5-4   Simple spool valve: (a) on; (b) off.

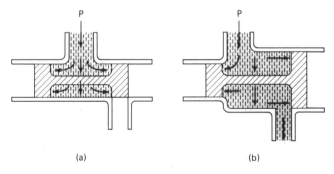

FIGURE 5-7   (a) Inlet pressure, *P*, exerts same force on both faces so spool valve does not move; (b) right face has greater area than left, so spool valve moves to right under inlet pressure (see Chapter 2).

also incorporates a boost valve that is actuated by hydraulic pressure to assist the spring, thus increasing the regulated pressure (Figure 5-8). This idea of auxiliary pressure, or one pressure working against another, is called the **balanced valve** principle, and it is common to automatic transmission regulating valves, such as the governor valve, throttle valve, and oil pump pressure regulator valve.

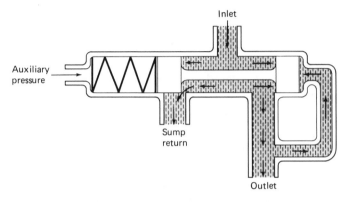

FIGURE 5-8   Pressure-regulating valve. Spring and auxiliary pressure oppose inlet/outlet pressure.

Most **shift valves** are spool valves operated by two auxiliary hydraulic pressure sources that oppose each other. As one source gains pressure over the other from certain subsystems in the transmission, the valve shifts in the direction of lower pressure. (Other shift valves are electrically operated by solenoids, which are discussed later.)

Some spool valves operate inside a sleeve or bushing that fits into the valve body. The mating surfaces of the land and the bushing, sleeve, or body are very precisely machined, allowing only a thin film of fluid for lubrication. This is why it is so important to keep transmission fluid clean.

SERVOS

A **servo** is a piston and cylinder at the output end of a hydraulic circuit. The piston is connected to some part requiring force, such as a band or clutch pack, and when a valve is opened to apply hydraulic pressure, the piston, cylinder, and linkage serve to transform hydraulic force into mechanical force. (In an automotive brake system, the wheel, or slave, cylinders can be thought of as servos, and the pres-

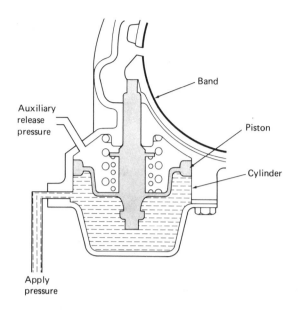

FIGURE 5-9   Servo applying band pressure.

sure is applied by a similar device—the master cylinder.)

Figure 5-9 shows a cutaway view of a servo connected directly to a transmission band. It is in the applied position. When the **apply pressure** is released, the piston is returned by auxiliary pressure at the opposite side and is assisted by the spring as well. The spring also acts as a cushion, or shock absorber, to soften the apply action. Servos can multiply force in two ways: (1) because pressure is measured in pounds per square inch, the larger the servo piston, the greater force it will exert from the same hydraulic pressure (Chapter 2), and (2) many servos are combined with levers to gain mechanical advantage. These are described later in this chapter under "Combination Devices."

The item of greatest wear on servos is the seals. Some servos have adjustable linkage to accommodate band wear. In other cases, the means for band adjustment is located on the reaction side of the band. Multiple-disc clutch servos (usually referred to as clutch piston and cylinder, rather than servo) are not adjustable.

ACCUMULATORS

An **accumulator** is similar to a servo in that it consists of a piston and cylinder. Its purpose is to cushion, or soften, hydraulic apply pressure.

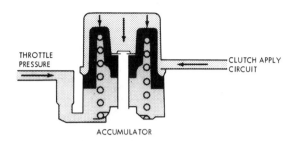

FIGURE 5-10   Simple accumulator.

A simple accumulator is shown in Figure 5-10. Notice that the accumulator piston works against a coil spring to help provide the cushioning or softening effect. As the spring compresses, pressure at the clutches increases. (Many *servos* are also equipped with springs that provide an accumulator effect as well as an assist to rapid piston return—and band release—when apply pressure is released. More about this later in this chapter under "Combination Devices.")

Instead of working only against spring pressure, some accumulators work against opposing hydraulic pressure which *bleeds* back through an orifice or regulator valve. For example, shifts at nearly wide-open throttle (WOT) must be made quickly (little or no accumulator effect) to avoid engine run-up between shifts, whereas those made at low speed and only slightly open throttle can be softened (full accumulator effect). To accommodate this variable need, some accumulators are designed to work against throttle pressure. This opposing throttle pressure is high at WOT, allowing little accumulator effect, and lower at smaller throttle openings to allow more and more accumulator effect (Figure 5-11).

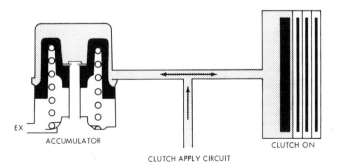

FIGURE 5-11   Variable accumulator.

GOVERNORS

A **governor** is a control device that senses speed and regulates other control devices accordingly. In an automatic transmission, it is mounted either in the case and driven off the output by a worm gear, or it is mounted directly on the output shaft, depending on the manufacturer's design. It is connected to the output shaft because its purpose is to respond to changes in vehicle road speed and provide hydraulic pressure to shift valves above certain speeds.

The design of mechanical governors uses movable weights that respond to centrifugal force. As output shaft speed increases, centrifugal force moves the weights farther and farther from the rotating axis. The weights bear against valves to regulate pressure to other control devices.

Figure 5-12 shows three types of mechanical governors. All have "primary" and "secondary" weights, springs, and valves, which extend the effect of centrifugal force. The heavier weights move out at lower speeds and the lighter ones at higher speeds. These governors all work *against* drive oil pressure. The spool valve weights in the shaft-mounted governor (Figure 5-12a) are mounted so that at low speed the primary valve spring holds it toward the center of rotation, and the secondary is held toward the center by control pressure. As speed increases, the primary moves out against its spring pressure which exposes a port feeding pressure to the shift valves. The case-mounted governor in Figure 5-12b uses ball-type check valves that are forced open by drive oil pressure to exhaust. This flow brings the lever-type weights toward the center of rotation. (Notice that each weight wraps around the governor shaft so that it closes the ball valve as the weight is moved by centrifugal force.) This allows governor oil pressure to increase, exerting force on the shift valves. The weights in the case-mounted governor of Figure 5-12c are also levers, but they act against a spool valve located in the governor shaft (which is also the valve body). This is shown in the cutaway view at the left. Notice the dashed line and circle at the upper end of the valve. That indicates a port (circle) and passage (dashed lines) that leads drive pressure to the chamber at the end of the valve. This helps balance the valve against the force of the weights. As road speed increases, centrifugal force moves the

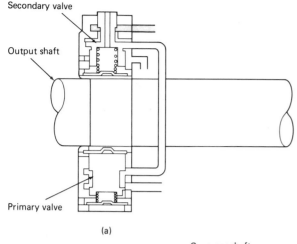

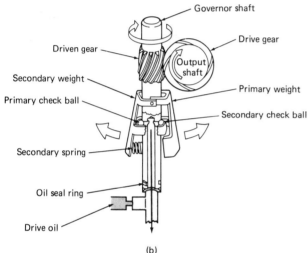

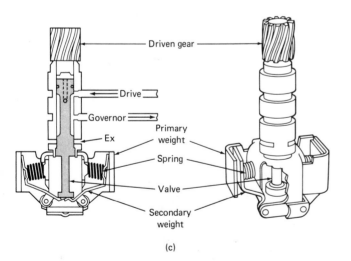

FIGURE 5-12 Mechanical governors: (a) shaft-mounted used by Ford, Chrysler, and most foreign manufacturers; (b) case-mounted ball valve type used by GM; (c) case-mounted spool valve type used by GM.

weights out and this moves the spool valve up (farther into the valve body), closing the exhaust port, as shown in the illustration, and increasing governor pressure.

Some transmissions have governor systems that include electrical circuits. As design engineers come to rely more and more on computer controls, governor systems incorporating electronic counters coupled with magnetic speed sensors will become more prevalent. Remember, however, that solid-state systems (electronic) do no work; there must be an electromechanical device if something is to be moved. These are discussed later in this chapter.

VACUUM MODULATOR

Engine vacuum varies with throttle opening and vehicle load. So do automatic transmission requirements. Mainline pressure, shift points, and shift action need to be modulated (or coordinated) with engine torque.

The **vacuum modulator** control unit (also called the vacuum diaphragm, vacuum control diaphragm, or vacuum capsule) operates a throttle valve, or modulator valve, that helps achieve this. It consists of a chamber divided by a diaphragm that has mechanical linkage on one side and a spring on the other. There is a port leading to the engine vacuum source (e.g., intake manifold) on the spring side, and a spool valve is connected to the other side. This valve, called a **throttle valve (T.V.)** or modulator valve, directs hydraulic pressure to other control devices at low vacuum and withholds it at high vacuum.

A vacuum diaphragm responds to differences in ambient, or atmospheric, pressure on one side and less than ambient, or vacuum, on the other. It is less effective at higher altitudes because atmospheric pressure and consequently, engine vacuum, is less there than at sea level. Figure 5-13a shows such a valve. Figure 5-13b shows an **altitude-compensating vacuum valve**. A spring **bellows** has been added to the atmospheric side. During bellows manufacturing, a vacuum is drawn—that is, some air is evacuated from inside—which causes the greater pressure outside to compress the bellows. The bellows is sealed to hold the vacuum. As altitude increases, the outside pressure that is com-

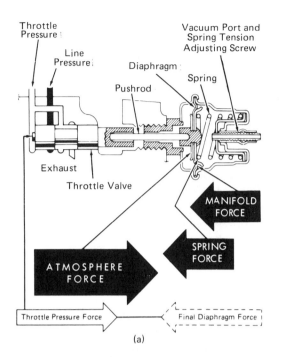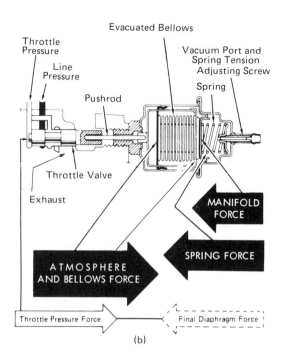

FIGURE 5-13   Vacuum-operated modulators: (a) optimum operation at sea level; (b) effective from sea level to high altitude.

pressing the bellows *decreases* (about 1 in. Hg for each 100 ft above sea level). This causes the spring bellows to exert pressure against the atmospheric side of the diaphragm to compensate for the lower atmospheric pressure at altitude. This is why the device illustrated in Figure 5-13b is called an altitude-compensating vacuum valve.

Some transmissions make use of mechanical linkage to control the throttle valve. Improper linkage adjustment can result in reduced clutch or band apply pressure, causing slippage and excessive wear. But the vacuum modulator requires no periodic adjustment once it is set. If a leak develops, high hydraulic pressure results, so no clutch or band slippage occurs. But a broken diaphragm can allow transmission fluid to be sucked into the engine combustion chambers, lowering transmission fluid level and causing wear if not detected.

There are also vacuum modulators that use two diaphragms. One draws engine manifold vacuum and the other draws **ported** vacuum. This means that it is drawn from the incoming side of the carburetor throttle body (above the throttle valve). Thus there is no vacuum at the closed throttle (idle) position, nor at WOT. But at intermediate throttle

positions, this ported vacuum is available to assist the lower engine vacuum typical of vehicles manufactured since 1973, when exhaust gas recirculation (EGR) was introduced.

COMPUTERS

The term *computer* has such widespread application that its meaning is most often misinterpreted. And this is no less true of its application to automotive technology. The modern definition of a computer includes four basic characteristics.

1. It is electronic.
2. It receives information.
3. It stores and processes information.
4. It communicates information.

The first characteristic means that it is solid state—no moving parts—and is incapable of doing work. The second, third, and fourth mean that it is programmable—that it can be made to receive and communicate information, but especially to store and process information according to procedures established in its storage system (memory).

ELECTRICITY VERSUS ELECTRONICS

What's the difference between *electricity* and *electronics*? Why isn't an *electronic* calculator called an *electric* calculator? Is there a clear distinction between an *electrical* system and an *electronic* system?

Until now, you would be hard put to find a quick answer. Oh, there are plenty of highly technical definitions, but none as simple as this contrast:

- An **electrical system** captures and distributes electrons (electricity) by mechanical means, using insulators and conductors.
- An **electronic system** captures and distributes electrons (electricity) by solid-state means—by the use of semiconductors, using diodes, transistors, and integrated circuits.

Semiconductors? Diodes? Transistors? Integrated circuit? Yes—hang on a minute! A semiconductor is a solid, crystalline substance, such as germanium (G) or silicon (Si), and its ability to conduct electricity falls somewhere between that of a good conductor and a good insulator. *It is the key difference* between an *electrical* system and an *electronic* system. It has permitted development, *in miniature*, of components that are *basic* to any electrical system. The electronic miniature of the electrical resistor is the *diode*, and a *transistor* is an electronic switch-ing device. *Both use semiconductors.* Since it is a property of a semiconductor that is being used, very little of the substance is needed, and very little electricity is required to make it work. As there are no moving parts (solid state), many diodes and transistors can be put together in a very small space to make *integrated circuits*.

So the difference between electricity and electronics is one of size, primarily, but also of form—sort of like the difference between a weight lifter and a ballerina. Although it certainly would be unusual to see those two working together, very often electrical circuits *are* teamed up with electronic ones.

In addition to programs built into a computer during manufacturing, some computers are programmable after they are made. Those that have any effect on automatic transmission operation include only built-in programs, however.

With the exception of what is called the governor computer on the Renault transaxle, computers that have an effect on automatic transmission operation are primarily for engine control. Their names vary: Computerized Engine Control (CEC), Micro Computer Unit or Microprocessor Control Unit (MCU), Electronic Control Unit (ECU), Electronic Engine Control (EEC), and Electronic Control Assembly (ECA) are a few. Since these are made not to be programmed or reprogrammed after assembly, it is probably best to think of them as electronic units that process pulses of electrical energy for the purpose of signaling as well as coordinating the operation of certain electromechanical devices. They cannot be repaired, only replaced as complete units. Most automobile manufacturers make testing equipment to diagnose the complete electronic circuitry so that the source of a problem can be isolated.

The use of computers in engine controls has produced a 5 to 10% improvement in fuel economy. Some automatic transmission designs (both foreign and domestic) now include electronically controlled solenoid valves for the opening and closing of certain hydraulic shift circuits. This allows precision timing of optimum shift sequences with respect to a multitude of electronically sensed engine conditions. The continual emphasis on developing environmentally clean and more efficient automotive power indicates that electronic, or computer-controlled, shifting will probably become more and more prevalent.

SENSORS AND COUNTERS

If you are familiar with the numerous emissions components, you know that there are electronic sensors of all kinds, shapes, and sizes. Most are not repairable and must be replaced as units.

Electronic shifting requires an electronic signal of road speed—the job usually done by a mechanical governor. This is achieved by a speed sensor and a counter. The **speed sensor** is a magnetic pick up, a device that senses and transmits low-voltage impulses. These are generated each time a small magnet, usually located on the circumference of some transmission output member, passes the coil in the sensor. The pulses are transmitted to a **counter**, which converts the information to engine speed and feeds it to the computer memory for processing with other information.

A **thermistor** is another type of sensor. It is made of semiconductors whose resistance changes according to temperature. It is used to sense fluid temperature. In one application it delays torque converter lock up until the transmission fluid exceeds a predetermined temperature.

Other sensors that affect transmission operation include ones indicating throttle position, altitude, engine coolant, and vacuum. These are discussed in Chapter 8.

SWITCHES AND SOLENOIDS

One of the most common electrical devices, **switches**, simply "make" or "break" an electrical circuit. They range from simple "on-off" to complex multiple-circuit types that simultaneously switch from one circuit to another, and they are often an integral part of another electrical device. Sensors, for example, are usually heat-, pressure/vacuum-, or magnetically-operated switches. Other switches in automatic transmissions include the neutral or safety switch, backup lights, torque converter clutch, overdrive, and shift valve switches.

In electronics, **transistors** perform switching functions and are fundamental components of computers. The complexity of many electrical devices and subassemblies can be simplified by recognizing the switching functions.

Solenoids are a vital link between the signal or control capabilities of electronics and the power capabilities of mechanics. They are electromechanical devices that use the power of a magnetic coil to accomplish work.

A simple magnetic coil consists of a wire winding with a loosely fitting iron core. When an electric current is applied to the winding, it creates a magnetic field (**electromagnet**). The iron core is influenced by the magnetic field and it, too, be-

WHY SO MANY GROUND STRAPS?

Use of vehicle frame and metal housings as a path for the flow of electricity back to the battery to complete a circuit is as old as the automobile itself. Early vehicles had very simple electrical circuits, and one ground strap from battery post to engine or frame was adequate for those unsophisticated machines. Most vehicle manufacturers mounted the major power train assemblies metal to metal—without rubber mounting blocks—so a complete ground path was no problem. Even later models with rubber-mounted engine and transmission required only a single ground strap because the electrical circuits were few and very simple: ignition, generator, and lights.

Today's vehicles are webbed with electrical circuits: emission control, high-energy ignition, electronic fuel injection, signaling and computerized systems, and of course, all the automatic systems for convenience—electric windows, trunk lids, clocks, courtesy lights, door locks, radio antennas, windshield wipers—and what may be the greatest convenience of all, the automatic transmission. If there were still only one ground strap, electricity—seeking to complete its circuit back to the battery—would run rampant throughout all metal parts. Without a solid path provided by a ground strap, electricity returning from automatic transmission

control devices would have to travel through shafts, bearings, and thrust washers—jumping from one to the other, arcing (sparking) slightly each time it jumped a gap, causing oxidation and premature bearing surface failure. With a ground strap from transmission housing to frame, electricity takes a path of least resistance—the one requiring no jumping effort: through the ground strap. The result is a better operating electrical circuit *and* longer-lasting internal transmission parts. Do not overlook this important electrical link, the ground strap.

comes a magnet. Both the coil and the core now have north and south poles. Since opposite poles attract and like poles repel each other, the core moves to a point within the coil where the repelling and attracting forces are equal. When current through the coil is switched off, the iron core is no longer influenced by the magnetic field, and it loses most of its magnetism. (If it were steel rather than iron, it would retain more of the magnetism, becoming a permanent magnet.)

On a simple solenoid, a spring moves the core partly out of the coil where there is no current flowing. As soon as the coil is activated, the magnetic field magnetizes the core, which is drawn into the coil by the attraction of like-poles, overcoming the spring force and exerting a mechanical (push or pull) motion through linkage to whatever the solenoid has been designed to move.

Many automobile starter solenoids are simply high-amperage switches; others also simultaneously engage the starter pinion to the flywheel ring gear. The horn relay is an example of a device whose major components are a switch activated by a small electromagnet.

The difference between a solenoid and an electromagnet such as that used in an electrical relay is the distance through which the device can be effective. In a solenoid the longer the coil and core is, the greater the coil movement, or throw, can be. But an electromagnet is effective only over a relatively small air gap. The strength of a coil or solenoid depends greatly on the number of turns of the wire and the current passing through it.

In automatic transmissions, solenoids are used to operate hydraulic shift valves and torque converter clutches by computer command as well as being manually operated for downshifts (kickdown) and cruise control.

CONTROL LINKS

The term *links* is not an established automotive term. It is a general term used here to identify the function common to four methods of providing the connection between initiation of a control at one device and its fulfillment at another. These are: mechanical links, vacuum links, electrical links, and hydraulic links. Link failure or maladjustment through damage, wear, leakage, and electrical discontinuity is at the root of many common problems or substandard automobile performance and failure.

Mechanical Links

Rods and *cables* are the primary forms of mechanical linkage. Rods are effective for both push (*compression*) and pull (*tension*), whereas cables, unless they are in a housing, are effective only when pulled in one direction. Both rods and cables are often connected to levers or **bellcranks** (Figure 5-14). The latter is simply a lever whose ends form an

---

WHAT DO SPRINGS AND BATTERIES HAVE IN COMMON?

Lots of things: They both come in all sizes and shapes, they are both made from various materials, and most important, *they both store energy.*

You cannot get electricity out of a battery unless you first put it in (charge it). And you cannot get force out of a spring unless you first put it in (stretch it).

Neither a weak battery nor a weak spring will store as much energy as new ones will. And do not fool yourself into thinking a weak spring can be restored by stretching—it cannot. It is suffering from metal fatigue and must be replaced. (Some very large springs that have been stretched, twisted, or bent beyond their limit can be "rebuilt" or reshaped, but none that you will come across in an automatic transmission.) The size of a spring determines its power, and its length determines how long the power will last.

Springs are used in external control linkages (e.g, to "return" a cable-operated device), as well as inside the transmission and on virtually all automotive subassemblies. They also serve as a stabilizing device when used with servo and accumulator pistons and spool valves by extending the duration of travel. If it were not for springs, these devices would snap from one position to another or flutter back and forth.

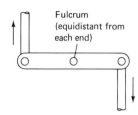

Lever as link to reverse direction
(no mechanical advantage)

Fulcrum
(equidistant from
each end)

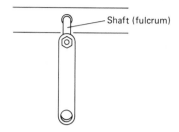

Levers as simple control devices
(mechanical advantage—increase torque)

Shaft (fulcrum)

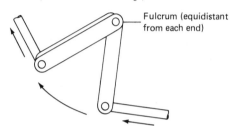

Bellcrank as link to change direction
(no mechanical advantage)

Fulcrum (equidistant
from each end)

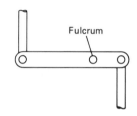

Increase speed or force
while reversing direction

Fulcrum

FIGURE 5-14   Levers and bellcranks.

angle to its fulcrum point. All—rods, cables, levers, and bellcranks—may be assisted by *springs*.

Levers and bellcranks are used to change linear motion to rotary motion to reverse direction, or to make sharp turns in a linkage assembly. (They can also be considered as simple control devices, when their fulcrum distance from each end is *unequal*, or when they are used in various lengths for torque advantage.)

Most cables are contained in a flexible housing which keeps the cable from buckling when it is under compression. Cables can be quickly and easily routed around obstacles, and their length is not as critical as that required for rods. As long as a cable is of equal or greater length than the distance from one control device to another, it will work. The ends of the cable housing must be firmly anchored for it to be effective.

Mechanical control linkage adjustment is made by disconnecting the rod or cable at one terminal point, setting the control devices at specified positions, and adjusting the length of the rod or cable to fit. The length of smaller rods (usually limited to carburetor linkage) is adjusted by bending, whereas larger rods and nearly all cables have clamped or threaded **trunnions** (pegs). After adjusting a rod, check that it does not interfere with

other parts in such a way as to prevent it from operating from one extreme position to the other.

Rod wear, of course, occurs mostly at joints. Wear can be corrected by replacing **grommets** (similar to bushings, but made from rubber or plastic) when they are used, or by welding to restore the worn surfaces. Cable wear usually consists of *frayed* (unraveled) or broken ends. The cable (or wire) can be replaced if the housing is still in good condition, but it is getting more and more difficult to find replacement cable without the housing included as an assembly.

Vacuum Links

Although vacuum links are less positive and more limited in application than mechanical links, they are ideal for engine/transmission-related controls and control signals. Since engine vacuum varies over the extremes of engine acceleration and deceleration, it can be used directly or as a signal to effect optimum transmission power flow.

The link itself is very simple, consisting of some type of airtight conduit, such as rubber or plastic hose, metal tubes, and so on, connected to a vacuum source at one end (e.g, engine intake manifold) and a vacuum-operated device at the other.

Leakage is one of the major causes of substandard vacuum system operation or failure and can cause incorrect shift points in some transmissions. Leakage is often the fault of loose vacuum link connections. Rubber and plastic hoses lose their elasticity with age, which keeps them from making a good seal. Rubber hoses also **check** (small "checkerboard" cracks). Checking can be detected by sharply bending the hose. If the hose shows cracks, replace it. Plastic hose seems to harden with age more than rubber, but it does not check as readily. Plastic is alright when it is hard as long as it seals at the connections, but it snaps easily.

Electrical Links

Wire is usually wrapped together with other wire in a **wiring harness.** This keeps the wires away from moving or hot engine parts, protects the insulation from chaffing, and is the only way to organize what would otherwise be a tangled mass. But a wiring harness also prevents visual tracing of a wire from one terminal to another. So wires are color-coded and assigned to specific locations in both the **male** and **female terminals** of a connector for correct mating.

Connectors are designed in various shapes and sizes to reduce the chances of making wrong connections (Figure 5-15). Mitchell's *Wiring Harness and Component Locator* identifies connector holes, or terminals, and saves both time and patience.

Sometimes breaks that are difficult to detect, or locate, occur in insulated wire; that is, the wire breaks, but the insulation does not. If the wire is feeding a device whose operation you can see, hear, or feel, the first test is to bend, twist, and otherwise move the wire (or harness) along its entire length to try to make or break contact. Otherwise, a test light or other continuity tester has to be used (Chapter 7).

Two other problems to watch for in electrical links are (1) frayed, broken, or burned wire insulation, and (2) broken or weak connections.

"Hot" wires are those leading from the battery source to the *load.* The load is any electrical device—even a simple lamp or switch. If the hot wire touches metal or a wire leading from the electrical device back to the battery (**ground wire**) it completes a **"short" circuit** (one without a load),

and full circuit power flows, burning the wire insulation, sparking, and even causing fire. Insulation can be repaired with tape or shrink tubing if it is isolated damage, but if the insulation has gotten too hot, or is too old and has lost its flexibility, it is best to replace the wire.

Small electrical loads require only small wires, but large loads must have large enough wires to meet the load demand; otherwise, it is just like directly grounding a hot wire. The smaller the wire size, the greater the resistance in the circuit, so always replace with a wire of *equal* or *larger* size so that you do not add more resistance to the circuit (remember, gage *decreases* with *increasing* wire size). A wire too small for a device that has a high electrical demand can overheat, even burn the wire. It is like grounding, because the device can carry more electricity than the wire can.

Connections should always be clean and tight; otherwise, resistance is added to the circuit and substandard performance results. Loose connections cause arcing (sparking) and corrosion, which create the added resistance. Corrosion is evident by the presence of a white powdery substance, resulting from oxidation of the metal from moisture between a loose connection interface. Loose connections are a common problem. In a connector, the terminals sometimes get bent or lose their tension and do not make good contact. This causes arcing—sometimes to the extent that the plastic connector housing partly melts from the heat. The terminals on most connectors can be disconnected and bent to restore tension for good contact. If the connector has minor damage from arcing, it can be taped or patched with **RTV** (room-temperature vulcanizing) **rubber.**

Hydraulic Links

Automatic transmission hydraulic links consist of fluid confined in (1) tubing outside the transmission, and (2) in passages machined and/or cast into the valve body, case, shafts, and other moving parts inside the transmission. These links connect valves, servos, accumulators, and other hydraulic devices, which together with one or more pumps, make a hydraulic system (Chapter 6).

Some hydraulic links are under greater pressure than others and require steel tubing or reinforced hose with special high-pressure fittings. The links within an automatic transmission valve body

FRONT END COMPONENTS

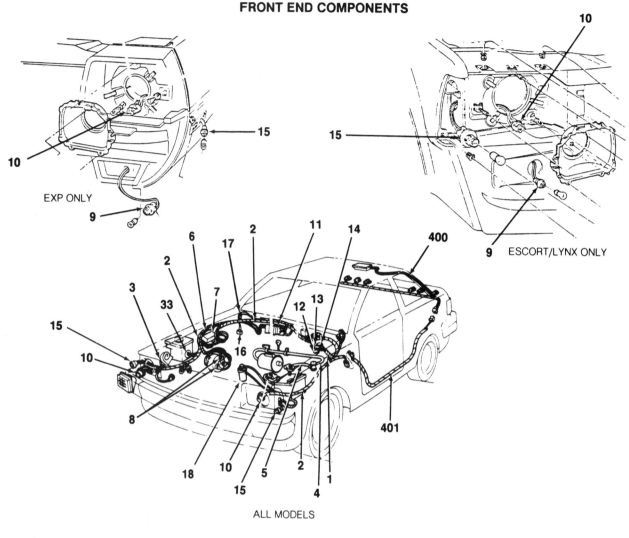

ALL MODELS

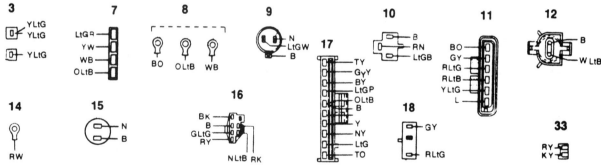

1. Dash Panel-to-Engine Gauge Feed Harness
2. Dash Panel-to-Headlight Junction Harness
3. Horn Connector
4. Starter Relay-to-Starter Harness
5. Starter Relay-to-Battery Harness
6. Alternator-to-Voltage Regulator Harness
7. Voltage Regulator Assembly Connector
8. Alternator-to-Voltage Regulator Harness Connector
9. Park & Turn Signal Light Connector
10. Headlight Connector
11. Breakerless Ignition Modulator Connector

12. Neutral Start Switch Connector
13. Carburetor Float Solenoid Connector
14. Coolant Temperature Indicator Sender Connector
15. Side Marker Light Connector
16. Dual Warning Buzzer Connector
17. A/C Fan Controller Connector
18. Ignition Coil Connector
33. Windshield Washer Reservoir Low Washer Fluid Switch Connector
400. Interior/Courtesy Light Switch Harness
401. Rear Lighting Harness

FIGURE 5-15   Connector sizes and shapes help identify the right connection (1981-84 Escort, EXP, LN7, and Lynx engine compartment wiring harness).

depend greatly on correct valve body mounting bolt torque for proper sealing.

For a hydraulic link to work, air must not be allowed to enter the fluid. Because the fluid is incompressible, it transmits power. But if air is mixed with the fluid, power is absorbed because the air compresses. Air gets into automatic transmission hydraulic links when fluid is too high or when fluid is too low. Even though transmission fluids include antifoaming agents (see Chapter 6), moving parts in an overfilled automatic transmission have an egg-beater effect on the fluid, filling it with miniscule bubbles of air which compress, rendering the system substandard or even useless. When fluid is too low to fill all hydraulic links and devices, the pump brings air into the system and the system fails.

COMBINATION DEVICES

There are many examples of two or three control devices combined into one unit: Switches are combined with servos, sensors, and solenoids; servo-accumulator combinations are common—often with linkage added to gain mechanical advantage.

Figure 5-16 shows an intermediate band servo-accumulator combination. On the shift from second to third, the servo apply pressure is released, and the hydraulic pressure to the third gear clutch is also directed to the spring side of the servo piston. This permits a pressure-accumulating effect, or pressure buildup, for third gear clutch apply because it is working against the orificing effect of the servo

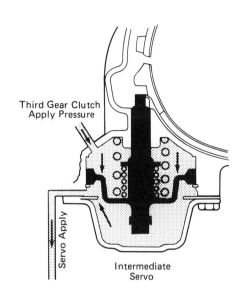

FIGURE 5-16   *Servo–accumulator combination.*

apply line as it moves the piston to its fully released position, evacuating the apply fluid.

Solenoids are the electromechanical equivalent of the hydraulic servo. They are especially important because they can be controlled electronically. Some combination devices using solenoids have already been mentioned (starter switch–gear and horn relay); some automatic transmissions (Ford, Renault, and Toyota) use solenoid-operated valves for shift control, and many others use solenoids for kickdown and torque converter clutch operation. In Figure 5-17, three solenoid-operated valves are shown.

TRADE TERMS

Accumulator	Electronic	Separator plate
Altitude-compen-	Electronic shifting	Servo
sating vacuum	Female terminal	Shift valve
valve	Governor	Short circuit
Apply pressure	Grommet	Solenoid
Back flow	Ground wire	Solid state
Balanced valve	Male terminal	Speed sensor
Bellcrank	Orifice	Spool valve
Bellows	Ported vacuum	Switch
Check	Pressure regulat-	Thermistor
Check valve	ing valve	Throttle valve (T.V.)
Counter	Pressure relief	Transistor
Electromagnet	valve	Trunnion
Electromechanical	RTV rubber	Vacuum modulator
		Wiring harness

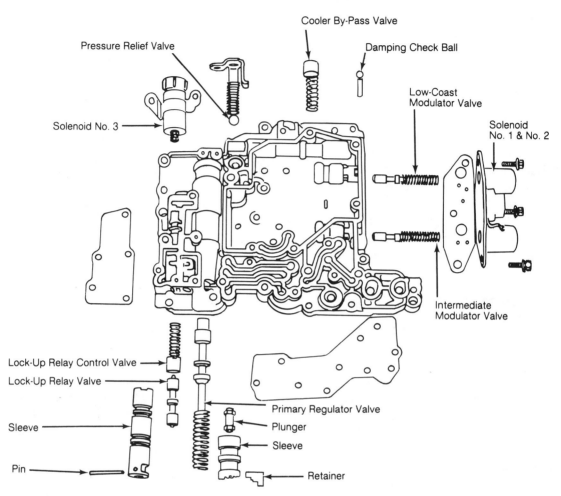

FIGURE 5-17   Valve body showing three solenoids.

REVIEW QUESTIONS

5–1. Control devices are powered by all but which of the following?

(a) Hydraulic.

(b) Vacuum.

(c) Combustion.

(d) Electricity.

5–2. Check valves are operated by fluid flow.

T   F

5–3. The balanced valve principle is common to all but which of the following?

(a) Throttle valve.

(b) Oil pump pressure regulator valve.

(c) Pressure relief valve.

(d) Governor valve.

5–4. Weak compression coil springs can be restored by stretching to their original length.

T   F

5–5. How many different types of control links are there?

(a) 3.   (c) 4.

(b) 5.   (d) 2.

5–6. Which of the following statements is true?

• As links, levers and bellcranks are used to convert from linear to rotary motion or to reverse or change direction.

• When the fulcrum point is *not* the same distance from each end of a lever or bellcrank, it can be considered a simple control device.

• When a lever is used to increase torque, it is considered a simple control device.
  - (a) First.
  - (b) Second.
  - (c) Third.
  - (d) First and third only.
  - (e) All.
  - (f) None.

5–7. Match the terms in the first column with those in the second.
  - (a) Slave cylinder.
  - (b) Land.
  - (c) Bushing.
  - (d) Back flow.
  - (1) Sleeve.
  - (2) Servo.
  - (3) Valley.
  - (4) Spring.

5–8. In automatic transmissions, servos are actuated by:
  - (a) Other servos.
  - (b) Governor pressure.
  - (c) Master cylinder pressure.
  - (d) None of the above.

5–9. A device incorporating a piston and cylinder at the end of a hydraulic circuit is called a:
  - (a) Slave cylinder.
  - (b) Accumulator.
  - (c) Servo.
  - (d) All of the above.

5–10. All but one of the following are basic to both servos and accumulators.
  - (a) Spring.
  - (b) Piston.
  - (c) Cylinder.
  - (d) Linkage.

5–11. An accumulator's effect results from:
  - (a) Bleed back or orificing.
  - (b) Spring action.
  - (c) Both of the above.
  - (d) Neither of the above.

5–12. The following terms are all common to what automatic transmission control device?_____ Springs, rotary motion, weights, centrifugal force, hydraulic pressure.

5–13. Which of the following statements best relates to vacuum modulator?
  - (a) Senses vehicle road speed.
  - (b) Engine vacuum varies with throttle opening and vehicle load.
  - (c) Applies clutch and band pressure.
  - (d) None of the above.

5–14. Match the terms in the first column with those in the second.
  - (a) Ambient.
  - (b) Vacuum.
  - (c) Bellows.
  - (d) 100 ft.
  - (e) Solid state.
  - (1) Pressure.
  - (2) Atmosphere.
  - (3) No moving parts.
  - (4) Altitude compensated.
  - (5) 1 in.

5–15. All governors have spool valves.   T   F

5–16. The function of an automatic transmission governor can be accomplished electronically by:
  - (a) Counter.
  - (b) Computer.
  - (c) Speed sensor.
  - (d) All of the above.

5–17. Fluid temperature can be sensed electronically by a:
  - (a) Diode.
  - (b) Thermistor.
  - (c) Transducer.
  - (d) All of the above.
  - (e) None of the above.

5–18. An electromagnet and a solenoid have which of the following in common?
  - (a) Transistor.
  - (b) Coil.
  - (c) Thermocouple.
  - (d) Moveable core.

5–19. Which of the following best describes a solenoid?
  - (a) Electrical.
  - (b) Switch.
  - (c) Electromechanical.
  - (d) Electronic.

5–20. Common electrical failures are caused by:
  - (a) Shorts.
  - (b) Corrosion.
  - (c) Loose connections.
  - (d) All of the above.

ESSAY QUESTIONS

5–1. Explain the differences between servos and accumulators, and describe how the two are sometimes combined.

5–2. Describe the four types of control links; give examples of each and what control they might link together.

CHAPTER ACTIVITIES

5–1. Carefully inspect the holes in a clean, used, valve-body separator plate. See if you can identify those that serve as ball check valve seats by locating the ones with shiny, chamfered edges. Notice that this will give the locations for each ball, too, in case you forgot to make note of them during disassembly.

5–2. If a case-mounted governor valve is available, carefully examine its mechanism to see how it functions.

5–3. On an available shop vehicle, conduct a cursory check of some of the vacuum hoses for checking and loose (poorly sealed) connections.

5–4. How many ground straps can you locate on one of your shop vehicles—or on your own vehicle, if you have one?

6

Hydraulic System

_____ **OBJECTIVES** _____

When you have completed this chapter, you should be able to:

- Name the three types of automatic transmission fluid currently used, and state the significant difference between them.
- Name the four functions of automatic transmission fluid.
- Identify the two types of automatic transmission filter.
- Discuss the various temperatures that occur in an automatic transmission, and explain what happens when fluid gets too hot.
- Show how to connect correctly the outlet and return lines on the transmission, on the cooler in a crossflow radiator, and to an auxiliary cooler used together with the original equipment cooler.
- Explain the three types of rotary pump and their differentiating characteristics.
- Trace any circuit given the hydraulic control diagram for any specific automatic transmission model.

Think of the hydraulic system in automatic transmission as consisting of two primary circuits: a control circuit that operates valves, servos, and accumulators, and a relatively free-flowing circuit that cools, lubricates, and couples the engine to the transmission through the torque converter. The system pumps automatic transmission fluid from a reservoir, or sump (the oil pan), routing it through

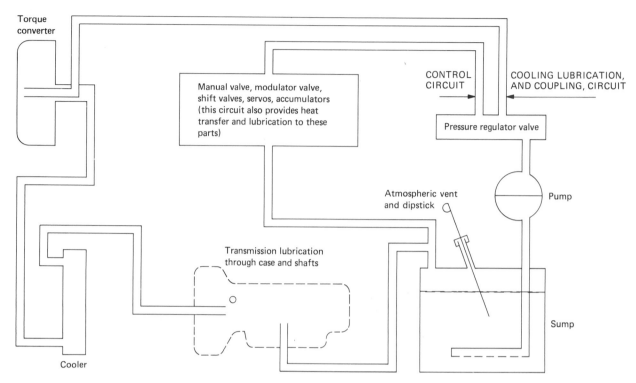

FIGURE 6-1   Two major circuits in an automatic transmission.

a pressure regulating valve where it branches to serve the two parts of the system described above (Figure 6-1).

The hydraulic system is complex; but it is not complicated as long as you concentrate on one thing at a time. Establishing a starting point and learning the circuits one by one allows you to then put the whole thing together. A thorough understanding of the hydraulic system is very important to building good diagnostic skills.

We investigate the hydraulic system in a logical manner by learning about fluids, filters, cooling, lubrication, pumps, fluid coupling, and finally, hydraulic control.

HYDRAULIC FLUID

Automatic transmission fluid (ATF) is a heavily refined, petroleum-based oil. It incorporates additives whose properties make it especially suitable for the flow and friction characteristics required for automatic transmission operation. It is customarily dyed red, primarily to help distinguish it from engine oil when determining leak sources.

ATF cools, lubricates, links control mechanisms, and serves as a coupling medium between torque converter impeller and turbine.

As many as 10 different additive types compose about 10% of total fluid volume. The first three in the following list contribute most to the unique properties of ATF.

Friction modifiers	Improves friction coefficient
Fluidity modifiers	Improves fluid flow
Seal swell agents	Helps protect seals from hardening and high-temperature decomposition
Viscosity stabilizers	Helps fluid retain body and fluidity over a range of temperature
Corrosion and rust inhibitors	Retards corrosion and rust from condensation
Antifoaming agents	Prevents aeration in churning fluid

Oxidation inhibitors	Retard oxidation at high temperature
Dispersants and Detergents	Suspending foreign particles and cleaning
High-pressure agents	Improves fluid surface tension
Pour point depressant	Reduces temperature at which fluid will still flow

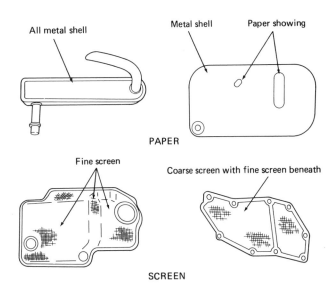

FIGURE 6-2 Examples of automatic transmission filters. (Courtesy of Allied Aftermarket Division.)

Of course, additives must be compatible with friction and bonding materials as well as various metal alloys in the transmission.

Early fluid formulations (1940s and 1950s) were designated Type A. Improvements in oxidation levels led to modified designations: Type A, Suffix A; Dexron: and Dexron II in 1973. Dexron II D has been acceptable for use in all automatic transmissions except Ford C-6 and JATCO in certain older-model vehicles. But Ford now recommends Type H for all its transmissions, and Chrysler recommends its Mopar 7176. The differences between Type H, Mopar 7176, and Dexron are in the static and dynamic friction coefficients. The **static friction coefficient** of fluid is a measurement of force (friction) resisting the movement of two stationary surfaces separated by the fluid, divided by the force holding the surfaces together. The **dynamic friction coefficient** of fluid is a measurement of force (friction) required to stop the movement of one surface over another moving surface when separated by the fluid, divided by the force holding the surfaces together. These friction coefficients obviously have a significant effect on shift quality and the holding power of friction elements.

FILTERS

There are two types of automatic transmission filter: (1) synthetic fiber or paper, and (2) metallic screen. Figure 6-2 shows some examples of each. Either type is encased in a sheet metal body in the oil sump. Dirty filters of the first type must be replaced, but often screen filters can be cleaned. If there is considerable varnish buildup from fluid oxidation at high temperatures, even the screen-type filters must be replaced.

A dirty filter can restrict fluid flow to the point that it seriously affects transmission operation and causes excessive wear. Generally, it is best to replace the filter if conditions indicate that the fluid should be replaced (see Chapter 9).

COOLING

Under heavy-duty operation, local temperatures in an automatic transmission can reach as high as 600°F. And although normal cruising speed temperature is about 180°F, driving in heavy city traffic, long uphill climbs, and heavy towing or hauling loads can raise fluid temperatures to 250 to 300°F surprisingly fast. Excessive heat causes oxidation of ATF. This deposits varnish on transmission parts, causing sticking valves, plugged filters, and a general loss of additive effectiveness.

Obviously, cooling is a very important function. The usual cooling design routes ATF to a large cooling tube in the outlet tank of the engine radiator. The outlet tank is always the one to which the bottom radiator hose is attached. On the transmission case, the fitting for the outlet line is *always* located below the return line fitting. That outlet line—the lower one that routes hot ATF to the cooler—must always be connected to the lower fitting on a

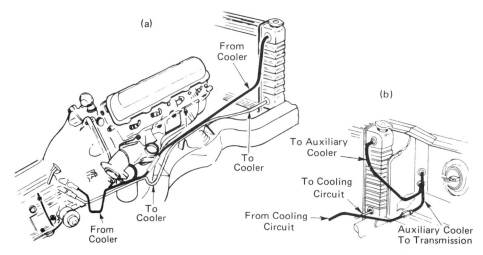

FIGURE 6-3 ATF cooling: (a) normal connection; (b) auxiliary cooler hooked in series for heavy-duty operation. (Courtesy of Oldsmobile Division, General Motors Corporation.)

crossflow radiator, as shown in Figure 6-3. This routing fills the cooling tube inside the radiator from the bottom, expelling air as it does. If it were hooked up in reverse, the cooling tube would drain before it would fill, introducing air into the system.

Additional cooling is provided on many motor homes and heavy-duty trucks by an **auxiliary cooler** connected in series with the standard cooler. It is usually mounted in front of the radiator (and air-conditioning condenser when so equipped). In addition to this **original equipment manufacturer (OEM)** item, **aftermarket** coolers are popular for vehicles hauling or pulling heavy loads, those subject to many starts and stops (such as delivery vehicles), and vehicles operating in very hot climates.

PUMP

Fluid under pressure is supplied to the automatic transmission hydraulic system by a single, rotary-type hydraulic pump located at the front of the transmission. The pump is driven by the engine through the torque converter housing. It draws fluid from the sump and builds pressure against a pressure regulator valve, which causes fluid to be passed to other parts of the system at controlled pressures.

Rotary pump designs include gear or rotor types and vane types. Although Mercedes-Benz incorporates a rear (secondary) pump designed

around two *external*-meshing spur gears, its primary pump uses the *internal-external* (IX) gear configuration that is used by many American and foreign makers. IX *rotary* pumps are also used in some Chrysler and American Motors transmissions. Gear and rotor pumps are **fixed displacement pumps** delivering the same amount of fluid on each revolution. **Variable displacement vane pumps** are becoming more and more popular, however, because their output can be varied within certain limits. Figure 6-4 shows how rotary pumps work.

The IX gear pump is shown in Figure 6-5. The external gear, keyed to the torque converter housing by the two drive lugs, drives the off-center in-

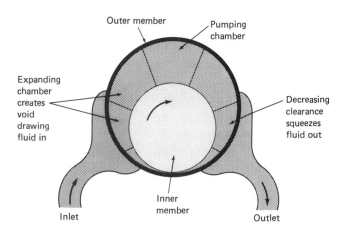

FIGURE 6-4 Schematic of how a gear, rotor, or vane rotary pump works. (Courtesy of Chrysler Motors Corporation.)

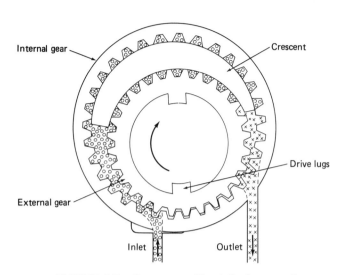

FIGURE 6-5   Gear pump (fixed displacement).

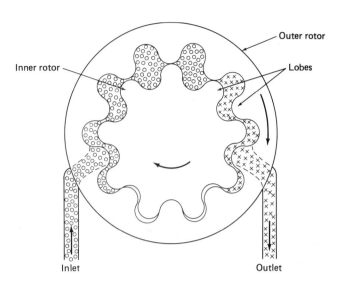

FIGURE 6-6   Rotor pump (fixed displacement).

ternal gear. As rotation proceeds, the space between the gear teeth (as they begin to disengage near the inlet chamber) increases. This creates a low pressure (vacuum) which draws fluid from the sump. The **crescent** is part of the pump body casting and serves to retain fluid entrapped between the teeth of the internal and external gears. As rotation continues, the space between the gear teeth decreases.

This "squeezes" the fluid, increasing its pressure and accelerating its flow through the outlet to the pressure regulator valve.

The IX rotor pump (Figure 6-6) is very similar to the IX gear pump. But notice that it has no crescent divider as the gear pump does. This is because of the unique shape of the intermeshing lobes. Like the gear pump, the space between the lobes in-

creases as the lobes begin to disengage on the inlet side. But the shape of the lobes is such that the surfaces of each are always tangent and nearly touching. This retains the fluid. As rotation continues, the space decreases, forcing the fluid through the outlet under pressure.

Figure 6-7 shows two views of the vane pump. Look at the left view. The vanes float freely in the rotor slots. The outer end of each vane butts against the inside diameter of the slide (really a movable pump body), and the other end butts against the vane ring. The ring "floats" and serves as a spacer so that the outer ends of the vanes always follow the **eccentric** (off center) inside diameter of the slide to retain the entrapped fluid. That is, when a vane approaches the right side, it is pushed into the rotor slot; this moves the ring to push out the vanes on the left side.

TWO PUMPS—BETTER THAN ONE?

Many older-model vehicles could be push-started or towed without concern about transmission lubrication because they were equipped with a second pump driven by the transmission output shaft.

Enough pressure was generated by the rear pump to engage the transmission when the vehicle was pushed and to lubricate the transmission when the vehicle was towed on the rear wheels.

Except for Mercedes, which still uses a rear (secondary) pump in its type 025 and type 040 automatics, there has been no rear pump since the pre-1967 Chevrolet Powerglide.

This is the reason for the practice of towing with front or rear wheels off the ground, depending on whether the vehicle is front- or rear-wheel drive.

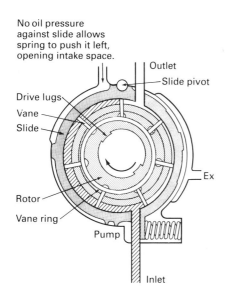

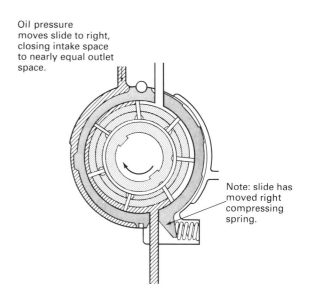

FIGURE 6-7   Vane pump (fixed displacement).

Now look at the right side of Figure 6-7 and compare the position of the slide (body). Hydraulic pressure against its left side has moved it to the right (notice the spring compression), so that the space between it and the rotor is nearly equal around the entire circumference (displacement has been varied: variable displacement). In this configuration the pump pumps less oil, and it requires less horsepower to turn it. Much of the time, the pressure developed by a gear or rotor (fixed displacement) pump is not needed and is exhausted by the pressure regulator valve back to the sump, and the horsepower to turn the pump to develop that fixed (and high) pressure is wasted. This is why the use of the vane-type rotary pump is increasing in popularity.

TORQUE CONVERTER

The fluid that enables the torque converter to connect engine and transmission is provided by the transmission oil pump through the pressure regulator valve. Substantial heat is generated as the fluid moves through the torque converter, so it is routed directly to the transmission cooler, then it continues through the lubrication circuit. There is a bypass valve between the cooler inlet and outlet lines that

ensures lubrication, should flow through the cooler become restricted.

The circuit for torque converter lock-up is discussed in the following section.

HYDRAULIC CONTROL CIRCUIT

Diagrams of automatic transmission hydraulic circuits appear confusing at first. Here are some pointers that help in interpreting them.

1. Trace only one circuit at a time. (Duplicate copies on a copying machine, then shade in the circuit in which you are interested.)
2. Start from the pump.
3. Note how the manual valve circuit and the modulator valve (throttle valve) circuit is fed.
4. Trace the main path of your circuit first, then trace the effect of the alternate circuits.
5. Understand that the diagram does not always show a valve in the position it should be in to depict accurately the condition you are tracing.
6. Understand that the layout of the diagram (position of valves, servos, accumulators, clutches, and bands with respect to each other does not necessarily reflect the relative positions of parts and circuits in the transmission itself.

TABLE 6-1

Terminology variation among manufacturers

Common or Descriptive Name	General Motors	Ford	Chrysler	Other
Mainline, or line pressure	Drive oil	Control pressure	—	Working pressure
Full throttle downshift	Detent	—	—	W.O.T. (wide–open throttle)
Vacuum modulator	—	Vacuum diaphragm	—	—
Throttle valve (T.V.)	Modulator valve	—	—	—
Downshift valve	Detent valve	—	—	(passing gear)
Throttle pressure	Modulator pressure	—	—	—
Downshift pressure	Detent pressure	—	—	—
Impeller	Torque converter pump	—	—	—
Input shaft	Turbine shaft	—	Reactor shaft support	—
Stator support	—	Front clutch	Rear clutch	—
High–reverse clutch	Direct clutch	Rear clutch	Front clutch	—
One–way roller clutch	—	—	Overrunning clutch	Sprag clutch
Clutch drum	Clutch housing	Clutch cylinder	Clutch retainer	—
Input shell	Sun gear drive shell	—	Sun gear driving shell	Input drum
Low–reverse servo	Rear servo	—	—	—
Low–reverse band	—	Rear band	—	—
Intermediate servo	Front servo	—	—	—
Ring gear	Internal gear	Internal gear	Annulus gear	—
Low gear	—	—	Breakaway	First gear
Intermediate gear	—	—	Kickdown	Second Gear
Intermediate band	—	Front band	Kickdown band	—
Front ring gear	Input ring gear	—	—	—
Front carrier	Output carrier	—	—	—
Rear ring gear	Output ring gear	—	—	—
Rear carrier	Reaction carrier	—	—	—
Output carrier	Rear carrier	—	—	—

7. Read the fluid passages as they are drawn. When one passage crosses another, one may be continuous as though it crosses over the other, which in effect it does (but the one it crosses over is also continuous). Also, notice that passages that cross each other without intersecting are always drawn continuous when they are horizontal (running from side to side) and interrupted when vertical (running up and down the page). Take note of orifices, direction of flow (sometimes indicated by arrows), and check valves.

Table 6-1 summarizes different terminology among manufacturers for what is essentially the same part. For example, the clutch pack that is engaged in both high and reverse is called the *direct* clutch by General Motors, the *rear* clutch by Ford, and the *front* clutch by Chrysler! Knowing of these differences in terminology helps when reading a hydraulic circuit diagram.

Automatic transmission hydraulic systems vary from one model to the next, and changes will be made as new models come out. But by analyzing one representative system, you will easily be able to trace through the hydraulic circuit diagrams of any other to become familiar with its essential differences. We use the Turbo Hydra Matic 350 (THM-350), since more than 25 million of it and its derivatives—250, 250C, 350C, 375B—have been manufactured.

Neutral

The simplest circuit—and logical beginning—is neutral.

Referring to Figure 6-8, trace the following:

- *From the pump to the pressure regulator valve* (Notice that the line branches to other significant parts of the system *before* it enters

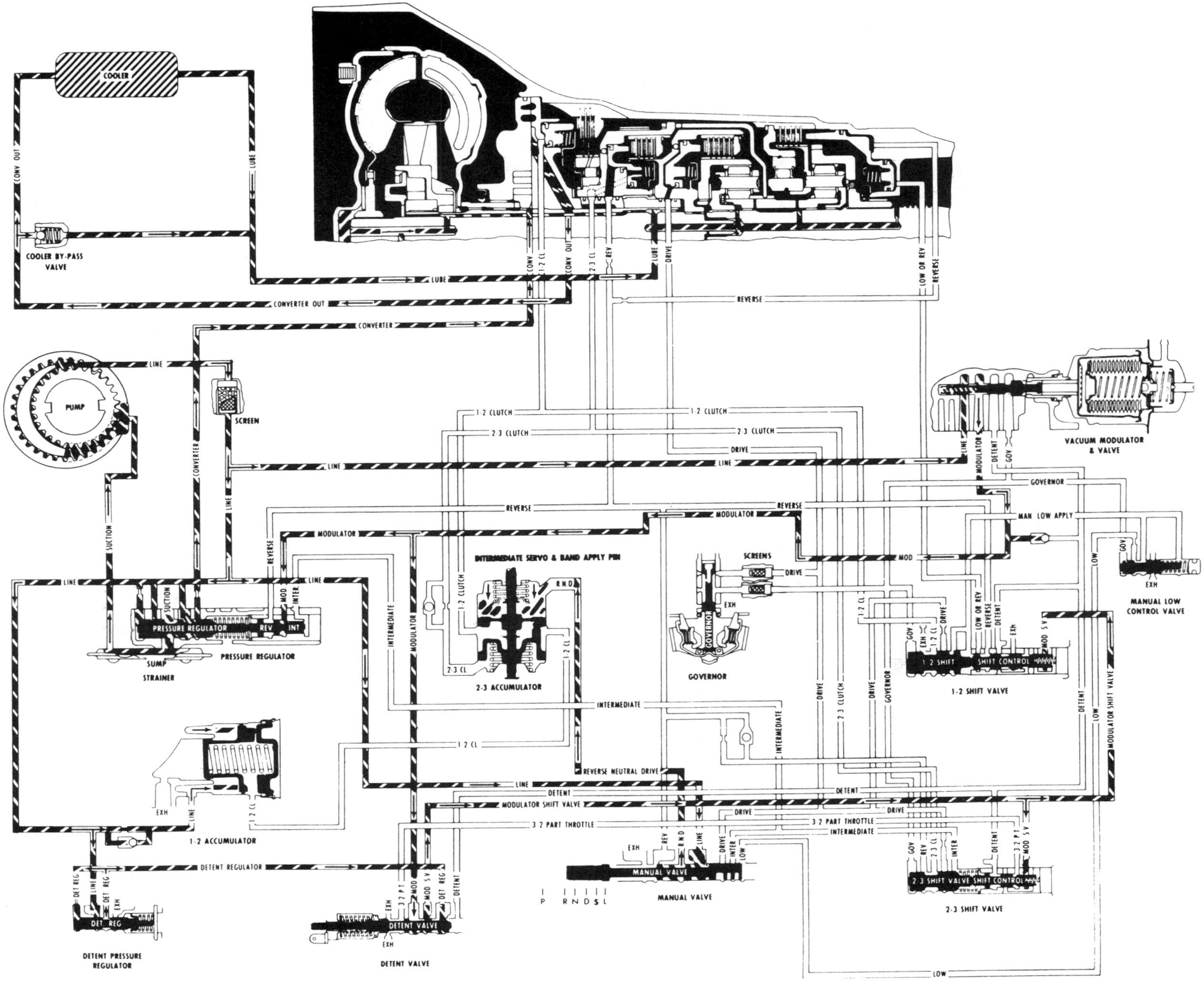

FIGURE 6-8 THM 350 in neutral. (Courtesy of General Motors Corporation.)

the pressure regulator valve. That does not mean that pressure is unregulated. The pressure regulator valve *exhausts fluid back to the sump when line pressure gets too high.*)

- *The torque converter–cooler–lubrication circuit:* charged (as it always is in gear).

- *The control circuits that are always charged in neutral or any gear:* vacuum modulator, manual valve, 1-2 accumulator, detent valve (through detent pressure regulator), modulator-to-reverse-intermediate boost valve, modulator-to-detent valve, and (through detent valve) modulator-to-shift valves.

- *The only other control circuit required for neutral: reverse–neutral–drive* (R.N.D.) from manual valve-to-intermediate servo. This circuit holds the intermediate band *disengaged.*

Notice that the governor circuit is not charged and no pressure is reaching any of the apply devices—as should be the case for "neutral."

Drive Low

With the selector lever at "D" (for drive) and the vehicle standing still, trace the circuit for "drive low" in Figure 6-9.

- *Pump to pressure regulator valve.*

- *Torque converter–cooler–lubrication circuit*

- *The control circuits that are always charged:* vacuum modulator, manual valve, 1-2 accumulator, detent valve, (through detent pressure regulator), modulator-to-reverse-intermediate boost valve, modulator-to-detent valve, and (through detent valve) modulator-to-shift valves.

- *Other control circuits required:* RND, drive oil (previously line pressure) from manual valve-to-governor, forward clutch servo and shift valves (always required for forward gears); governor pressure-to-shift values, manual low control valve (prohibits manual shift to low at excessive road speed), and modulator valve. (Governor pressure is there to react with modulator and/or spring pres-

sure, depending on speed and throttle opening.)

Note that low and reverse clutch is disengaged. It is called the low and reverse clutch because it is disengaged in low and engaged in reverse—the only two possible conditions.

Drive Intermediate

With the selector lever in "D" and the vehicle speed and throttle opening conditions suitable for governor pressure and modulator (throttle) pressure to shift into intermediate (second) gear, trace the circuit for "drive intermediate" in Figure 6-10.

- *Pump to pressure regulator valve*

- *Torque converter–cooler–lubrication circuit*

- *The control circuits that are always charged:* vacuum modulator, manual valve, 1-2 accumulator, detent valve (through detent pressure regulator), modulator-to-reverse-intermediate boost valve, modulator-to-detent valve, and (through detent valve) modulator-to-shift valves.

- *Other control circuits required:* R.N.D., drive oil from manual valve-to-governor, forward clutch and shift valves; governor pressure-to-shift valves, manual low control valve, and modulator valve; 1-2 clutch pressure from 1-2 shift valve (opened by balance between governor pressure and modulator pressure)-to-intermediate clutch servo, and on to 1-2 accumulator (notice check valve allowing line pressure to exhaust) through intermediate servo (helping to hold intermediate band disengaged).

The purpose of the intermediate band in the THM 350 is to prevent the sun gear from overrunning the intermediate overrun roller clutch so that there is no "freewheeling" during deceleration. It is applied during manual intermediate but not during drive intermediate.

Drive

With the selector lever in "D" and the vehicle speed and throttle-opening conditions suitable for gover-

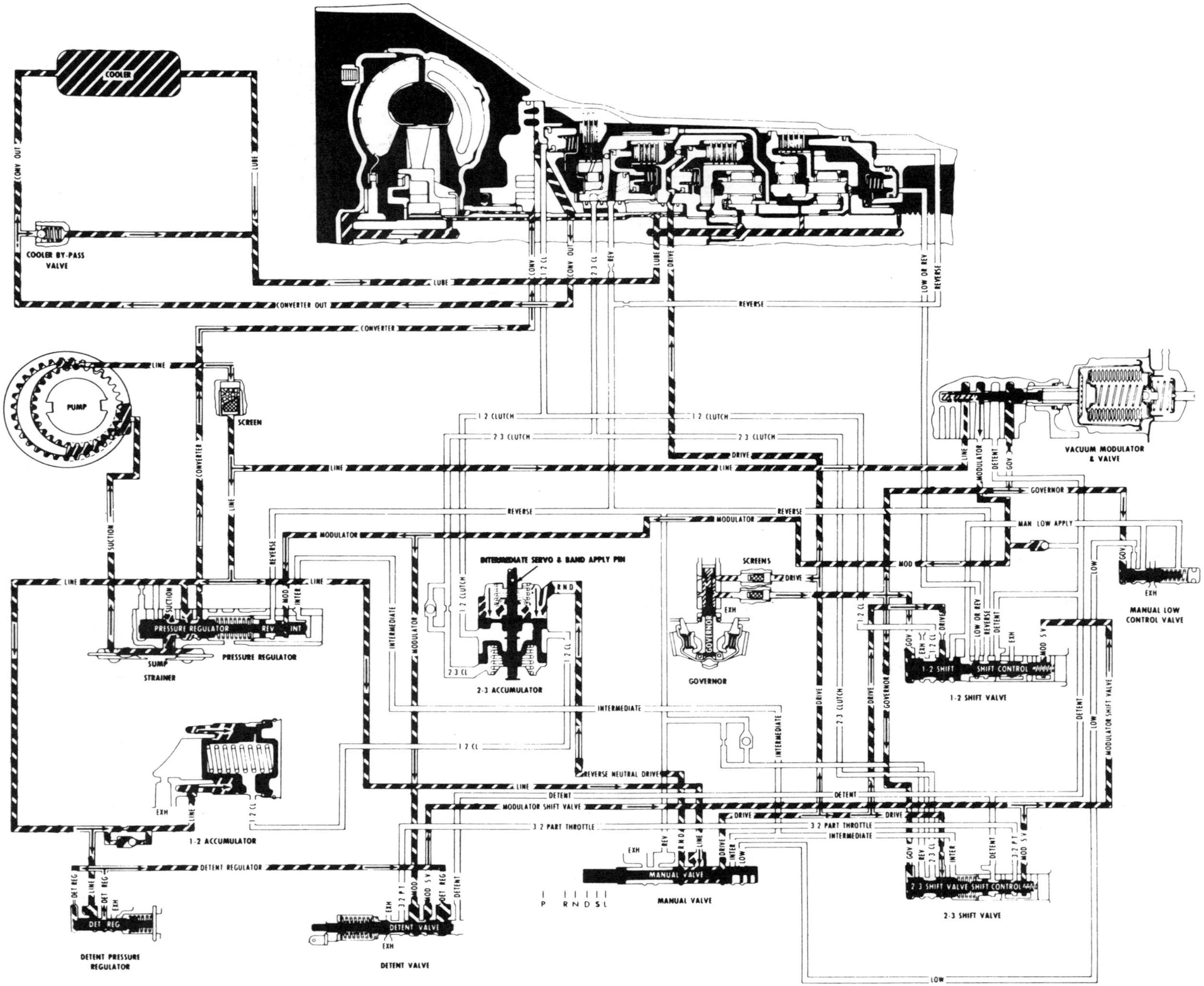

FIGURE 6-8. TURBOGLIDE in drive range, first gear. (Courtesy of General Motors Corporation.)

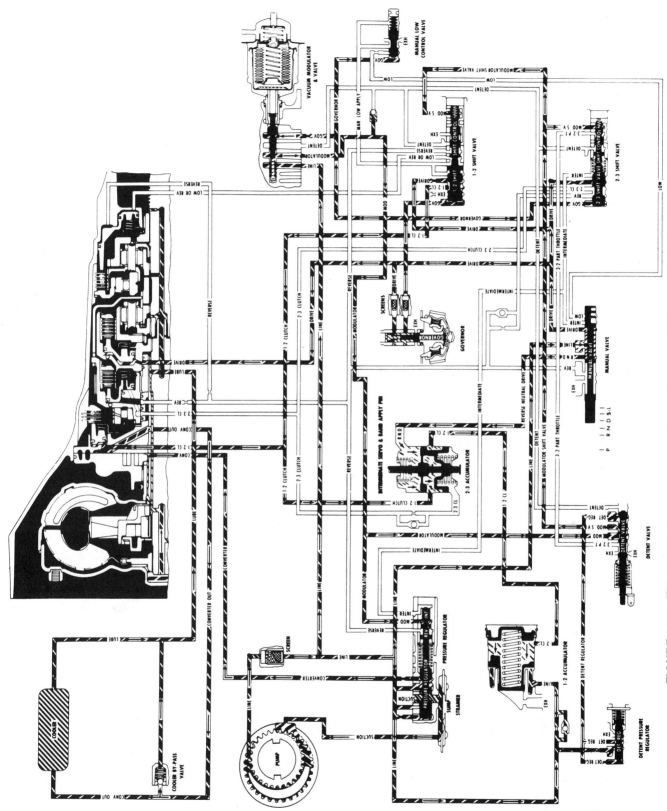

FIGURE 6-10 THM 350 in drive range, second gear. (Courtesy of General Motors Corporation.)

79

nor pressure and modulator (throttle) pressure to shift into direct gear (direct drive—transmission output shaft turning engine speed), trace the circuit for "drive" in Figure 6-11.

- *Pump to pressure regulator valve*
- *Torque converter–cooler–lubrication circuit*
- *The control circuits that are always charged:* vacuum modulator manual valve, 1-2 accumulator, detent valve (through detent pressure regulator), modular-to-reverse-intermediate boost valve, modulator-to-detent valve, and (through detent valve) modulator-to-shift valves.
- *Other control circuits required:* R.N.D., drive oil from manual valve-to-governor, forward clutch and shift valves; governor pressure-to-shift valves, manual low control valve, and modulator valve; 1-2 clutch pressure from 1-2 shift valve-to-intermediate clutch servo and on to 1-2 accumulator through intermediate servo (it does not act against intermediate servo or 2-3 accumulator because it is working against equal accumulator and R.N.D. pressure); 2-3 clutch pressure to direct clutch and on 2-3 accumulator. (Note that it passes through the one-way check valve going into the accumulator and through an orifice going out.)

Manual intermediate

With the selector level at intermediate ("S" or "L_2"), the vehicle is limited to automatic shifting between low and intermediate. It also provides engine braking in intermediate gear. The selector lever can be moved from direct ("D") to intermediate or low ("L_1") to intermediate at any speed. Trace the circuit "manual intermediate" in Figure 6-12.

- *Pump to pressure regulator valve*
- *Torque converter–cooler–lubrication circuit*
- *The control circuits that are always charged:* vacuum modulator, manual valve, 1-2 accumulator, detent valve (through detent pressure regulator), modulator-to-reverse-intermediate boost valve, modulator-to-

detent valve, and (through detent valve) modulator-to-shift valves.

- *Other control circuits required:* drive oil from manual valve-to-governor, forward clutch and shift valves; intermediate (line) pressure from manual valve-to-2-3 shift valve (to keep it from shifting) and reverse intermediate boost valve at pressure regulator; governor pressure-to-shift valves, manual low control valve, and modulator valve; 1-2 clutch pressure from 1-2 shift valve-to-intermediate clutch servo and on to 1-2 accumulator through intermediate servo.

Notice that without R.N.D., 1-2 clutch pressure applies the intermediate band when it passes through the intermediate servo. It also exhausts the metered line pressure at the 1-2 accumulator through a one-way check valve, does the same with the residual (unpressurized) 2-3 clutch fluid at the 2-3 accumulator, and exhausts residual R.N.D. fluid through the manual valve.

Application of the intermediate band prevents the sun gear from overrunning the intermediate overrun roller clutch so that transmission input and output shafts remain locked together during deceleration.

Manual Low

With the selector lever at low ("L_1"), the transmission will not shift regardless of speed or throttle opening. If the selector lever is moved to low ("L_1") above 50 mph (80.5 km/h), the transmission will automatically shift into intermediate, then to low at 50 mph. As with "manual intermediate," "manual low" also provides engine braking. Trace the circuit "manual low" in Figure 6-13.

- *Pump to pressure regulator valve*
- *Torque converter–cooler–lubrication circuit*
- *The control circuits that are always charged:* vacuum modulator, manual valve, 1-2 accumulator, detent valve (through detent pressure regulator), modulator-to-reverse-intermediate boost valve, modulator-to-detent valve, and (through detent valve) modulator-to-shift valves.

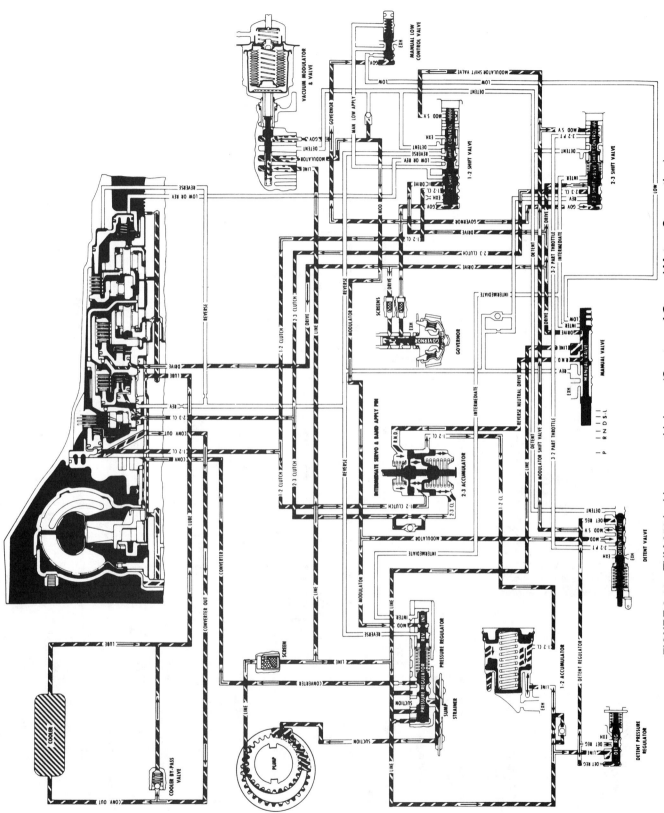

FIGURE 6-11 THM 350 in drive range, third gear. (Courtesy of General Motors Corporation.)

81

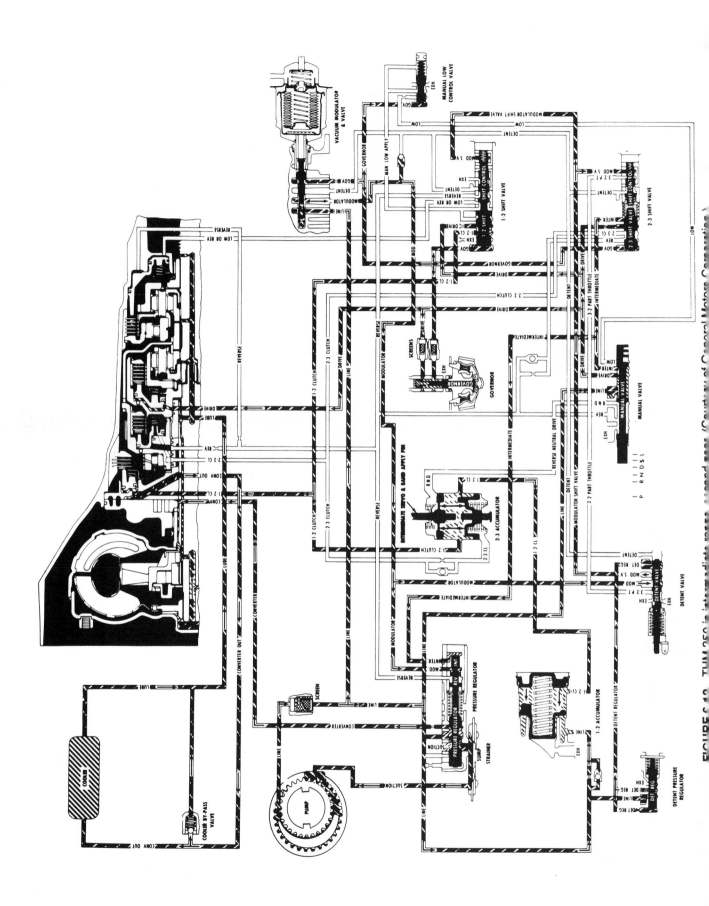

FIGURE 6-12. THM 350 is intermediate range geared sore. (Courtesy of General Motors Corporation.)

82

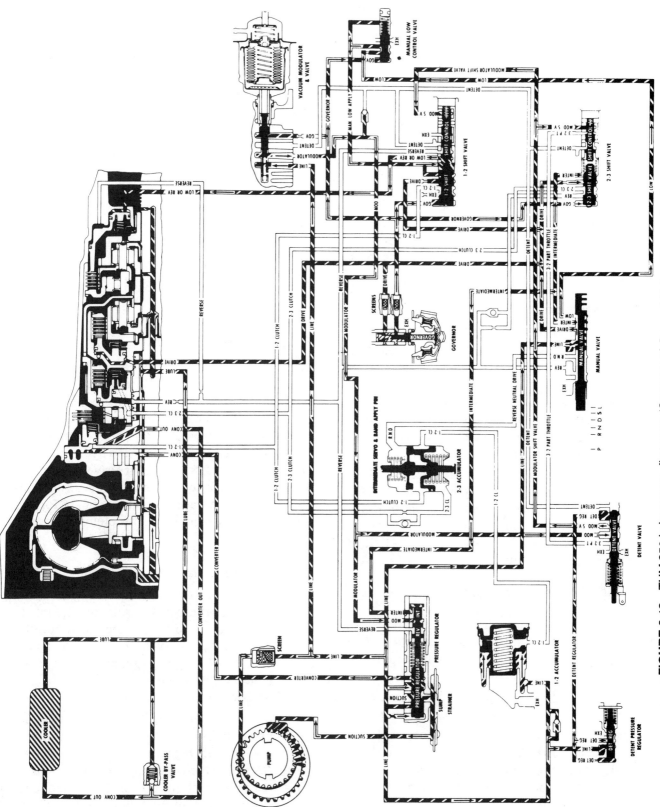

FIGURE 6-13 THM 350 in low range, first gear. (Courtesy of General Motors Corporation.)

Other control circuits required: drive oil from manual valve-to-governor, forward clutch and shift valves; intermediate (line) pressure from manual valve-to-2-3 shift valve and reverse-intermediate boost valve; low (line) pressure from manual valve-to-manual low control valve then to 1-2 shift valve (to keep it closed) and on to rear (low-reverse) servo.

Note that it is governor pressure that keeps the manual low control valve closed above 50 mph.

Reverse

There is more to this circuit than you might expect. Trace it in Figure 6-14.

- *Pump to pressure regulator valve*
- *Torque converter–cooler–lubrication circuit*
- *The control circuits that are always charged:* vacuum modulator, manual valve, 1-2 accumulator, detent valve (through detent pressure regulator), modulator-to-reverse-intermediate boost valve, modulator-to-detent valve, and (through detent valve) modulator-to-shift valves.
- *Other control circuits required:* R.N.D., reverse (line) pressure from manual valve-to-reverse-intermediate boost valve, shift valves, direct clutch, low-reverse and reverse servo, and from 2-3 shift valve to 2-3 clutch servo and accumulator.

Detent (Full-Throttle Downshift)

With the selector lever in drive, Figure 6-15 shows what takes place to shift to intermediate gear at *wide-open throttle (W.O.T.)* and at part throttle.

- *Pump to pressure regulator valve*
- *Torque converter–cooler–lubrication circuit*
- *The control circuits that are always charged (except for modulator-to-shift valves:* vacuum modulator, manual valve, 1-2 accumulator, detent valve (through detent pressure regulator), modulator-to-reverse-intermediate boost valve, and modulator-to-detent valve; here there is departure from the

usual manner in which shift circuits are charged:

(a) At *part throttle*, modulator pressure is still directed to the shift valves.

(b) At *wide-open throttle*, modulator pressure and regulated detent pressure is directed to the 2-3 shift control, and regulated detent pressure continues to the 1-2 shift control and into the modulator circuit through a one-way check valve as well as to the modulator valve itself.

- *Other control circuits required:* R.N.D., drive oil from manual valve-to-governor, forward clutch, and shift valves, and to modulator valve; 1-2 clutch pressure from 1-2 shift valve to intermediate clutch servo and on through the combined 2-3 accumulator/intermediate servo without effect on the 1-2 accumulator.

Torque Converter Clutch

There are two designs: one locates the control valve in the pump cover and the other locates it in a separate valve body. The converter clutch valve controls both clutch application and release. (To review the design of the torque converter clutch, refer to Chapter 4.) Transmission hydraulic circuits are charged the same as that for Drive (Figure 6-11). The torque converter clutch circuit is a supplemental one. It can be traced from Figure 6-16 for clutch application and Figure 6-17 for clutch release.

- Pump to pressure regulator
- Mainline through circuits as shown in Figure 6-11
- 2-3 clutch pressure to a solenoid-operated exhaust and on to switch the converter clutch valve to the apply circuit (the solenoid exhausts 2-3 clutch pressure to the converter clutch valve until it is energized by the governor switch at 30 to 45 mph (48 to 72 km/h).
- Solenoid closes, switching converter clutch valve to allow converter feed from pressure regulator to reach converter apply passage. (Note that converter apply deadends—this oil does not reach the cooler since it requires no cooling in lock-up—but fluid is metered through an orifice to the cooler circuit to continue lubrication.)

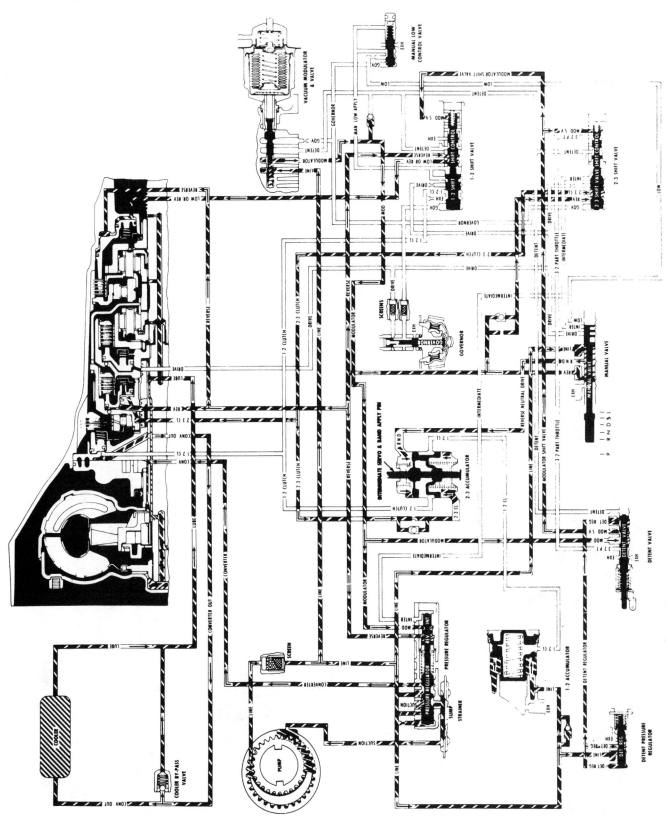

FIGURE 6-14 THM 350 in reverse. (Courtesy of General Motors Corporation.)

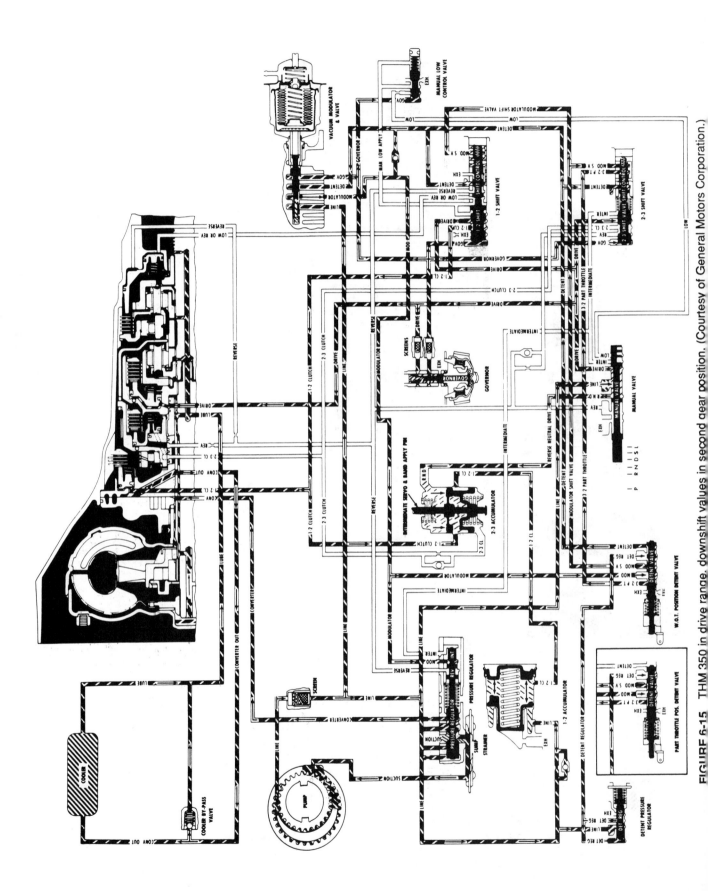

FIGURE 6-15   THM 350 in drive range, downshift values in second gear position. (Courtesy of General Motors Corporation.)

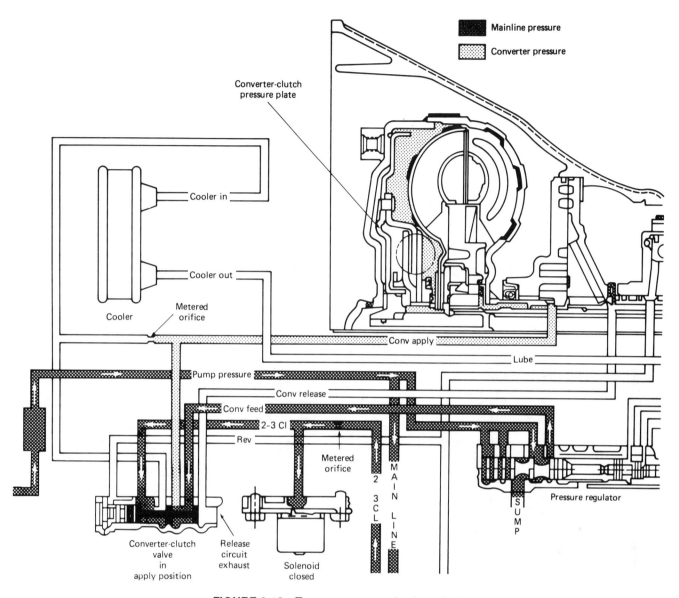

FIGURE 6-16   Torque converter, clutch applied.

• Converter release is achieved when the solenoid opens, exhausting 2-3 clutch pressure from the converter clutch valve, allowing spring pressure to move it to the release circuit, which feeds the front side of the clutch and disengages it.

TRADE TERMS

Aftermarket	Eccentric	Static friction
ATF	Fixed displacement	coefficient
Auxiliary Cooler	Mopar 7176	Sump
Crescent	OEM	Type H
Dexron II D	R.N.D.	Variable displacement
Dynamic friction	Rotary pump	vane pump
coefficient		W.O.T.

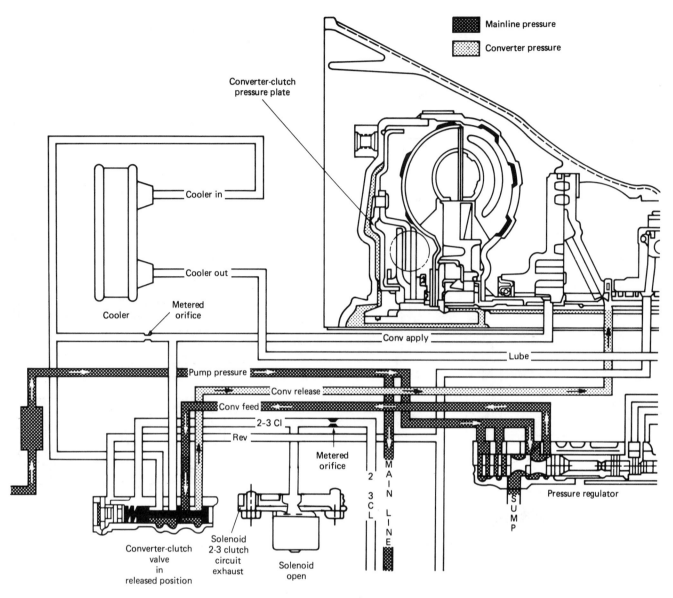

FIGURE 6-17 Torque converter, clutch released.

REVIEW QUESTIONS

6–1. Which of the following best differentiates Type F from Dexron II D transmission fluid?

(a) Antifoaming agent.

(b) Dispersant.

(c) Fluid friction coefficient.

(d) Viscosity.

6–2. ATF can be exposed to what approximate temperature during operation?

(a) 180°F

(b) 250 to 300°F.

(c) 600°F.

(d) All of the above.

6–3. Type A, Suffix A, ATF is the most recent improvement.   T   F

6–4. On a crossflow radiator the transmission to outlet tank lines should be connected:

(a) Top line from transmission to bottom of outlet tank.

(b) Bottom line from transmission to top of outlet tank.

(c) Bottom line from transmission to bottom of outlet tank.

(d) None of the above.

6–5. An auxiliary cooler must be connected:

(a) Separately from the original.

(b) In parallel with the original.

(c) In series with the original.

(d) None of the above.

6–6. Which of the following are rotary pumps?

(a) IX gear.

(b) Variable displacement vane.

(c) Spur gear.

(d) IX rotor.

(e) All of the above.

6–7. The crescent is an integral part of any rotary pump.   T   F

6–8. The best place to start tracing a hydraulic circuit is:

(a) Manual valve.

(b) Pressure regulator valve.

(c) Pump.

(d) Any of the above.

6–9. Lubrication is achieved by the lubrication circuit only.   T   F

6–10. Control circuits that are always charged are:

(a) Throttle or vacuum modulator valve.

(b) Manual valve.

(c) Pressure regulator valve.

(d) All of the above.

6–11. "Mainline" or "line" pressure is always unregulated pressure.   T   F

6–12. Shift valves are moved by all but which of the following pressures?

(a) Drive oil pressure.

(b) Modulator pressure.

(c) Governor pressure.

(d) Spring pressure.

6–13. In the THM-350, the intermediate band is applied during manual intermediate but not during drive intermediate. This is not true of all transmission makes.   T   F

6–14. A circuit that is always charged when the engine is running includes all but which of the following?

(a) Torque converter.

(b) Cooler.

(c) Lubrication.

(d) R.N.D.

6–15. Engine braking occurs in which of the following?

(a) Drive.

(b) Manual low.

(c) Drive intermediate.

(d) None of the above.

6–16. The selector lever can be moved to manual low at any speed without damaging the transmission.   T   F

6–17. In which of the following selector positions does automatic shifting *not* take place?

(a) Drive.

(b) Drive low.

(c) Drive intermediate.

(d) Manual low.

(e) Manual intermediate.

6–18. Match the terms in the first column with those in the second.

(a) ATF.   (1) Intermediate.
(b) OEM.   (2) Lubrication.
(c) R.N.D.   (3) Part throttle.
(d) W.O.T.   (4) Aftermarket.

6–19. Variable displacement is achieved in the vane pump by:

(a) Pump speed.

(b) Crescent.

(c) Sliding pump body.

(d) Pressure regulator valve.

6–20. The torque converter clutch apply circuit is opened through use of 2-3 clutch pressure and a solenoid valve.   T   F

ESSAY QUESTIONS

6–1. Discuss the various temperatures that occur in an automatic transmission, and explain what happens when fluid gets too hot.

6–2. Describe the three types of rotary pump and their differentiating characteristics.

CHAPTER ACTIVITIES

6–1. Applying the pointers you have learned about reading hydraulic diagrams in general and drawing on your experience in tracing circuits of the THM-350, trace the circuits in specific model diagrams for at least two other automatic transmission makes (e.g., Chrysler and Ford).

6–2. On a vehicle that has an auxiliary cooler added to the system, follow the lines to determine whether or not the auxiliary cooler is correctly connected in series.

7

Automatic Transmission Electrical Systems

OBJECTIVES

When you have completed this chapter, you should be able to:

- Recognize electrical and electronic circuits involved with automatic transmissions.
- Cite examples of circuits that control the transmission as well as circuits that are controlled by the transmission.
- Recognize circuit schematics, wiring diagrams, and test charts used for identification and repair of transmission-related electrical circuits.
- State the difference between electrical and electronic shifting.
- Compare governor and vehicle speed sensor fundamentals.
- Compare throttle/modulator pressure and throttle position sensor (potentiometer) fundamentals.
- Name the four major automatic transmission circuits that feed into the computer in an electronically shifting transmission.

In the past, electrical devices and systems in automatic transmissions were mostly limited to neutral start circuits and backup light switches. Then came lock-up converters and overdrives engaged by solenoid-controlled hydraulic pressure. This was followed closely by electronically controlled transmission shifting, which uses computers, electronic sensing devices, and solenoids to achieve **shift pattern** precision unattainable with the straight hydraulic control systems.

EARLY ELECTRIC TRANSMISSION EFFORTS

In 1927, an electric drive with no gear shift was developed by E.M. Frazer. In 1935, a car called Hudson introduced the "electric hand"—remote control gear shifting.

Although some foreign manufacturers have been involved with electronic shifting since the early 1970s, it took over 10 years before the system appeared in foreign imports (Renault and Toyota) and another couple of years before appearing in domestic applications (Allison).

So electricity and electronics (see Chapter 5 sidebar, *"Electricity versus Electronics"*) are playing a bigger role each year as the automotive industry pursues performance efficiency. But what does this mean in terms of automotive maintenance and repair—hundreds of feet of wire, a multitude of switches, sensors, solenoids, and so on, making it too difficult to handle? Not really; here's why:

- Testing can be done with a simple volt-ohmmeter (and in some cases, dedicated test devices are available from manufacturers).

- Because much of the system is solid state (no moving parts), there are fewer parts to wear out. Faulty parts rarely can be rebuilt and must be replaced (this includes wiring—much of which is in printed circuit form or in sealed wiring harness and connectors.) Replacement avoids the uncertainties of tear-down-parts cleaning-rebuild.

- Any confusion from the presence of so many wires, switches, and sensors can be handled by:
  (a) Isolating one circuit at a time.
  (b) Starting from the beginning (electrical source).
  (c) Tracing the main path of the circuit first, then tracing the effect of any alternate or branch circuits.

Before proceeding, you might wish to review the electrical sections in Chapter 5. There we looked separately at electrical and electronic devices and the means by which they are linked together—that is, how power is transferred from one to another. In this chapter we take a closer look at these and the circuits they make up.

TRANSMISSION-CONTROLLED CIRCUITS

These circuits do not affect the operation of the transmission; rather, it is the operation of the transmission that, through them, affects the operation of other devices.

Neutral Switch

The **neutral switch** is a safety circuit to prevent cranking the engine when the transmission is in gear. This circuit was used in some models only in "Park," but if those vehicles stalled—during acceleration from a traffic light, for example—they had to be brought to a complete stop before the selector lever could be moved to "Park" to complete the circuit to the starter. Today, this circuit is wired into both "Park" and "Neutral" positions in most vehicles, so that the starter circuit can be activated while the vehicle is coasting in neutral.

It is a simple switching circuit which, in effect, completes the starter solenoid circuit by grounding. Figure 7-1 shows a "Park/Neutral" circuit for late-model General Motors vehicles, but it is repre-

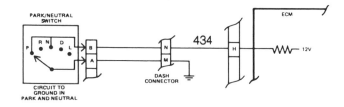

The P/N switch is closed when the gear selector is in Park or Neutral. One side of the switch is connected to the ECM which supplies a buffered 12 volts, the other side is grounded. The P/N switch is an input to the ECM. When the voltage at ECM term. "H" is high (12 volts), the ECM allows activation, at the proper time, of other controls such as TCC, EST, VSS and others.

FIGURE 7-1 Representative neutral start circuit. (Courtesy of General Motors Corporation).

sentative of many. Note that it feeds into the Electronic Control Module (ECM) and through that device has an effect not only on the starter circuit but also on the Torque Converter Clutch (TCC), Electronic Spark Timing (EST), and Vehicle Speed Sensor (VSS). But this is not important if you are checking only the park/neutral circuit.

Backup Light Switch

This is a very simple circuit incorporating a mechanically or hydraulically activated switch on the transmission. The switch completes the circuit when the selector lever is in the reverse gear position. Sometimes this switch is combined with the neutral start switch.

Transmission-Controlled Spark

One means of achieving more complete combustion to meet environmental standards is to control spark timing precisely under various driving conditions. One of these conditions is vehicle speed. A vacuum solenoid valve (VSV) is installed in the vacuum line between the carburetor and distributor. It is connected to a pressure-activated switch in the governor hydraulic circuit. The switch closes at speeds under about 30 mph, sending current to the solenoid, which shuts off vacuum, preventing spark advance at low speeds. (Figure 7-2).

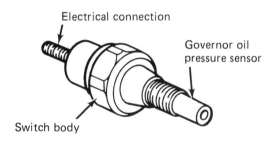

Electrical connection

Governor oil pressure sensor

Switch body

AUTOMATIC TRANSMISSION SWITCH

FIGURE 7-2 Pressure switch for automatic transmission control of vacuum advance.

ELECTRICAL SHIFTING

Electrical shifting through solenoids is an idea that has been around for quite a while. Its applications are found in manual transmissions and independent overdrive units as well as automatics. Subaru's M-41A automatic, for example, uses a solenoid that is actuated by a switch under the accelerator pedal. The solenoid operates the hydraulic kickdown valve at W.O.T. Several of the Toyota transmissions are designed with a switch-operated solenoid to control overdrive shifts. The overdrive circuit for a Celica is shown in Figure 7-3.

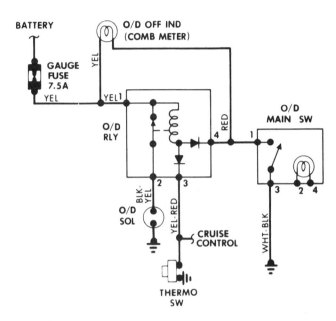

FIGURE 7-3 Celica overdrive circuit wiring diagram. (Courtesy of Toyota Motor Sales, USA.)

These electrical shifting applications were easily tied into electronic shifting when the computer came along. We cover that later in the chapter.

TORQUE CONVERTER LOCK-UP CIRCUITS

These circuits utilize solenoids to direct pressure to hydraulic spool valves for torque converter lock-up devices. On some models, lock-up takes place in all but first gear; in others, it can occur only in direct drive.

Figure 7-4 shows a schematic for a system designed to lock up in third gear only. Notice in the diagram that certain conditions of both the governor and third (direct) gear must be in effect before the solenoid is activated for lock-up to take place: (1) the vehicle must reach or exceed a specified speed, and (2) the transmission must be in third

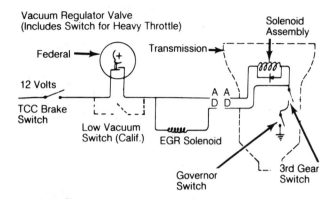

FIGURE 7-4 Solenoid-operated torque converter clutch schematic. (Courtesy of General Motors Corporation.)

gear. Also notice the TCC **brake switch**. It deactivates the solenoid when the brake is applied. This causes the hydraulic pressure to the TCC valve to exhaust, unlocking the torque converter clutch.

With computer control, as we will discuss soon, a number of other conditions can determine when the torque converter can be applied: both engine coolant and transaxle lubricant temperature, manifold pressure, throttle position, barometric pressure (altitude), and **pulse relay** (closes TCC circuit during gear changes), among others. All these are refinements—present on some makes and models, not on others.

Figure 7-5 shows the connector-to-solenoid wiring along the valve body for several models of the THM 200-4R, which lock up in fourth gear only. Most shop manuals include schematics such as these, as well as diagnostic test charts for the various transmission models.

Figure 7-6 is one of several test charts produced by General Motors for their torque converter clutch. These may appear too difficult to bother with at first, but you will find them quite simple when you start reading through them. Simply begin at the top and follow each set of boxed instructions. Follow the line to where it branches off, and take the shortest branch to the next box. Perform the instructions. If there is no line after a box, go back to the branch and follow the other line to the next set of boxed instructions. That is all there is to it. They present a nearly foolproof way to isolate circuit problems, and all they require is a voltmeter and a continuity tester, such as an ohmmeter or test light.

ELECTRONIC SHIFTING

Appearing first on imports in the early 1980s, electronically controlled shifting is now incorporated in some domestic heavy equipment (Allison), but systems for domestic passenger car and light trade applications have lagged behind.

The Electronic Control Unit (ECU) is a computer (again, different manufacturers use different names; see the Glossary). It is an electronic unit that receives, processes, and sends pulses of electrical energy for the purposes of signaling and operating certain electromechanical devices. Because it can process information so fast, there is no practical limit to the number of sensing devices, counters, timers, and electromechanical circuits that it can handle. Through the electromechanical devices, it can control nonelectrical systems, such as vacuum and hydraulic, as well. In fact, this is exactly what happens in electronic shifting.

Figure 7-7 is a schematic of the electronic and electrical components of the Toyota Supra transmission. Notice the following:

- Separate computers (ECU) for engine and transmission; both interact, however.
- Various electronic and electrical sensors (coolant, throttle position) that affect shifting and clutch lock up.
- Two speed sensors:(1) a **digital** speed sensor for the speedometer that displays numerical speed values, and (2) an **analog** speed sensor that functions as a governor. It reacts with a magnet in the rotor sensor to generate voltage pulses in direct proportion to speed; the pulses affect other circuits and devices that must respond to certain speeds and speed ranges.
- **A select pattern switch** allows the driver to select one of three built-in (programmed) shift patterns most nearly suitable to the type of driving anticipated: normal mode, power mode, or economy mode.

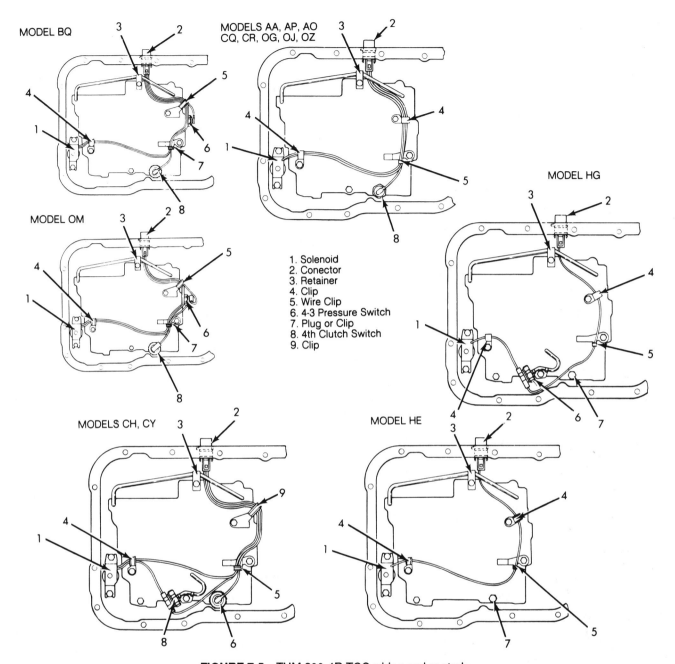

FIGURE 7-5   THM 200-4R TCC wiring and controls.

1. Solenoid
2. Conector
3. Retainer
4. Clip
5. Wire Clip
6. 4-3 Pressure Switch
7. Plug or Clip
8. 4th Clutch Switch
9. Clip

- The brake light switch, better called the **brake switch** since it feeds into the ECU, uses that information wherever it is needed in addition to brake lights (e.g., disengage torque converter clutch).
- The "DG," or diagnostic, terminal provides testing access to the entire electronic system. Specified voltage values from the shop

manual relate to certain system conditions to isolate defective circuits.

Figure 7-8 presents a wiring diagram showing the transmission-related circuits. Look at the major components: Electronic Controlled Transmission (ECT) computer, three shift solenoids, an unlabeled speed sensor (feeding information to the computer

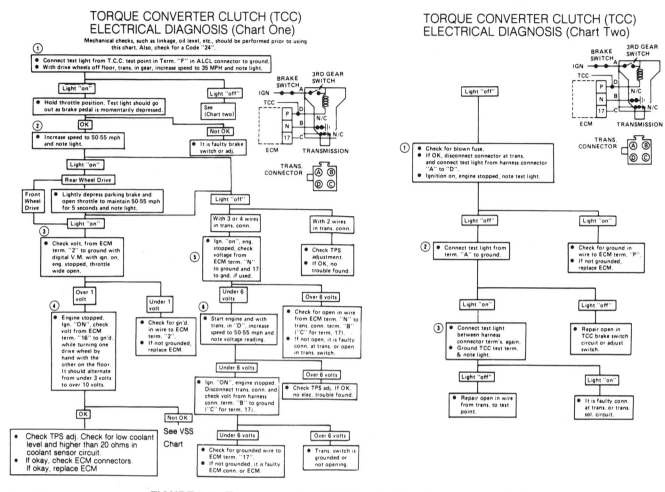

FIGURE 7-6 Torque converter clutch test chart for computer-controlled engines with carburetor (Courtesy of General Motors Corporation).

for cruise control, clutch lock-up, etc.), a shift pattern selection switch (Economy, Power, Normal), an analog speed sensor (governor function), overdrive switch, digital speed sensor (speedometer), and throttle position sensor—fewer than 10 major components in all.

Computer Control

Without a computer, automatic shift control is accomplished by the opposing pressures of governor and throttle on shift valves. With a computer, the shift valves are still shifted by hydraulic pressure, but the fluid is routed by solenoid valves activated by the computer. Electrical shifting requires manual switch activation or switching by comparatively bulky mechanical or hydromechanical means. The

computer, even at its small size, handles those switching functions many, many times faster and can make instantaneous "decisions" based on preset data programmed into its memory.

The governor function and throttle function are still needed, but they take a different form and feed directly to the computer. The governor function is accomplished by the **vehicle speed sensor (VSS)** which is explained in detail in Chapter 5.

The throttle function is achieved by a **throttle position sensor (TPS)**, or **potentiometer**, that varies voltage with the position of the throttle (much like the volume control on a stereo).

Figure 7-9 shows these major transmission circuits feeding to a computer. This one happens to be patterned after a Renault model which incorporates both transmission and engine computers in one unit.

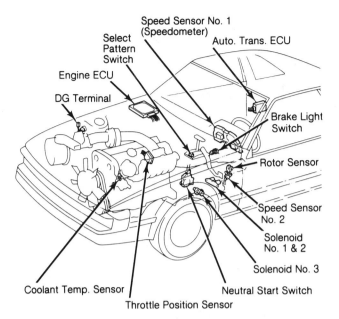

FIGURE 7-7 Electronic and electrical components of the Toyota Supra electronic shifting transmission. (Courtesy of Toyota Motor Sales, USA.)

Notice four major circuits affecting the transmission: (1) neutral switch. (2) throttle position sensor, (3) vehicle speed sensor, and (4) solenoid valves (in this case two valves for a three-speed transmission). The Self-Test Connector is for a test device available only from the manufacturer. The 6-Way Connector feeds other nontransmission related circuits. In units designed by other manufacturers, this connection might include any number of sensing devices, some of which might directly or indirectly affect the transmission.

Those of us in automotive technology need not learn the intricacies of computer repair, but it should be of interest to you to have some familiarity with what's inside "the box." Figure 7-10 is a complete electronic shift circuit with an indication of the relationship of the following computer components:

• The **counter** interprets pulses from the speed sensor and relays speed information to the ROM.
• **RAM** (random access memory) responds to variable vehicle conditions, including speed and throttle opening, and constantly updates that information.

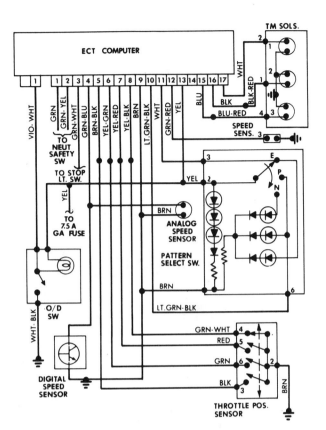

FIGURE 7-8 Toyota Cressida electronic shift circuits. (Courtesy of Toyota Motor Sales, USA.)

• **ROM** (read-only memory) consists of fixed data programmed by design to be used together with the variable RAM.
• The **microprocessor** (not shown) is a programmed integrated circuit that accepts one set of data as input (RAM), compares those data to its programmed data (ROM), and generates another set of data, based on that comparison, as output to the flip-flops.
• The **flip-flops** alternate between two possible circuits and accept continuously updated output from the microprocessor and pass it on to the power drivers.
• The **power drivers** are like relay switches—they utilize the weak electronic power to switch in electrical power sufficient to energize the solenoids.
• The **interval timer** feeds the flip-flops for the time duration needed to make a shift.

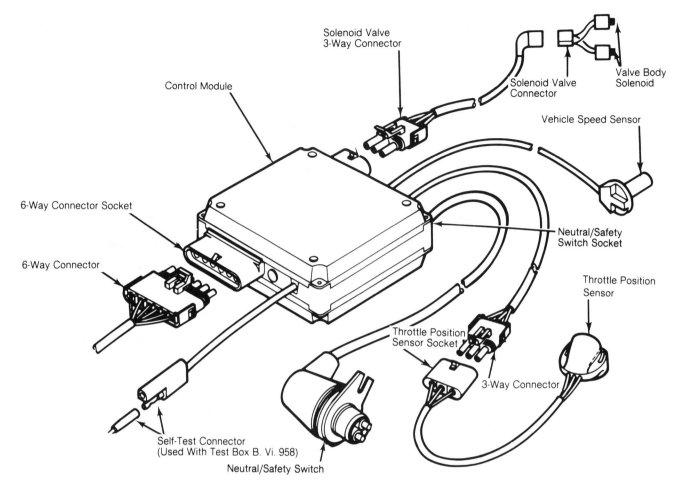

FIGURE 7-9   Computer (Renault electronic control module, ECM) showing major electonic shifting automatic transmission connections. (Courtesy
of American Motors Corporation.)

TESTING

Testing is taken up in greater detail in Chapter 9. But it should be helpful to reiterate here that most manufacturers' test procedures are thorough and plentiful and can be carried out with a voltmeter and continuity device. However, it is extremely important to follow testing steps in detail and in their proper sequence. Pay close attention to any test warnings. Electronic test procedures are very methodical and can be relied on to confirm normal operation as well as to detect defects.

TRADE TERMS

Analog	Microprocessor	ROM
Brake switch	Neutral switch	Select pattern switch
Counter	Potentiometer	Shift pattern
Digital	Power driver	Throttle position
Flip-flops	Pulse relay	sensor
Interval timer	RAM	Vehicle speed sensor

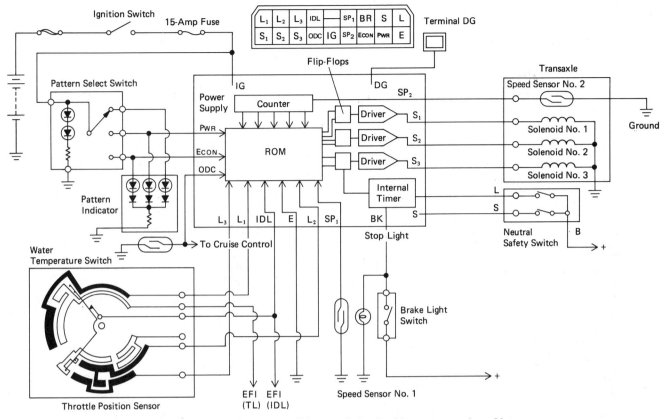

FIGURE 7-10 Electronic shift control circuit with representation of internal computer circuits.

REVIEW QUESTIONS

7–1. Indicate which of the following circuits control the transmission (CT) or are transmission controlled (TC).

(a) Throttle position sensor.

(b) Neutral switch.

(c) Back-up light switch.

(d) Brake switch.

7–2. Which of the following are *not* among the advantages of electronic shifting?

(a) Plug-in diagnostic test devices are often available from the manufacturer.

(b) Testing can be done with a volt-ohmmeter.

(c) Components can be easily rebuilt in the shop.

(d) Shift patterns can be tailored to many driving conditions.

7–3. When analyzing any electrical or electronic circuit diagram, which of the following are helpful?

(a) Isolating one circuit at a time.

(b) Starting from the beginning.

(c) Tracing the main path first.

(d) All of the above.

(e) None of the above.

7–4. Because electronics is playing a bigger part in automatic transmission operation, electricity is hardly used at all anymore.
T   F

7–5. The transmission controlled spark system uses:

(a) Vacuum advance.

(b) Solenoid valve.

(c) Pressure switch.

(d) All of the above.

(e) None of the above.

7–6. Electromechanical devices are no longer necessary in electronic shifting.   T   F

7–7. A transmission solenoid shift valve that is activated by a switch under the accelerator pedal is:

(a) An electronic shift circuit.

(b) A manual shift circuit.

(c) An overdrive circuit.

(d) None of the above.

(e) All of the above.

7–8. One way that a torque converter clutch is released is by applying the brakes.
T   F

7–9. In electronic shifting, the solenoid:

(a) Is attached directly to the spool valve.

(b) Directly controls mainline pressure to the apply device.

(c) Directly controls pressure to the shift valve.

(d) Has no effect on shift valves, because there are none.

7–10. In electronic shifting transmissions, which of the following can also affect shifting?

(a) Engine coolant temperature.

(b) Manifold pressure.

(c) Barometric pressure.

(d) None of the above.

(e) All of the above.

7–11. Automatic transmissions with solenoid-controlled hydraulic lock-up valves may, or may not, have electronic shifting.   T   F

7–12. Electronic control units, through elecro-mechanical devices, can control which of the following systems?

(a) Vacuum.

(b) Hydraulic.

(c) Neither of the above.

(d) Both of the above.

7–13. There must be separate computers for engine and transmission.   T   F

7–14. What is the difference between analog and digital?

(a) Digital displays numbers to be read and interpreted.

(b) Analog directly affects other devices through voltage or resistance.

(c) Both of the above.

(d) Neither of the above.

7–15. A shift pattern is:

(a) The option of shifting either partly or entirely through the lowest-to-highest gears.

(b) A gear shifting sequence timed to give optimum vehicle performance under certain driving conditions.

(c) Always built into the transmission and cannot be changed.

(d) The sequence on the selector indicator.

7–16. Match the terms in the first column with their function in the second.

(a) Counter
(b) ROM
(c) Microprocessor
(d) Flip-flops
(e) Power drivers
(f) Timer

(1) Responds to vehicle speed and throttle opening; sends commands to flip-flops.

(2) Enables data to flow from the ROM to the power drivers.

(3) Feeds flip-flops for the time duration needed to make a shift.

(4) Interprets speed sensor, signals ROM.

(5) Programmed circuit that accepts data, compares them to the programmed data, and outputs resulting new data.

(6) Enables weak electronic power to direct electrical power to activate solenoids.

ESSAY QUESTIONS

7–1. Explain the difference between electric and electronic shifting.

7–2. Explain what a Throttle Position Sensor does, how it operates mechanically and electrically, what device it replaces, and what it feeds to.

CHAPTER ACTIVITIES

7–1. Different manufactures have different names for computers and electronic control devices (which often contain the computer). Match the names with the abbreviations to find the manufacturer.

(a) Electronic Control Module.
(b) Electronic Control Unit.
(c) Electronic Control Assembly.

(1) ECM American Motors (Renault/General Motors).
(2) ECA Ford.
(3) ECU General Motors, American Motors, Ford.

7–2. Different manufacturers have different names for the entire computer system. Match the names with the abbreviation to find the manufacturer.

(a) Computerized Engine Control.
(b) Electronic Engine Control.
(c) Computer Command Control.
(d) Electronically Controlled Transmission.

(1) EEC Ford.
(2) CCC General Motors.
(3) CEC American Motors.
(4) ECT Toyota.

8

Interfacing Systems and Assemblies

```
_____ OBJECTIVES _____

When you have completed this chapter, you should be able to:

• Identify drive shaft and U-joint types.

• Differentiate between final drive gearsets and differential gearsets.

• Describe the operation of a differential gearset.

• State in general terms how one goes about adjusting bevel gear
  ring and pinion final drives.

• Recognize external transaxle configurations.

• Describe the significant difference between part-time and full-time
  four-wheel-drive transfer cases.

• Explain the general inspection and installation procedures for a flex
  plate.

• Identify engine-related connections and systems that have a direct
  or indirect effect on automatic transmissions.
```

The point at which one thing attaches to another is called an *interface*, and each thing can be said to **interface** with the other. Because the two things interface, they also have an effect on each other.

Located in the middle of the power train, the automatic transmission affects, and is affected by, two major systems: the engine and the final drive. In this chapter we examine each of these interfac-

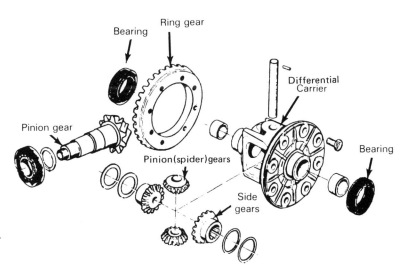

FIGURE 8-1 Final drive gears (engine mount at right angle to axle).

ing systems, and other assemblies within the power train, that need to be considered in transmission troubleshooting (diagnosis) and repair.

FINAL DRIVE

The last gear assembly in the power train, or drive train, is called the **final drive**. This term originally labeled the last set of gears (reduction) at each drive wheel on tractors and other heavy equipment—it still does, for that matter. But when applied to highway vehicles, its range of definition often encompasses the entire assembly of shafts, gears, and even clutches used to transmit power from the transmission to the drive wheels. Strictly speaking, however, it is the **ring and pinion**, or final gearset, excluding the differential gears. How the term is used depends partly on the whim of the user and partly on the vehicle or assembly under discussion.

Third Member

This labels what is considered the final drive for a front-engine, rear-wheel-drive power train. The **third member** is the assembly housing the beveled reduction ring and drive pinion gear, the **differential** carrier and **spider** (pinion) **gears** and the **axle** (side) **gears** (Figure 8-1). Its housing is either bolted to the axle housing or sometimes is an integral part of the axle housing. In the case of independent rear suspension, it becomes the final housing in the drive train. The third member also

has been called the differential—a name that ignores the presence of the ring and pinion—or simply "rear end," an unimaginative but equal alternative. But with the popularity of mid-engine, rear-engine, and front-wheel-drive designs, to which the term cannot apply, the descriptive "final drive" has returned to popularity. So much for terminology.

Drive Shaft. Rear-wheel-drive vehicles with front-mounted engines transmit torque over a considerable distance. Part of the distance is taken up by the transmission and final drive; in between the two is a **drive shaft**, also called a **propeller shaft**. There are two types: (1) an exposed, hollow-tube, shaft design incorporating universal joints at both ends (**Hotchkiss drive**), and (2) a (usually) solid shaft enclosed in a housing (**torque tube**) that connects transmission to final drive, or rear-axle, housing.

The Hotchkiss drive is the more popular of the two (Figure 8-2). It uses either the **cross-and-yoke (cardan) U-joint** (Figure 8-3) or the **ball-and-trunnion** U-joint (Figure 8-4), and it may consist of two lengths joined by a **double cardan joint**, as shown in Figure 8-5.

The torque tube drive has been used extensively, but it was dropped by Ford in favor of the Hotchkiss drive in 1948; Chevrolet followed suit in 1955, Buick in 1961, and Rambler (American Motors) in 1963. Some Porsche models use a torque tube that is flange mounted at both ends, thus requiring no drive shaft U-joints, and Chevette combines Hotchkiss and torque tube, using the latter to stabilize axle housing rotation or **wind-up**, by a fixed

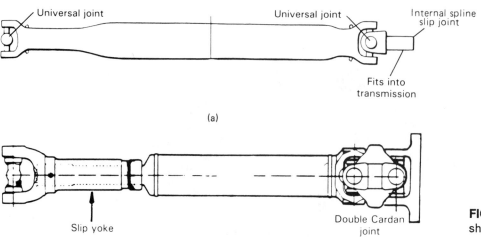

(a)

FIGURE 8-2 Hotchkiss drive shafts: (a) cross and slip yoke to transmission; (b) cross and slip yoke to shaft with double-cardan joint.

(b)

mount to the vehicle frame at one end and the axle housing at the other (Figure 8-6).

Oddly enough, the Hotchkiss drive has more wear points and is more easily damaged. The shaft can be bent by road hazards and there are at least eight bearings to maintain. Whether caused by drive shaft damage or universal joint bearing damage, an out-of-balance drive shaft can quickly damage rear transmission seals and put a lot of strain on output shaft bearings. Visual inspection of the drive shaft can usually reveal any damage. Rotate the drive shaft back-and-forth by hand and watch for looseness of trunnion bearings. Inspect the circumference of the drive shaft along its entire length for dents and missing balance pieces. Start the engine, apply the brakes, and shift from forward to reverse several times, listening for excessive looseness, crackling, and squeaks; road test to detect the same, especially squeaks with a frequency three or four times faster than wheel rotation. Also road test to detect significant vibration at that frequency—usually between 35 and 55 mph.

One other drive shaft problem is often overlooked: the U-joint operating angle. The simple cardan joint used at each end of many Hotchkiss drives can set up a torsion vibration if operated at too great an angle. This is because there is a difference in speed (velocity) between the driving and driven side; the driving side rotates at a constant speed, but the driven side speeds up and slows down

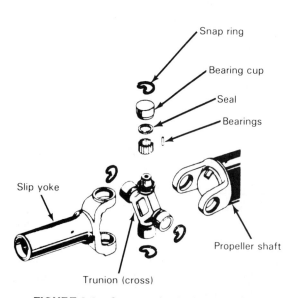

FIGURE 8-3   Cross-and-yoke U-joint.

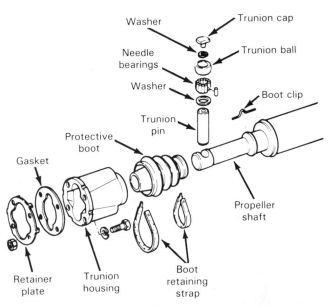

FIGURE 8-4   Ball-and-trunnion U-joint.

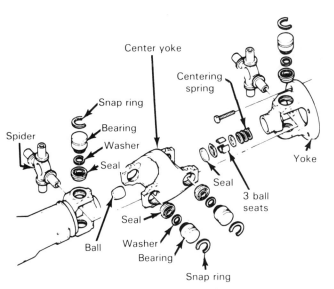

FIGURE 8-5   Double cardan U-joint.

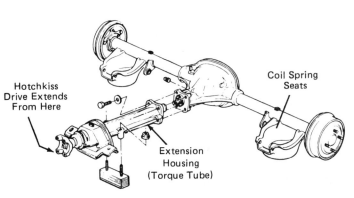

FIGURE 8-6   Chevette combined Hotchkiss/ torque tube drive.

two times during each revolution. This fluctuation is directly proportional to the operating angle. Although the U-joints will "work" at angles up to about 40°, the *difference* in angle between transmission output shaft and pinion shaft should be only 1 or 2° to minimize velocity fluctuation when single cross-and-yoke joints are used. Constant-velocity joints such as double cardan, Rzeppa, Bendix, and others do not have this limitation.

Ring and Pinion.   In an automobile, the true final drive is a reduction gearset of about 3 or 4:1— for every turn of the drive wheel, the transmission output shaft turns three or four times (the actual ratios range from about 2.5 to over 4:1). In many transaxles, this gearset is a pair of helical cut gears,

which we examine in the next section. But where the engine is mounted at a right angle to the wheel axis, it is a bevel gearset (see Chapter 3).

This particular bevel gearset is commonly called the "ring and pinion." It meshes off-center (Figure 8-7), and the resulting shape of the teeth follow a complex geometric figure called a hyperbolic paraboloid, from which the term **hypoid** has been coined. The off-center mesh allows the drive-shaft and the vehicle's center of gravity to be lowered. It is also quieter because the teeth engage in more of a sliding fashion. A hypoid gearset must mesh correctly or it will be noisy and subject to excessive wear. Fortunately, the difference between excessive-wear sounds in an automatic transmission and those of a ring and pinion is the difference between a whine and a growl, so it is pretty easy to isolate the problem. This is not true in a transaxle because: (1) the two units are combined in what is essentially the same housing, and (2) the helical gear mesh is not as critical nor is it adjustable.

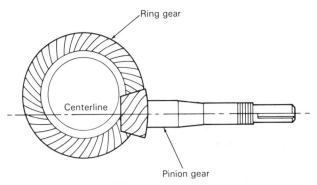

FIGURE 8-7   Ring and pinion: hypoid bevel gearset for reduction.

The ring and pinion adjustments are summarized in Figure 8-8. *Backlash* (gear mesh clearance) is adjusted by moving ring gear/differential carrier bearings to one side or the other; *pinion depth* (gear mesh position) is adjusted by shimming. Both sets of bearings have a required *preload*.

Differential.   When a vehicle turns a corner, the outer wheels turn more times than the inner wheels because they travel farther. The differential gearset splits the drive torque to compensate for this difference. It is like a planetary made up of bevel gears (Figure 8-9). All differentials are essentially the same design, whether bevel gear final drives or

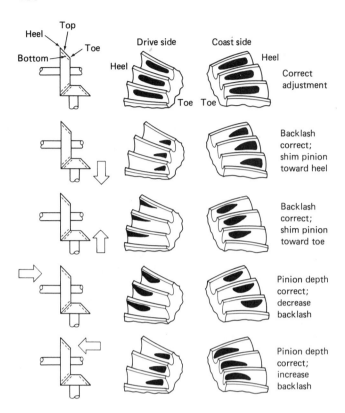

FIGURE 8-8 Hypoid ring and pinion gear meshing patterns and adjustments.

transaxles; some may have four spider gears instead of just two, and others may be fitted with clutches to limit wheel spin (**limited slip differential**) during traction loss (Figure 8-10).

Differential problems are rare. Road testing for differential noise must include turns because that is the only time the differential is working. Jacking up one drive wheel (be sure to block all others) will also operate the differential, but it is a no-load condition and cannot really be conclusive. Limited slip differentials may make a creaking noise during sharp, slow turns on dry pavement. This is caused by clutch pack slippage and may indicate that the wrong lubricant has been used or that the lubricant has become water contaminated.

Transaxle

The combined unit called a **transaxle** contains transmission (automatic or manual), differential, and final drive, the latter often connecting the two. Vehicles with engines mounted parallel to the axle can be connected through a final drive that is a helical cut gearset, such as that shown in Figure 8-11.

Or the connection can be made by a 1:1 chain drive with some form of reduction, such as the planetary gearset used by General Motors (Figure 8-12). This makes an extremely compact and efficient unit, as can be seen in Figure 8-13: transmission at left, final drive and differential at right, with valve body, pump, and torque converter placed adjacent. All share a common lube system. Notice that the transmission output shaft is a natural extension of, and connects directly to, the left axle, and the right axle leads directly into the differential.

Vehicles with engines mounted across the axle rather than parallel to it require a bevel gear final drive to change the direction of power flow to the drive wheels. Some makes locate the final drive in front of the transmission and torque converter housing (e.g., Cadillac El Dorado, Oldsmobile Toronado, Saab, Toyota Tercel (Figure 8-14); others locate it between the transmission and the torque converter [e.g., Audi, some Porsche, Volkswagen, and Renault models, Subaru, (Figure 8-15).]

Attempting to isolate transaxle wear or damage noise to the transmission, final drive, or differential is difficult because these units are so close together. But any bench repair can lead to disassembly of the complete transaxle, permitting a thorough check of the entire assembly.

FOUR-WHEEL DRIVE

Formerly limited to heavy equipment and other vehicles intended for off-road operation, four-wheel drive now appears in several makes of passenger cars and light trucks.

All four-wheel-drive designs incorporate an assembly called a **transfer case**. Some mount directly on the transmission housing, others separately to the vehicle frame between transmission and axles. Traditionally, the transfer case contained gearsets that could be shifted to provide two-wheel or four-wheel drive as well as **high** or **low range gearing**. It had to be shifted out of four-wheel drive during operation on dry, hard surfaces to avoid wind-up between front and rear axles from differences in tire circumferences, slippage and so on. So the need to develop a four-wheel drive that could operate on any surface—full time—was recognized. The solution seemed simple: add a dif-

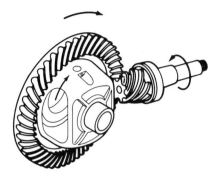

Ring gear is bolted to differential carrier that turns on bearings in axle housing—all on same axis.

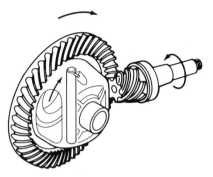

A shaft to hold the spider (pinion) gears inserts through two holes in the carrier and pins in place.

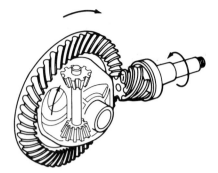

As the ring gear and carrier turn, the shaft and spider gears turn end over end.

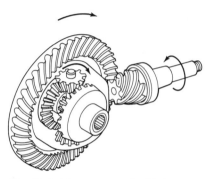

The side (axle) gears now mesh with the spider gears and, except when the vehicle turns a corner or one wheel slips, they turn with the carrier and ring gear as one unit. The spider gears do not turn on their axis, but power is evenly transferred through them.

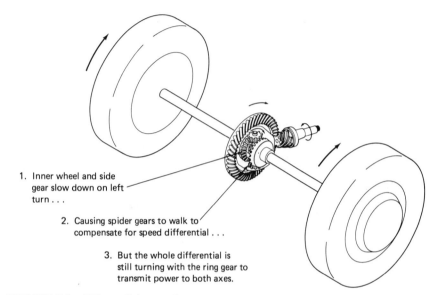

1. Inner wheel and side gear slow down on left turn . . .

2. Causing spider gears to walk to compensate for speed differential . . .

3. But the whole differential is still turning with the ring gear to transmit power to both axes.

FIGURE 8-9   Differential operation.

ferential gearset between the front and rear axles. But on very slippery surfaces, the differential allowed all the torque to go to the slipping axle, rendering the four-wheel drive useless.

The biggest problem associated with *full-time* four-wheel drive was solved by adding a coupling consisting of an assembly of clutches in a housing filled with **viscous, silicone fluid**—a unique property of this fluid is that it does not thin out when heated or subjected to high shear forces. (See Chapter 4 for a more complete description under "Lock-up Torque Converters.") When one axle starts slipping its increased speed is transferred to the coupling. This causes the clutch plates to begin to rotate through a silicone fluid, which in turn, creates shear friction that resists further speed in-

GENERAL PURPOSE VEHICLE

In March, 1940, a group of automotive engineers were invited to Fort Benning, Georgia, by Colonel Arthur W.L. Herrington. They were to see a demonstration of a small armed vehicle that was designed and built by Captain Robert G. Howie. So successful was this demonstration that it led to development of the Jeep, certainly the most popular vehicle that came out of World War II and the one to which the popularity of four-wheel-drive passenger vehicles can be credited. The Jeep was designated a General Purpose vehicle, or GP, hence the name.

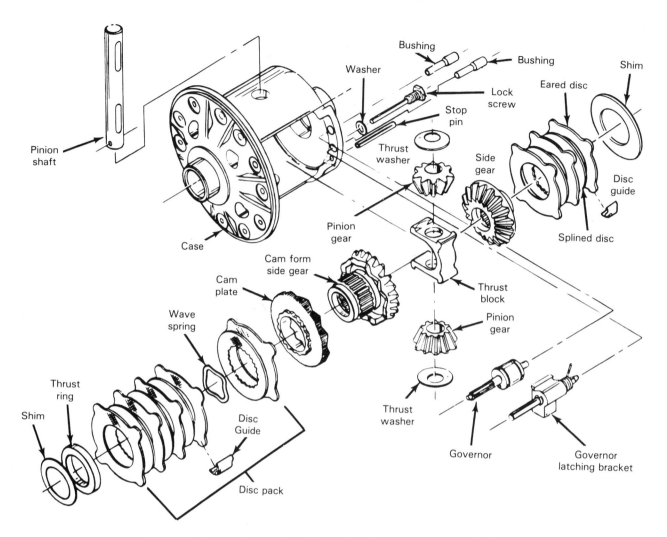

FIGURE 8-10 Limited-slip differential (Courtesy of Ford Motor Company).

crease. The resistance increases with increasing speed, thus limiting the amount of slippage, yet differential gearing still works at low speed differences normally encountered on highway driving, which avoids wind-up.

The successful development of full-time four-wheel drive has broadened its application to passenger cars for highway driving safety. So what we knew for many years as simply "four-wheel drive," we now distinguish as **part-time four-wheel drive** and **full-time four-wheel drive**.

Transfer Cases

There are a number of popular transfer cases. Most are for part-time four-wheel drive, but we will

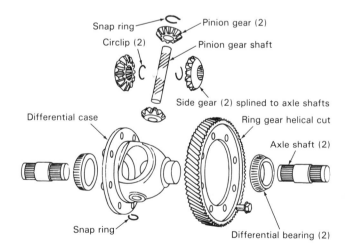

FIGURE   8-11 Final-drive   gears   (engine mounted parallel to axle.

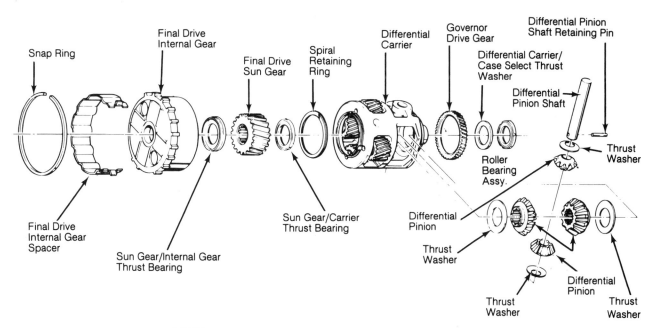

FIGURE 8-12   Differential and planetary gearset final drive.

review one full-time and one part-time/full-time unit as well. Transfer cases have little effect on transmission diagnosis and repair—some effect perhaps, from the transmission-mounted ones, but because of their direct connection more than anything else. However, it helps to become familiar with them. Here is a summary:

New Process Model 205. This transfer case is a helical-gear-driven, heavy-duty, two-speed, part-time unit used by both Chrysler and General Motors (Figure 8-16).

New Process Models 207 and 208. The design of these two assemblies includes aluminum cases and the use of a planetary gearset for low range. Both are part-time, two-speed, chain-driven units used by Chrysler and General Motors (Figures 8-17 and 8-18), Ford (Figure 8-19), and Jeep (Figures 8-17 through 8-20.

Spicer Model 300. This helical-gear-driven, heavy-duty, two-speed, part-time unit is used by Jeep (Figure 8-21); similar ones are used by Nissan/Datsun (Figure 8-22), and Toyota Land Cruiser (Figure 8-23). Notice that Jeep uses a one-piece housing that bolts directly to the transmission (manual or automatic). Nissan/Datsun uses a three-

piece housing that bolts to both transmission and frame, and Toyota uses a two-piece that bolts directly to the transmission.

Toyota 4WD Pickup. This is similar to the Spicer Model 300 in that it is a helical-gear-driven, two-speed, part-time transfer case. But note that it uses a five-part housing, counting the adapter housing for mounting to the transmission and the rear case extension housing (Figure 8-24). It also incorporates a screw-type oil pump to feed the speedometer gear and rear bearing (Figure 8-25).

Mitsubishi (Chrysler Imports). This is the only two-speed, chain-driven, helical gear, part-time transfer case made (Figure 8-26). It mounts directly to the three-speed automatic transmission case.

Borg-Warner 1345 and 1350. These are both aluminum cased, and they are the only transfer cases that have positive displacement pumps, which are driven by the output shaft. They are chain-driven, two-speed, part-time units that incorporate a planetary gearset for low-range operation. The 1345 is shown in Figure 8-27, and the 1350—used in Bronco II and Ranger—is shown in Figure 8-28.

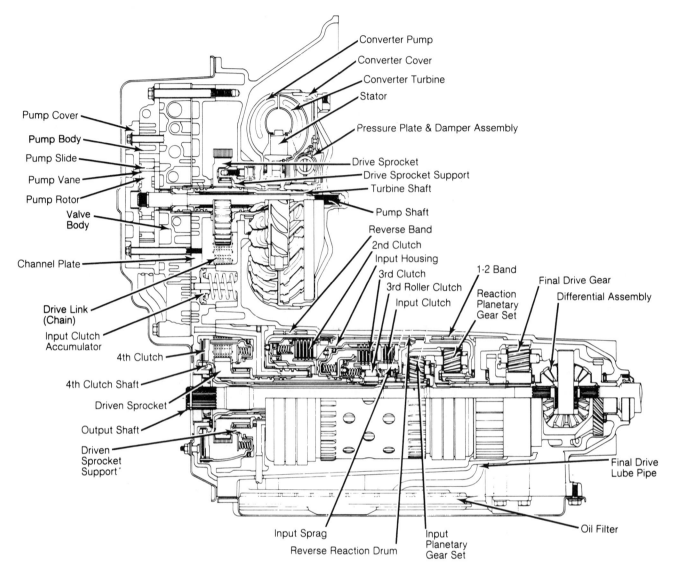

FIGURE 8-13   Transaxle cross section for transverse-mounted engine.

American Motors Model 129.   This is a full-time, single-speed, chain-driven, independently mounted, aluminum transfer case. It incorporates a viscous silicone fluid coupling and differential gearset to accommodate full-time operation. It is used in the Eagle passenger car and can be optionally equipped with a vacuum-operated front hub and 4WD axle disconnect that is actuated by a dash-mounted switch (Figure 8-29). Note the screw-type oil pump.

American Motors Selec-Trac Model 229. Available only with automatic transmission, this transfer case can be operated either full-time or part-time. It is a two-range speed, chain-driven unit with a planetary gearset for low range and a viscous silicone fluid coupling and differential gearset (Figure 8-30). Selec-Trac controls full-time or part-time operation from a mode selector on the instrument panel (Figure 8-31). It is installed with a Model 44 front axle and disengages both front hubs and transfer case in part-time mode.

It is identical to the optional Select Drive on Model 129, and the outward appearance of the case is very similar to the Model 129. Note also the screw-type oil pump.

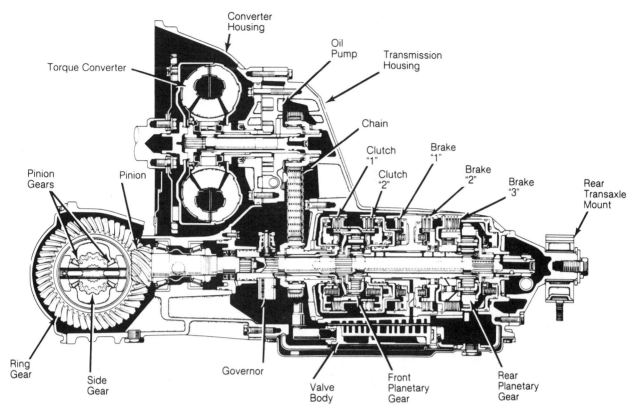

FIGURE 8-14 Example of longitudinally mounted engine "transaxle" with final drive located in front (Courtesy of Toyota Motor Sales, USA).

ENGINE

The engine interfaces with the automatic transmission mechanically, as well as through vacuum and electrical systems. These, too, must be considered for a thorough automatic transmission trouble diagnosis.

Flex Plate

The mechanical connection from engine to transmission in nearly all designs is between the torque converter housing and a flex plate. The **flex plate** is made of a steel alloy about 3/32 in. thick. It is bolted to the crankshaft near its center and to the torque converter housing around its perimeter. It most often includes the starter ring gear, although some designs locate the starter ring gear on the torque converter housing. The bolt patterns around the center or perimeter, or both, may not be symmetrical, which assures that the units are always

bolted together the same way. Some bolt patterns *are* symmetrical, however, so it is good practice to mark flex plate-to-converter and flex plate-to-crankshaft during disassembly. Special high shear-strength bolts are used, and bolts of unknown properties must never be used in their place.

Always remove the flex plate if the transmission has been removed. Clean and visually inspect it for metal-fatigue cracks, especially in the areas around the perimeter bolt holes. At reassembly, observe bolt-tightening torque values—excessive torque can lead to stress fractures. Of course, undertorquing risks developing a loose connection. Runout should be checked against specifications, too.

Also, during transmission installation, it is important to follow the manufacturer's specifications for converter installation (to make certain that it engages the oil pump) and for the distance the converter must be slid forward to meet the flex plate. If this distance is too great, the slots in the converter

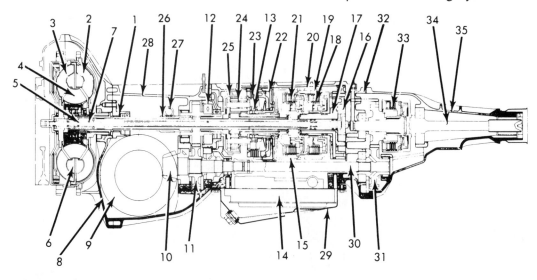

1. Stator Shaft	13. One-Way Clutch	25. Parking Gear
2. Impeller	14. Valve Body	26. Speedometer & Governor Drive Gear
3. Turbine	15. Connecting Shell	27. Governor Shaft
4. Stator	16. Oil Pump	28. Final Drive Housing
5. Turbine Shaft	17. Oil Pump Carrier	29. Oil Pan
6. Torque Converter	18. Reverse Clutch	30. Transfer Drive Shaft (4WD)
7. Oil Pump Drive Shaft	19. Brake Band	31. Transfer Gear (4WD)
8. Converter Housing	20. Transmission Housing	32. Intermediate Housing (4WD)
9. Ring Gear	21. Forward Clutch	33. Transfer Clutch (4WD)
10. Drive Pinion	22. Center Support	34. Rear Drive Shaft (4WD)
11. Reduction Gear	23. Low & Reverse Brake	35. Extension Housing (4WD)
12. Oil Seal Holder (4WD)	24. Planetary Gear	

FIGURE 8-15   Example of longitudinally mounted engine "transaxle" with final drive mounted between transmission and torque converter (Courtesy of Subaru of America).

boss might not completely engage the pump lugs, causing excessive wear or even disengagement.

Vacuum

For automatic transmissions that use a vacuum modulator, engine tune-up is critical. An engine with a faulty ignition system, leaky or burned valves, or bad rings will produce insufficient vacuum and affect modulator operation. This, in turn, can affect shift quality and shift points. Of course, other parts of the engine vacuum system should also be checked for leaks, since overall vacuum could be diminished by a collection of small leaks instead of one big one.

Computer Control

Even when there is no computer-controlled electronic shifting, computerized engine controls

should also be checked when diagnosing evident transmission problems. This assures that the engine is operating properly, thus eliminating it as a source of any detrimental effect on transmission operation.

On vehicles using electronically controlled solenoids for torque converter lock-up, there can be a number of sending and switching mechanisms that have a direct or indirect effect: air conditioning, engine temperature, governor pressure, high or low vacuum, and gear shifting and position. It is important to keep up to date in your familiarity with computerized controls and to refer to the latest manufacturing information when on the job. You will find little basic difference from one manufacturer to the next as to how its devices sense and control emissions (crankcase, fuel, exhaust) and engine efficiency (coolant temperature, ignition timing, fuel consumption). But you will find different names for what is essentially the same device.

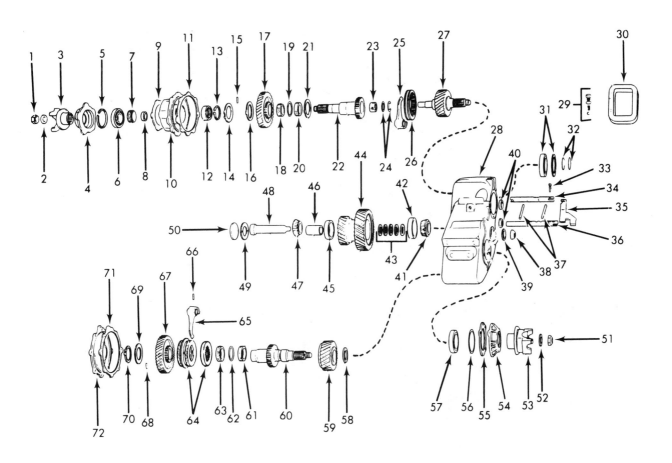

1. Rear Output Shaft Lock Nut	25. Shift Fork	49. Cover Gasket
2. Washer	26. Sliding Clutch	50. Rear Cover
3. Rear Output Shaft Yoke	27. Input Shaft	51. Front Output Shaft Lock Nut
4. Bearing Retainer & Seal	28. Transfer Case	52. Washer
5. Snap Ring	29. Poppet Plug, Spring & Ball	53. Yoke
6. Bearing	30. PTO Gasket & Cover	54. Bearing Retainer & Seal
7. Speedometer Gear	31. Input Shaft Bearing & Snap Ring	55. Gasket
8. Spacer	32. Snap Ring & Rubber "O" Ring (General Motors Only)	56. Snap Ring
9. Gasket	33. Shift Link Clevis Pin	57. Front Bearing
10. Rear Output Shaft Housing	34. Range Shift Rail	58. Thrust Washer
11. Gasket	35. Shift Rail Connector Link	59. 4WD-High Gear
12. Bearing	36. 4WD Shift Rail	60. Front Output Shaft
13. Snap Ring	37. Interlock Pins	61. Needle Bearing
14. Thrust Washer	38. Rear Idler Lock Nut	62. Spacer
15. Thrust Washer Lock Pin	39. Washer	63. Needle Bearing
16. Thrust Washer (Tanged)	40. Shift Rail Seals	64. Sliding Clutch Gear
17. Low Speed Gear	41. Idler Shaft Bearing	65. Shift Fork
18. Needle Bearings	42. Bearing Cup	66. Roll Pin
19. Spacer	43. Shims	67. Front Output Low Gear
20. Needle Bearings	44. Idler Gear	68. Thrust Washer Lock Pin
21. Thrust Washer (Tanged)	45. Bearing Cup	69. Thrust Washer
22. Rear Output Shaft	46. Spacer	70. Snap Ring
23. Needle Bearings	47. Idler Shaft Bearing	71. Rear Cover Gasket
24. Washer & Retainer	48. Idler Shaft	72. Rear Cover & Bearing

FIGURE 8-16   New Process Model 205 transfer case.

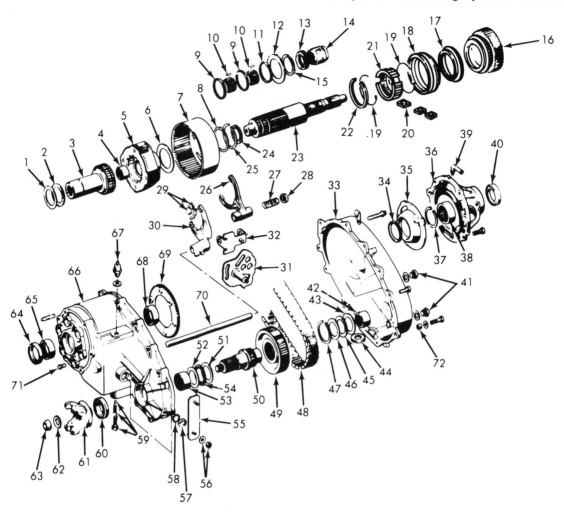

1. Input Gear Thrust Washer
2. Input Gear Thrust Bearing
3. Input Gear
4. Mainshaft Pilot Bearing
5. Planetary Assembly
6. Planetary Thrust Washer
7. Annulus Gear
8. Annulus Gear Thrust Washer
9. Needle Bearing Spacers
10. Mainshaft Needle Bearings (120)
11. Needle Bearing Spacer
12. Spacer Washer
13. Oil Pump Gear
14. Speedometer Gear
15. Drive Sprocket Snap Ring
16. Drive Sprocket
17. Blocker Ring
18. Synchronizer Sleeve
19. Synchronizer Spring
20. Synchronizer Key
21. Synchronizer Hub
22. Synchronizer Hub Snap Ring
23. Mainshaft
24. Mainshaft Thrust Bearing
25. Internal Gear Snap Ring
26. Mode Fork
27. Spring
28. Spring Retainer

29. Range Fork Pads
30. Range Fork
31. Range Sector
32. Mode Fork Bracket
33. Rear Case
34. Seal
35. Oil Pump Housing
36. Rear Retainer
37. Bearing Snap Ring
38. Rear Output Bearing
39. Vent Tube
40. Rear Seal
41. Drain & Fill Plugs
42. Front Output Shaft
    Rear Bearing
43. Front Output Shaft Rear
    Thrust Bearing Race (Thick)
44. Magnet
45. Front Output Shaft
    Rear Thrust Bearing
46. Front Output Shaft Rear
    Thrust Bearing Race (Thin)
47. Driven Sprocket Retaining Ring
48. Drive Chain
49. Driven Sprocket
50. Front Output Shaft
51. Front Output Shaft Front
    Thrust Bearing Race (Thin)

52. Front Output Shaft Front
    Thrust Bearing Race (Thick)
53. Front Output Shaft Front Bearing
54. Front Output Shaft Front
    Bearing Thrust Race
55. Operating Lever
56. Washer & Lock Nut
57. Range Sector Shaft
    Seal Retainer
58. Range Sector Shaft Seal
59. Detent Ball, Spring
    & Retainer Bolt
60. Front Seal
61. Front Yoke
62. Yoke Seal Washer
63. Yoke Nut
64. Input Gear Oil Seal
65. Input Gear Front Bearing
66. Front Case
67. 4WD Indicator Light
    Switch & Washer
68. Input Gear Rear Bearing
69. Lock Plate
70. Shifter Fork Shaft
71. Lock Plate Bolts
72. Alignment Dowels

FIGURE 8-17 New Process Model 208 transfer case (Chrysler and General Motors version).

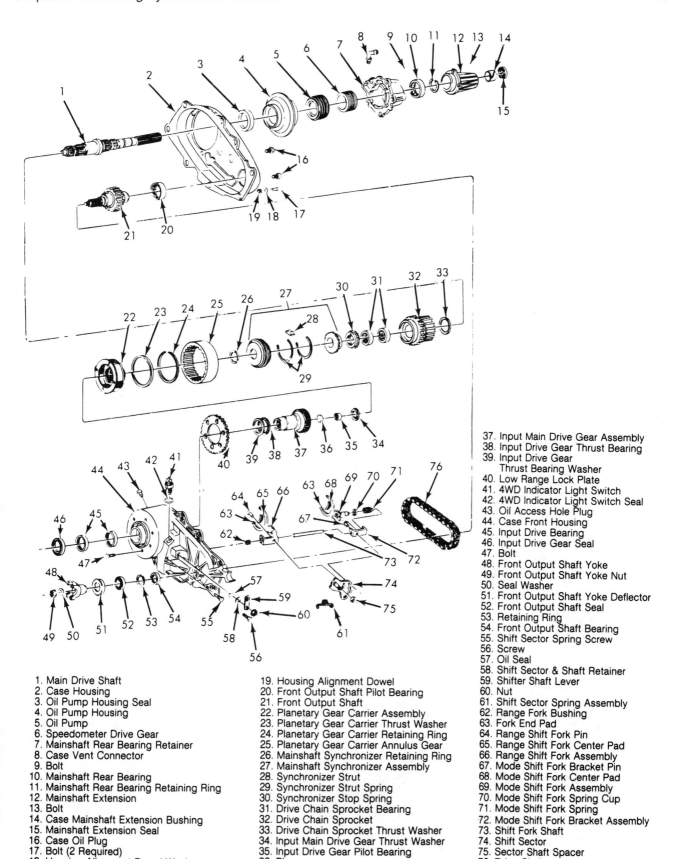

37. Input Main Drive Gear Assembly
38. Input Drive Gear Thrust Bearing
39. Input Drive Gear
    Thrust Bearing Washer
40. Low Range Lock Plate
41. 4WD Indicator Light Switch
42. 4WD Indicator Light Switch Seal
43. Oil Access Hole Plug
44. Case Front Housing
45. Input Drive Bearing
46. Input Drive Gear Seal
47. Bolt
48. Front Output Shaft Yoke
49. Front Output Shaft Yoke Nut
50. Seal Washer
51. Front Output Shaft Yoke Deflector
52. Front Output Shaft Seal
53. Retaining Ring
54. Front Output Shaft Bearing
55. Shift Sector Spring Screw
56. Screw
57. Oil Seal
58. Shift Sector & Shaft Retainer
59. Shifter Shaft Lever
60. Nut
61. Shift Sector Spring Assembly
62. Range Fork Bushing
63. Fork End Pad
64. Range Shift Fork Pin
65. Range Shift Fork Center Pad
66. Range Shift Fork Assembly
67. Mode Shift Fork Bracket Pin
68. Mode Shift Fork Center Pad
69. Mode Shift Fork Assembly
70. Mode Shift Fork Spring Cup
71. Mode Shift Fork Spring
72. Mode Shift Fork Bracket Assembly
73. Shift Fork Shaft
74. Shift Sector
75. Sector Shaft Spacer
76. Drive Chain

1. Main Drive Shaft
2. Case Housing
3. Oil Pump Housing Seal
4. Oil Pump Housing
5. Oil Pump
6. Speedometer Drive Gear
7. Mainshaft Rear Bearing Retainer
8. Case Vent Connector
9. Bolt
10. Mainshaft Rear Bearing
11. Mainshaft Rear Bearing Retaining Ring
12. Mainshaft Extension
13. Bolt
14. Case Mainshaft Extension Bushing
15. Mainshaft Extension Seal
16. Case Oil Plug
17. Bolt (2 Required)
18. Housing Alignment Dowel Washer

19. Housing Alignment Dowel
20. Front Output Shaft Pilot Bearing
21. Front Output Shaft
22. Planetary Gear Carrier Assembly
23. Planetary Gear Carrier Thrust Washer
24. Planetary Gear Carrier Retaining Ring
25. Planetary Gear Carrier Annulus Gear
26. Mainshaft Synchronizer Retaining Ring
27. Mainshaft Synchronizer Assembly
28. Synchronizer Strut
29. Synchronizer Strut Spring
30. Synchronizer Stop Spring
31. Drive Chain Sprocket Bearing
32. Drive Chain Sprocket
33. Drive Chain Sprocket Thrust Washer
34. Input Main Drive Gear Thrust Washer
35. Input Drive Gear Pilot Bearing
36. Plug

FIGURE 8-18   New Process Model 207 transfer case.

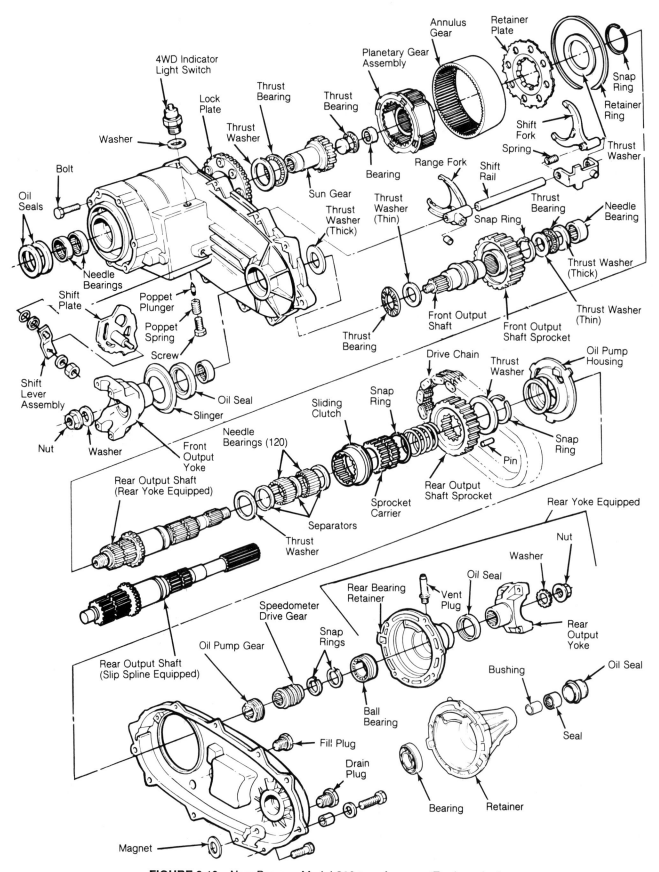

FIGURE 8-19   New Process Model 208 transfer case (Ford version).

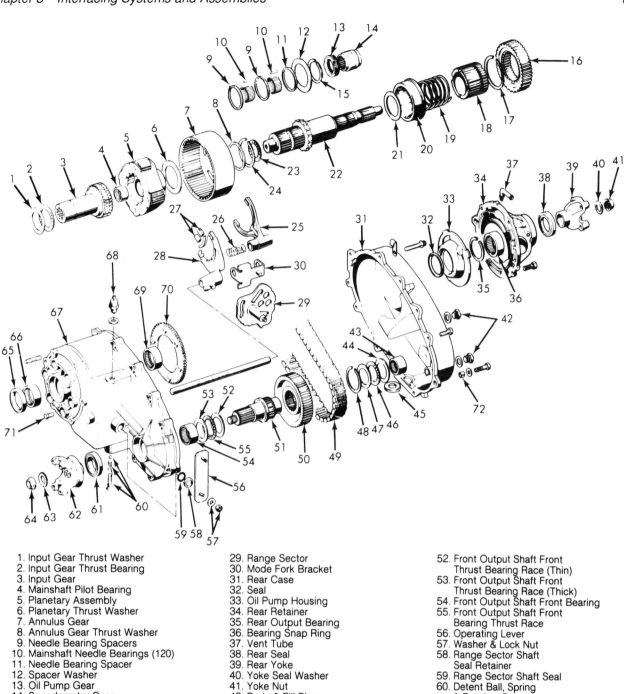

1. Input Gear Thrust Washer
2. Input Gear Thrust Bearing
3. Input Gear
4. Mainshaft Pilot Bearing
5. Planetary Assembly
6. Planetary Thrust Washer
7. Annulus Gear
8. Annulus Gear Thrust Washer
9. Needle Bearing Spacers
10. Mainshaft Needle Bearings (120)
11. Needle Bearing Spacer
12. Spacer Washer
13. Oil Pump Gear
14. Speedometer Gear
15. Drive Sprocket Snap Ring
16. Drive Sprocket
17. Sprocket Carrier Stop Ring
18. Sprocket Carrier
19. Clutch Spring
20. Sliding Clutch
21. Thrust Washer
22. Mainshaft
23. Mainshaft Thrust Bearing
24. Annulus Gear Retaining Ring
25. Mode Fork
26. Mode Fork Spring
27. Range Fork Pads
28. Range Fork

29. Range Sector
30. Mode Fork Bracket
31. Rear Case
32. Seal
33. Oil Pump Housing
34. Rear Retainer
35. Rear Output Bearing
36. Bearing Snap Ring
37. Vent Tube
38. Rear Seal
39. Rear Yoke
40. Yoke Seal Washer
41. Yoke Nut
42. Drain & Fill Plugs
43. Front Output Shaft
    Rear Bearing
44. Front Output Shaft Rear
    Thrust Bearing Race (Thick)
45. Magnet
46. Front Output Shaft
    Rear Thrust Bearing
47. Front Output Shaft Rear
    Thrust Bearing Race (Thin)
48. Driven Sprocket Retaining Ring
49. Drive Chain
50. Driven Sprocket
51. Front Output Shaft

52. Front Output Shaft Front
    Thrust Bearing Race (Thin)
53. Front Output Shaft Front
    Thrust Bearing Race (Thick)
54. Front Output Shaft Front Bearing
55. Front Output Shaft Front
    Bearing Thrust Race
56. Operating Lever
57. Washer & Lock Nut
58. Range Sector Shaft
    Seal Retainer
59. Range Sector Shaft Seal
60. Detent Ball, Spring
    & Retainer Bolt
61. Front Seal
62. Front Yoke
63. Yoke Seal Washer
64. Yoke Nut
65. Input Gear Oil Seal
66. Input Gear Front Bearing
67. Front Case
68. 4WD Indicator Light
    Switch & Washer
69. Input Gear Rear Bearing
70. Lock Plate
71. Lock Plate Bolts
72. Alignment Dowels

FIGURE 8-20   New Process Model 208 transfer case (Jeep version).

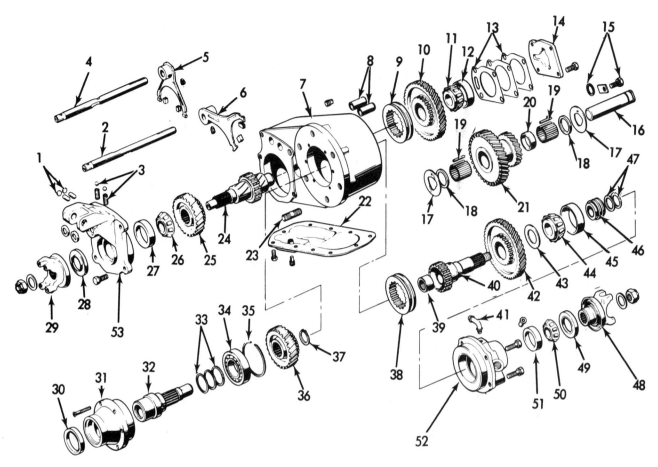

FIGURE 8-21   Spicer (Dana) Model 300 transfer case.

1. Interlock Plugs & Interlocks
2. Rear Output Shaft Shift Rod
3. Poppet Balls & Springs
4. Front Output Shaft Shift Rod
5. Front Output Shaft Shift Fork
6. Rear Output Shaft Shift Fork
7. Transfer Case
8. Thimble Covers
9. Front Output Shaft
   Clutch Sleeve
10. Front Output Shaft
    Clutch Gear
11. Front Output Shaft
    Rear Bearing
12. Bearing Race

13. Front Output Shaft End
    Play Shims
14. Cover Plate
15. Lock Plate, Bolt & Washer
16. Intermediate Gear Shaft
17. Thrust Washer
18. Bearing Spacer (Thin)
19. Intermediate Gear Shaft
    Needle Bearings
20. Bearing Spacer (Thick)
21. Intermediate Gear
22. Bottom Cover
23. Case-to-Transmission Stud
24. Front Output Shaft
25. Front Output Shaft Gear

26. Front Output Shaft
    Front Bearing
27. Bearing Race
28. Oil Seal
29. Front Yoke
30. Seal
31. Input Shaft Support
32. Input Shaft
33. Shims
34. Input Shaft Bearing
35. Bearing Snap Ring
36. Rear Output Shaft Gear
37. Snap Ring
38. Rear Output Shaft
    Clutch Sleeve

39. Input Shaft Rear Bearing
40. Rear Output Shaft
41. Vent
42. Rear Output Shaft
    Clutch Gear
43. Thrust Washer
44. Rear Output Shaft
    Front Bearing
45. Bearing Race
46. Speedometer Drive Gear
47. End Play Shims
48. Rear Yoke
49. Rear Output Shaft Oil Seal
50. Rear Output Shaft Rear Bearing
51. Bearing Race
52. Rear Bearing Cap
53. Front Bearing Cap

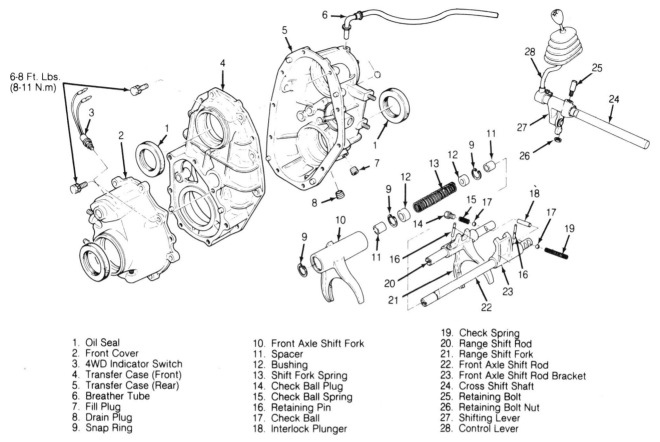

1. Oil Seal	10. Front Axle Shift Fork	19. Check Spring
2. Front Cover	11. Spacer	20. Range Shift Rod
3. 4WD Indicator Switch	12. Bushing	21. Range Shift Fork
4. Transfer Case (Front)	13. Shift Fork Spring	22. Front Axle Shift Rod
5. Transfer Case (Rear)	14. Check Ball Plug	23. Front Axle Shift Rod Bracket
6. Breather Tube	15. Check Ball Spring	24. Cross Shift Shaft
7. Fill Plug	16. Retaining Pin	25. Retaining Bolt
8. Drain Plug	17. Check Ball	26. Retaining Bolt Nut
9. Snap Ring	18. Interlock Plunger	27. Shifting Lever
		28. Control Lever

FIGURE 8-22   Nissan/Datsun 4WD pickup transfer case.

TRADE TERMS

Ball and trunnion	**Hotchkiss drive**	**Spider gears**
Cross and yoke	**Hypoid**	**Third member**
Differential	**Limited slip**	**Torque tube**
Double cardan	**differential**	**Transaxle**
Drive shaft	**Low range**	**Transfer case**
Final drive	**Part-time 4WD**	**Viscous silicone**
Flex plate	**Propeller shaft**	**fluid**
Full-time 4WD	**Ring and pinion**	**Wind-up**
High range	**Side gears**	

REVIEW QUESTIONS

8–1. The two major systems interfacing the transmission are _____ and _____.

8–2. The third member always has a bevel gearset final drive.   T   F

8–3. Automotive final drives are always reduction gearsets.   T   F

8–4. Which of the following is/are associated with drive shafts?

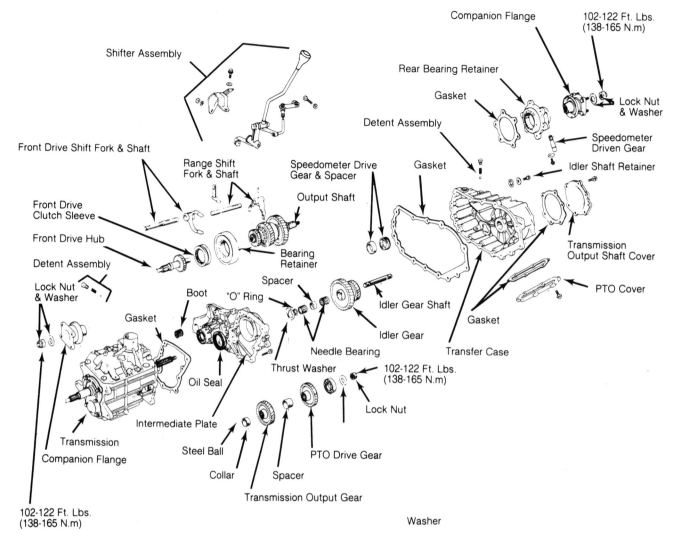

FIGURE 8-23   Toyota Land Cruiser transfer case.

(a) Hotchkiss drive.

(b) Propeller shaft.

(c) Torque tube.

(d) U-joint.

(e) All of the above.

8–5. Match the terms in the first column with those in the second.

   (a) Double cardan.   (1) Differential carrier.

   (b) Cross-and-yoke.   (2) Constant velocity.

   (c) Spider gears.   (3) Cardan.

   (d) Third member.   (4) Final drive.

8–6. Which of the following gears is not contained in the differential gearset?

   (a) Spider.

   (b) Pinion.

(c) Side.

(d) Ring.

8–7. Beveled gear final drives are used in rear-wheel drives only.   T   F

8–8. Drive shaft vibration and noise usually occurs _____ or _____ times faster than wheel rotation, depending on _____ _____ ratio.

8–9. The approximate difference between output shaft and pinion shaft angles required to minimize velocity variation with single cardan joints is:

   (a) 40°.

   (b) 25°.

   (c) 1 to 2°.

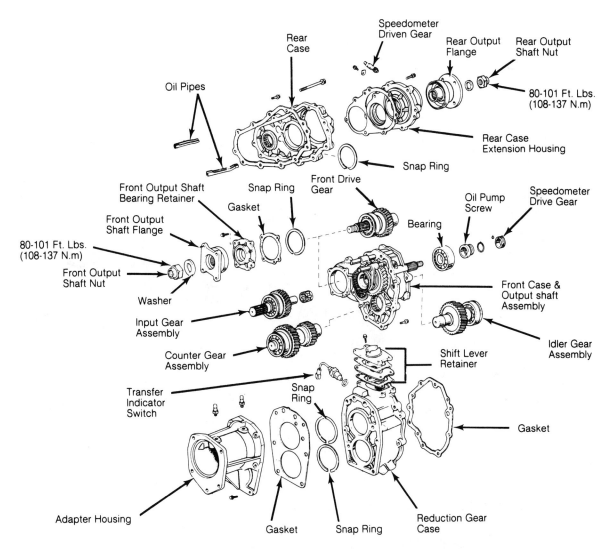

FIGURE 8-24 Toyota 4WD pickup truck transfer case.

(**d**) 28 1/2°.

8–10. Which of the following is not a constant-velocity joint?

(**a**) Rzeppa.

(**b**) Bendix.

(**c**) Single cross-and-yoke.

(**d**) Double cardan.

8–11. The term "hypoid" is derived from a mathematical term describing the shape of the teeth of a bevel ring pinion gearset that meshes _____.

8–12. The adjustments required for a bevel ring and pinion final drive are _____, _____ _____ and _____ _____.

8–13. A differential gearset is similar to which of the following gearsets?

(**a**) Two spurs with an idler between.

(**b**) A rack and pinion.

(**c**) A planetary.

(**d**) An internal-external.

8–14. Road testing for differential noise must include _____.

8–15. Which of the following items does a transaxle not contain?

(**a**) Final drive.

(**b**) Flex plate.

(**c**) Transmission.

(**d**) Differential.

8–16. Most transfer cases are:

(**a**) Part-time 4WD.

(**b**) Part-time/full-time 4WD.

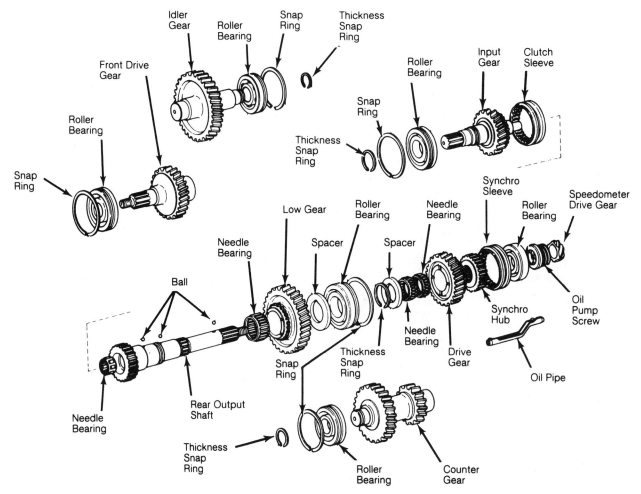

FIGURE 8-25   Toyota 4WD pickup truck transfer case gears showing oil pump screw.

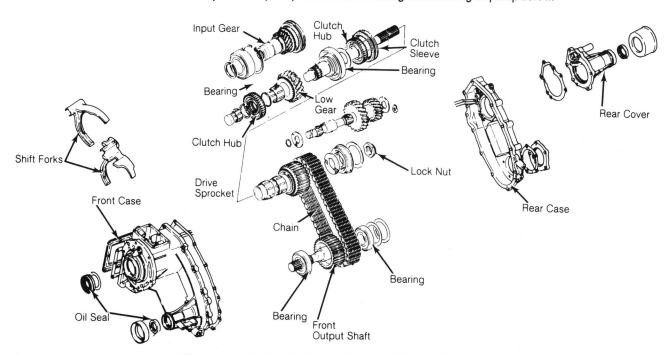

FIGURE 8-26   Mitsubishi transfer case (Chrysler imports).

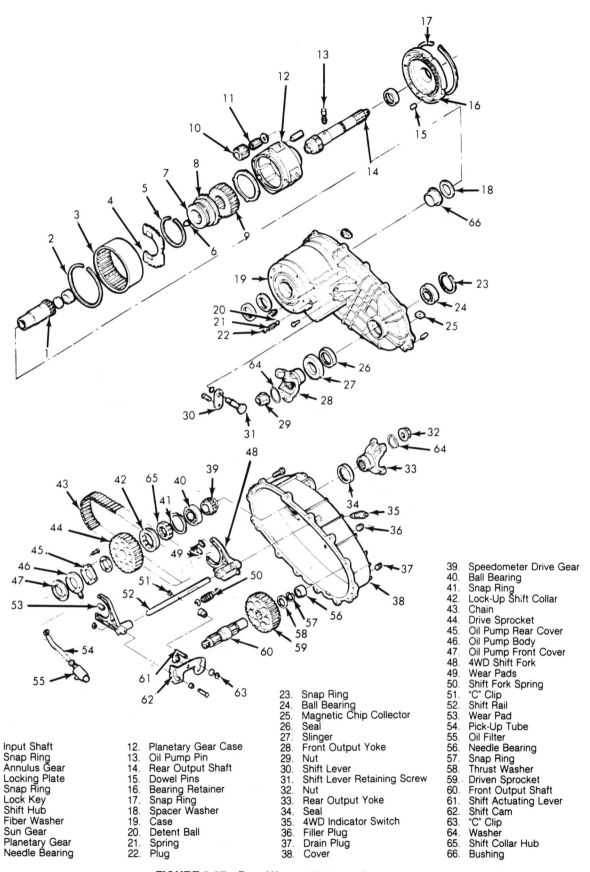

FIGURE 8-27   Borg-Warner 1345 transfer case.

1. Input Shaft
2. Snap Ring
3. Annulus Gear
4. Locking Plate
5. Snap Ring
6. Lock Key
7. Shift Hub
8. Fiber Washer
9. Sun Gear
10. Planetary Gear
11. Needle Bearing
12. Planetary Gear Case
13. Oil Pump Pin
14. Rear Output Shaft
15. Dowel Pins
16. Bearing Retainer
17. Snap Ring
18. Spacer Washer
19. Case
20. Detent Ball
21. Spring
22. Plug
23. Snap Ring
24. Ball Bearing
25. Magnetic Chip Collector
26. Seal
27. Slinger
28. Front Output Yoke
29. Nut
30. Shift Lever
31. Shift Lever Retaining Screw
32. Nut
33. Rear Output Yoke
34. Seal
35. 4WD Indicator Switch
36. Filler Plug
37. Drain Plug
38. Cover
39. Speedometer Drive Gear
40. Ball Bearing
41. Snap Ring
42. Lock-Up Shift Collar
43. Chain
44. Drive Sprocket
45. Oil Pump Rear Cover
46. Oil Pump Body
47. Oil Pump Front Cover
48. 4WD Shift Fork
49. Wear Pads
50. Shift Fork Spring
51. "C" Clip
52. Shift Rail
53. Wear Pad
54. Pick-Up Tube
55. Oil Filter
56. Needle Bearing
57. Snap Ring
58. Thrust Washer
59. Driven Sprocket
60. Front Output Shaft
61. Shift Actuating Lever
62. Shift Cam
63. "C" Clip
64. Washer
65. Shift Collar Hub
66. Bushing

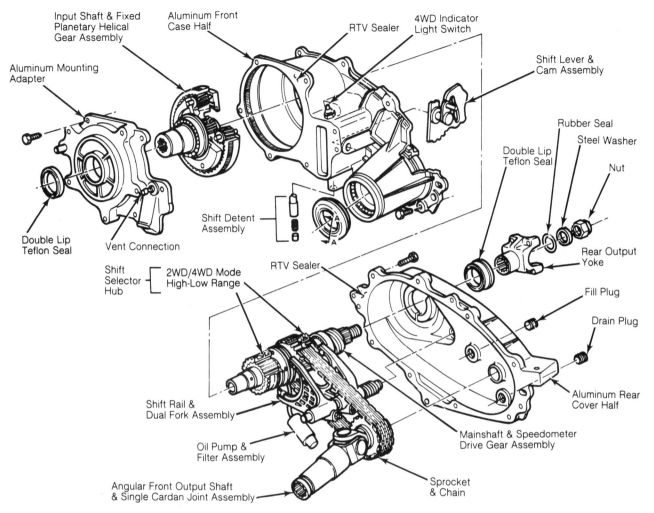

FIGURE 8-28   Borg-Warner 1350 transfer case.

(c) Full-time 4WD.

(d) Full-time/part-time 4WD.

8–17. The coupling that contains the differential gears on full-time 4WD units is filled with _____ _____ _____.

8–18. Transfer cases always mount separately, never to the transmission.   T   F

8–19. Always clean and inspect the flex plate for _____ and carefully observe _____ _____ when installing.

8–20. Engine-related systems that must also be checked when diagnosing automatic transmission problems are:

(a) Vacuum.

(b) Computer.

(c) Electronic Control Module.

(d) All of the above.

ESSAY QUESTIONS

8–1. Explain the difference between final drive gearsets and differential gearsets.

8–2. Describe the significant differences between part-time and full-time four-wheel-drive transfer cases.

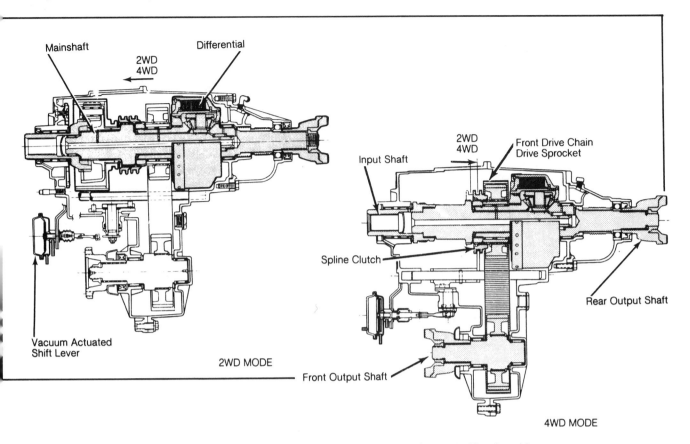

FIGURE 8-29   American Motors Model 129 transfer case with select drive option.

CHAPTER ACTIVITIES

8–1. Check under the hood of different makes and models of vehicles in your shop, and take note of engine and transaxle configuration and position.

8–2. Inspect the drive shafts on one or two front-engine, rear-wheel-drive vehicles to see if you can detect damage or wear.

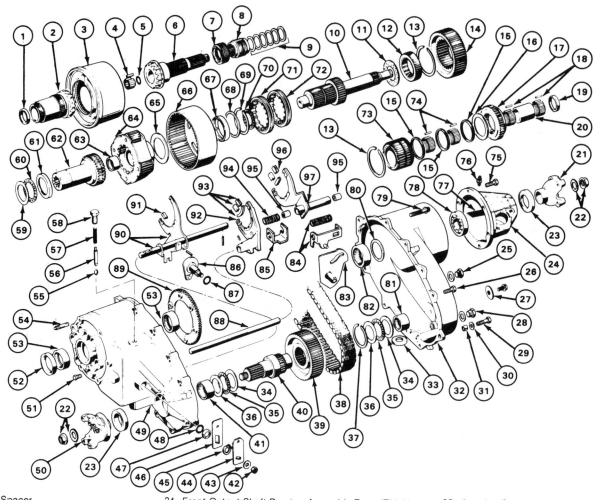

1. Spacer
2. Side Gear
3. Viscous Coupling
4. Pilot Bearing Rollers
5. "O" Ring Seal
6. Rear Output Shaft
7. Oil Pump
8. Speedometer Drive Gear
9. Shim Kit
10. Mainshaft
11. Manishaft Thrust Washer
12. Side Gear Clutch Gear
13. Retaining Ring
14. Sprocket
15. Spacer
16. Sprocket Thrust Washer
17. Viscous Clutch Gear
18. Side Gear Roller
19. Spacer (Short)
20. Spacer (Long)
21. Rear Yoke
22. Nut & Seal Washer
23. Seal
24. Rear Retainer
25. Plug Assembly
26. Bolt
27. Identification Tag
28. Plug Assembly
29. Dowel Bolt
30. Dowel Bolt Washer
31. Case Half Dowel
32. Rear Half Case
33. Magnet

34. Front Output Shaft Bearing Assembly Race (Thick)
35. Front Output Shaft Bearing Assembly Thrust
36. Front Output Shaft Bearing Assembly Race (Thin)
37. Retaining Ring
38. Chain
39. Driven Sprocket
40. Front Output Shaft
41. Front Output Front Bearing
42. Nut
43. Washer
44. Mode Lever
45. Snap Ring
46. Range Lever
47. "O" Ring Retainer
48. "O" Ring Seal
49. Front Half Case
50. Front Output Yoke
51. Low Range Plate Bolt
52. Input Shaft Oil Seal
53. Input Shaft Bearing
54. Stud
55. Ball
56. Plunger
57. Plunger Spring
58. Screw
59. Input Race
60. Input Thrust Bearing
61. Input Race (Thick)
62. Input Shaft
63. Input Bearing
64. Planetary Gear Assembly
65. Input Gear Thrust Washer

66. Annulus Gear assembly
67. Annulus Bushing
68. Thrust Washer
69. Retaining Ring
70. Thrust Bearing
71. High Range Sliding Clutch Sleeve
72. Mode Sliding Clutch Sleeve
73. Carrier
74. Carrier Rollers (120)
75. Rear Retainer Bolt
76. Vent
77. Vent Seal
78. Output Bearing
79. Bolt
80. Seal
81. Front Output Rear Bearing
82. Output Shaft Inner Bearing
83. Range Sector
84. Range Bracket (Outer) and Spring
85. Range Bracket (Inner)
86. Mode Sector
87. "O" Ring Seal
88. Range Rail
89. Low Range Lockout Plate
90. Mode Fork, Rail and Pin
91. Mode Fork Pad
92. Range Fork
93. Range Fork Pads
94. Range Bracket Spring (Inner)
95. Locking Fork Bushing
96. Locking Fork Pads
97. Locking Fork

FIGURE 8-30   American Motors Selec-trac Model 229.

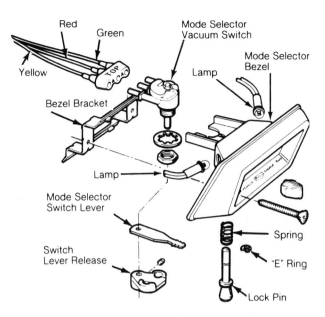

FIGURE 8-31 Selec-trac Model 229 mode selector.

9

Diagnosis, Testing Methods, and Special Tools

OBJECTIVES

When you have completed this chapter, you should be able to:

- Elicit your customer's observations by asking helpful, nontechnical questions.
- Analyze ATF condition for indication of existing or potential transmission problems.
- Follow a logical procedure of detection and testing that leads directly to a thorough diagnosis of the problem without jumping to conclusions.
- Follow established mechanical, hydraulic, vacuum, and electrical testing methods.
- Recognize the need for special tools, and select the ones that will best help complete the task safely and quickly.

DETECTION AND DIAGNOSIS

In the larger shops, one or more service managers will have the first contact with the customer. But a service manager sometimes puts the customer directly in touch with the technician, too. Of course, independent technicians—those in business for themselves—already know how important **customer contact** is. It ranks right up there with competent diagnosis and repair in conducting a successful repair business.

THERE ARE ALL KINDS OF CUSTOMERS

At one extreme, there are those to whom machinery is a total mystery and the automobile is a necessary evil tolerated only as long as it runs. Such persons simply do not detect symptoms—and problems only when they have become really major.("My engine won't start." "My car won't move." "The steering wheel doesn't work.")

The other extreme includes those who hear every tiny squeak, feel vibration and looseness in everything they touch, smell fumes that are sure to explode any minute, and see imperfection in every tiny detail. This is inevitably true of the new owner—of a new car or a used one; fortunately, it usually wears off as soon as they become accustomed to the "feel" of the car.

It is also fortunate that most customers fall between these two extremes and can be helpful in detecting real problems. Be pleasant to your customers, tolerant of their shortcomings or excuses, and helpful by asking questions: What? When? Where? And *listen*. The best way to listen is to tell them what you think you've heard them say: "OK, I want to make sure I've understood you—the noise only happens in drive, during acceleration..." etc.

When someone brings you their vehicle problem, the first thing they want to know is: "What's wrong with my car?" And the next thing they'll ask is: "How long will it take, and what's it going to cost?" This can put you under a lot of pressure; you are the expert in the situation, and your customer rightly expects you to answer these questions efficiently and accurately. This is why it is important to follow a well-planned *detection* and *diagnosis* sequence such as the following:

1. Listen to your customer describe the **symptoms** and how he or she detected them.
2. Check engine oil and ATF dipsticks. Note the level and condition of each.
3. Conduct a superficial check of mechanical, vacuum, hydraulic, and/or electrical connections that might be involved on the basis of the customer's description of the symptoms.
4. If the vehicle is driveable, have the customer take you for a ride so that you can interpret the performance that led to detection of the symptoms.

At this point you may be able to diagnose the problem. If not, you will have to conduct further shop inspections and/or road tests.

Diagnosis is a process of examination. At some point in this process, you draw a conclusion. If your conclusion turns out to have identified the problem correctly, you successfully concluded the

TOWING VEHICLES WITH AUTOMATIC TRANSMISSIONS

Almost without exception, the pump for automatic transmission lubrication is driven by the engine through the torque converter housing. If a vehicle with an automatic transmission is towed with the drive wheels on the ground, some gearsets, shafts, and bearings will spin with no lubrication, causing damage.

Vehicles with automatic transaxles must be towed with drive wheels suspended or on a dolly. Driveshafts may be removed from vehicles that have them if, for some reason, that is a better alternative.

Four-wheel-drive vehicles can be towed with the transfer case in neutral. Some manufacturers also instruct that the automatic transmission be put in park and the manual transmission be put in gear (but this is merely to assure that it is the transfer case that is in neutral, rather than the transmission being in neutral with the transfer case possibly being in low range, which could cause fly-apart gear speeds under tow!).

MAKING THE INVISIBLE VISIBLE

Whether you are trying to read a dipstick or detect an oil leak, clean hot oil on hot metal is difficult to see. Keep some typewriter carbon paper and a can of pressurized powdered footspray in your toolbox.

For a difficult-to-read dipstick, wipe with a clean rag, and rub the tip of the dipstick with carbon paper—your next dipstick check will be easily read.

When you are trying to zero in on oil leak sources, thoroughly

clean the suspected area with an aerosol cleaner such as that used for carburetors, dry with compressed air, then spray with the foot powder. Leaking oil will leave a clear trail through the powder.

---

examination process; if not, you did not. So your examination needs to be thorough and complete. Just because you have located a damaged or worn part at some point, do not jump to conclusions; check related circuits, systems, and assemblies as well.

Visual Checking

Like the detailed visual inspection of a part, **visual checking** is an examination of connections, systems, circuits, and assemblies. Begin first with the easiest and most obvious: for electrical, check the battery and ground connections; for vacuum, check the manifold connection; for hydraulic and lubrication, check dipsticks and leakages; for mechanical, check linkages and visible assembly connections and mountings.

Reading the Dipstick. Dipstick readings between cool and hot ATF will be different. The hot reading is usually higher on the dipstick than the cool reading, but not always. General Motors' THM-125C, for example, retains hot fluids in a separate reservoir for the valve body. When the fluid cools, a thermostatically operated valve opens, allowing the fluid to drain to the main reservoir; the dipstick then shows a higher reading. And the fluid level in some transmissions can be read accurately in neutral only. (Certain Chrysler models exhaust part of the pump circuit back to the sump in park. Checking in park position could result in running over a quart low.) Instructions are usually printed on the dipstick; if not, check the operating manual.

If the fluid level is too low or too high, do not road test until you have corrected it. Either condition can introduce air into the system (see Chapter

6); a high level can also force fluid out the vent or filler, which could be mistaken initially as a leak; an especially low fluid level not only affects transmission operation, but risks extensive damage from inadequate lubrication.

Interpreting ATF condition. Clean ATF should be translucent; that is, you should be able to see through it to the dipstick. Most ATF is dyed red—and this is mainly to help differentiate ATF leaks from engine oil leaks. Acceptable fluid shows some darkening and varnish deposit on the dipstick, but if it is very dark or opaque and has a burned odor, at least friction surface and seal damage has most likely occurred.

Also, the fluid should be dabbed onto a white paper towel; the towel will absorb the fluid and leave only significant contaminants, such as carbon (burned friction or seal material) or metallic particles (worn thrust washers, bushings, spacers, bearings, gears, etc.). If you find this kind of fluid contamination, you should at least plan on removing the pan for further examination, flushing the transmission, and cleaning or replacing the filter.

If the ATF appears pinkish and milky, water and/or antifreeze has leaked into the cooling circuit. The transmission must be completely overhauled, the leak repaired, and the cooling circuit and converter thoroughly flushed.

Locating Leaks. Although minor leaks can be tolerated, those big enough to wet an area upward of 10 square inches or so, are probably significantly affecting ATF consumption. If you notice a large wet area around the transmission or on the underside of the vehicle in that location, check the color of the oil. If it is red, it is a transmission leak, but if it is not, it could be either engine oil or dirty ATF. Engine oil and ATF will show up differently under black light, dirty or not. Compare the leaking oil to each dipstick under black light.

When trying to locate a leak, it helps to take note of the construction of the particular transmission. Is there a vent that is plugged? Does the seal appear to be tight around the extension housing? Linkage shafts? Pan? Servo cover? Output shaft? If these and other connections, such as pressure tap plugs, speedometer gear, and cooler lines, appear to be tight, a good steam cleaning followed by a road test is the best approach—it should be fairly easy to locate fresh ATF on the clean transmission if the leak is substantial.

It is not unusual to find evidence of leaks at the engine-to-transmission interface. These are usually from the pump body cover seals or the torque converter hub seal. Some makes and models have a large inspection plate that makes it easier to determine the exact leak source. But the transmission will have to be removed anyway to repair leaks in this area, as well as possible leaks in the converter itself.

If a vacuum-modulated transmission is using a lot of ATF but no leaks are evident, check for a broken modulator diaphragm. The break does not have to be very large to allow engine vacuum to draw a steady stream of ATF into the combustion chambers.

Checking Mechanical, Vacuum, and Electrical Connections. This aspect of visual checking can be governed somewhat by the nature of the symptoms. For example, if the vehicle creeps in gear at idle speed, check for sticking throttle linkage; or if idle seems high and rough, check for a leaking vacuum hose. If convertor clutch lockup isn't taking place, check the electrical connectors. In other words, it is okay to follow your first hunch, but do not stop there if it does not pay off. Start a methodical check. Conduct any simple checks that can be done visually, without shop instrumentation. Broken or disconnected return springs, pinched or hardened or cracked vacuum hoses, and hoses that have been reconnected to the wrong fitting are not unusual.

Especially check the vacuum modulator hose or the T.V. linkage. Also check for full, free-throttle operation—from idle to W.O.T.—and make certain that the downshift linkage is activated on transmissions so equipped. Some transmission downshift systems use a switch-activated solenoid.

Both engine and transmission mounts should be checked, as well as drive shaft U-joints—especially if one of the symptoms is vibration. When checking mounts, use a pry bar to make sure that the rubber-to-metal bond is intact.

Road Testing

Going out for a short demonstration ride with the customer driving is not a road test; it is meant for you to observe the kind of operation that has brought about the customer's complaint. When you have understood the customer's complaint, checked the ATF, and visually checked links and connections, but the exact source of the problem has not been revealed, send the customer to the waiting room—or home—if you cannot immediately schedule further diagnosis.

If possible, road test in a relatively quiet area with little or no traffic. It helps to conduct closed-throttle shift speed checks on a slight downhill grade. Bring someone along to record shift speeds and quality as you call them out.

Shift Speeds. When you are checking **shift speeds**, you are effectively evaluating throttle pressure, governor pressure, and valve-assembly performance. Specifications for shift speeds and conditions should be referred to for each model. Generally speaking, you will be checking shift speed and quality at three different throttle openings—both upshifts, downshifts, and forced downshift (detent or kickdown) in drive range and manual positions.

Tire size, final drive ratio, manufacturing tolerances, and variations in throttle position all have an effect on specified shift speeds. Some manufacturer's specification tables show more than one column of shift speeds, depending on tire size (Table 9-1), others are not as critical (Table 9-2), and still others merely suggest that upshifts should occur at one or two specific speeds at approximate throttle openings. It is a test that is somewhat difficult to control precisely, and although a record of the shift speeds experienced during your road test can be helpful, your observations of shift quality can be more revealing.

TABLE 9-1

Shift speed specifications (mph)

MODEL PKA-CH 5.0L MARK VII, 50 STATE

Throttle	Range	Shift	OPS—R.P.M.	Column Number 1	Column Number 2
Closed Throttle See Note	(D) ,D	1-2	310-460	9-13	8-13
	(D) ,D	2-3	660-820	18-23	18-22
	(D)	3-4	1180-1580	33-45	32-43
	(D)	4-3	1330-900	37-26	36-25
	(D) ,D	3-2	800-640	22-18	21-18
	(D) ,D	2-1	410-240	11-7	11-7
	1	3-1, 2-1	1100-730	31-21	30-20
Part Throttle See Note	(D) ,D	1-2	600-920	17-26	16-25
	(D) ,D	2-3	1200-1620	34-46	33-44
	(D)	3-4	1500-2140	42-61	41-59
	(D)	4-3	1500-1060	42-30	41-29
	(D) ,D	3-2	1250-780	35-22	34-21
	(D) ,D	2-1	670-440	19-12	18-12
Wide Open See Note	(D) ,D	1-2	1250-1760	35-50	34-48
	(D) ,D	2-3	2410-2760	68-78	66-75
	(D) ,D	3-2	2310-1950	65-55	63-53
	(D) ,D	2-1	1420-920	40-26	38-25

Tire Size	Axle Ratio 2.73
	Use Column No.
P215/70R15	1
P215/65R15	2

MODEL PKA-BD & PKA-BV 5.0L CONTINENTAL & MARK VII 50 STATE & HIGH ALTITUDE

Throttle	Range	Shift	OPS—R.P.M.	Column Number 1	Column Number 2
Closed Throttle See Note	(D) ,D	1-2	310-460	8-12	7-11
	(D) ,D	2-3	680-830	17-21	16-20
	(D)	3-4	1300-1680	32-42	32-41
	(D)	4-3	1440-1060	36-27	35-26
	(D) ,D	3-2	800-600	20-15	19-15
	(D) ,D	2-1	410-240	10-6	10-6
	1	3-1, 2-1	1110-730	28-18	27-18
Part Throttle See Note	(D) ,D	1-2	670-1020	17-26	16-25
	(D) ,D	2-3	1330-1710	33-43	32-42
	(D)	3-4	1600-2210	40-56	39-54
	(D)	4-3	1600-1200	40-30	39-29
	(D) ,D	3-2	1440-1020	36-26	35-25
	(D) ,D	2-1	690-480	17-12	17-12
Wide Open See Note	(D) ,D	1-2	1370-1800	34-45	33-44
	(D) ,D	2-3	2470-2810	62-71	60-68
	(D) ,D	3-2	2420-2080	61-52	59-51
	(D) ,D	2-1	1450-1020	36-26	35-25

Tire Size	Axle Ratio 3.08
	Use Column No.
P215/70R15	1
P215/65R15	2

Shift Quality. All shifts should be smooth and firm with no engine speed **flare-up**. And there should be no slippage after engagement of any gear. Torque converter "slippage" (normal operation) is characterized by an early leveling off; that is, it reaches a certain maximum as indicated by a leveling off of engine rpm, regardless of throttle opening. Clutch or band slippage caused by excessive

TABLE 9-2

Automatic shift speeds and governor pressures

Engine	2.2L or 2.6L	2.2L (Non-Turbo)	2.2L (Turbo)
Axle Ratio	2.78 or 3.22	3.02	3.02
Throttle Closed 1-2 Upshift 2-3 Upshift 3-1 Downshift	13-16 17-21 12-15	13-17 18-22 13-16	15-19 20-25 15-19
Throttle Wide Open 1-2 Upshift 2-3 Upshift	34-42 60-67	36-44 63-71	38-42 70-80
Kickdown Range 3-2 Downshift 3-1 Downshift	55-63 30-38	58-66 32-39	64-74 37-40
Governor Pressure [1] 15 psi 50 psi	23-26 57-65	26-29 61-68	28-31 69-76

[1] – Governor pressure should be from zero to 3.0 psi at stand-still or downshift may not occur.

wear or insufficient apply pressure tends to continue the slip indefinitely and is more evident in higher gears (direct and overdrive) than in the lower ones.

Most manufacturers publish clutch and band application charts, such as that shown in Table 9-3 for the Ford AXOD. These help to pinpoint faulty circuits as well as faulty bands and clutches. Of course, there can be a number of other reasons for substandard shift quality. Some, such as low ATF level and throttle valve adjustment, you should have checked already, but the fault might be in a sticking accumulator valve, a leaking accumulator or servo piston seal or broken spring, clutch piston seals, and so on. And this is where "troubleshooting" charts come in.

Stator Operation. A properly functioning torque converter multiplies torque at low speeds and couples at high speeds (see Chapter 4). A stator whose one-way clutch will not lock loses its ability to assist in directing vortex flow and contributing to torque multiplication. The vehicle will accelerate poorly at low speed (during vortex flow) but well at high speed (rotary flow).

On the other hand, if the one-way clutch seizes, the stator will not turn with rotary flow. This causes turbulence and so much resistance to torque that the vehicle's maximum speed will be significantly reduced.

Troubleshooting and Test Charts

Charts and diagrams, such as those for hydraulic control, electricity/electronics, clutch and band ap-plication, solenoid operating pattern (electronic shifting), shift speeds, and lock-up speeds are really specifications and blueprints. They tell you what a part, assembly, or circuit looks like and how it is supposed to perform. But there are two other types of performance summaries that are published by manufacturers especially to facilitate diagnosis: (1) troubleshooting charts and (2) test charts.

A **troubleshooting chart** attempts to list all possible symptoms (conditions) that might be detected in faulty transmission operation. Following each symptom is a list of possible causes accompanied by the suggested remedy (correction). Figure 9-1 shows a troubleshooting chart for General Motors' Torque Converter Clutches. This is a fairly simple chart, listing only three general symptoms. More complex assemblies require many more; that for AMC transmissions (Figure 9-2) lists over 40.

Test charts work differently. First they are usually for electrical circuits, including of course, electromechanical devices. And because it is not possible to check out electrical circuit operation visually, they present a logical testing procedure in the form of a **branching diagram**. The procedure usually begins with a set of conditions that can readily be confirmed as normal and operative. It proceeds with instructions to test specific subcircuits in the most logical sequence. By this process of elimination, it directs the testing in such a way as to check out each of the subcircuits as well as the inter-dependence of any subcircuit upon others. Figure 9-3 includes a test chart for a General Motor's Torque Converter Clutch designed for use with fuel injection. It also shows a schematic diagram identifying connectors and switches in the

TABLE 9-3

Clutch and band application

Gain	Lo-int Band	Overdrive Band	Forward Clutch	Intermediate Clutch	Direct Clutch	Reverse Clutch	Low-One-Way clutch	Direct One-Way Clutch
1st gear manual low	Applied		Applied		Applied		Applied	Applied
1st Gear (Drive)	Applied		Applied				Applied	
2nd Gear (Drive)	Applied		Applied	Applied			Holding	
3rd Gear (Drive)			Applied	Applied	Applied			
4th Gear (Overdrive)		Applied		Applied	Applied			Applied
Reverse (R)			Applied			Applied	Holding	
Neutral (N)								
Park (P)								

CONDITION	POSSIBLE CAUSE	CORRECTION
No Converter Clutch Apply	Problem in Electronic Control Module (if equipped with Computer Command Control)	Verify Electronic Control Module operation
	Electrical Problem	
	Voltage not reaching transmission	Ensure 12 volts reach transmission to engage solenoid
	Ground inside transmission	Ensure solenoid is not grounded inside case
	Defective connector, wiring harness, or solenoid	Check and repair or replace as required
	Defective pressure switch (if equipped)	Check and replace pressure switch as required
	3rd clutch switch inoperative (THM 440-T4)	Check and replace switch as required
	4th clutch switch inoperative (THM 440-T4)	Check and replace switch as required
	Valve Body Assembly	
	Sticking converter clutch apply valve	Clean, service and/or replace valve body as required
	Sticking converter clutch shift valve	Clean, service and/or replace valve body as required
	Sticking throttle valve	Clean, service and/or replace valve body as required
	No. 10 check ball missing (THM 440-T4)	Inspect valve body and service as required
	Oil Pump Assembly	
	Orifice plugged for converter signal oil in pump	Clean and inspect orifice for blockage
	Solenoid "O" ring damaged or missing	Check and replace "O" ring
	Oil pump wear plate or gasket mispositioned or damaged	Check and replace wear plate or gasket
	Improper torque on oil pump-to-converter housing bolts	Tighten bolts to specifications
	Turbine shaft seals damaged	Check and replace seals
	Orifice cup plug omitted from cooler in passage	Check and install plug
	Channel Plate (THM 440-T4)	Check and replace converter clutch blow-off check ball if not seated or if damaged; Check and replace torque converter clutch accumulator piston or seal if damaged
Converter Clutch Apply Rough, Slipping, or Shudders	Converter clutch pressure plate faulty	Check plate for damage and service as required
	Damaged or missing check ball in end of turbine shaft	Check and replace turbine shaft, if required
	Converter clutch regulator valve stuck	Clean, service and/or replace valve body as required
	Converter clutch accumulator piston or seal damaged	Check and service as required
	Channel plate spring damaged (THM 440-T4)	Replace channel plate
	Incorrect converter clutch blow-off spring installed (THM 440-T4)	Check and install correct spring

FIGURE 9-1   Troubleshooting chart for General Motor's torque converter clutch.

CONDITION	POSSIBLE CAUSE	CORRECTION
Converter Clutch Apply Rough, Slipping, or Shudders (Cont.)	Channel plate seals damaged or missing	Check and service as required
	Turbine shaft seals damaged or missing (THM 440-T4)	Check and replace turbine shaft seals or shaft
Converter Clutch Does Not Release	Solenoid does not exhaust	Verify Electronic Control Module operation (vehicles with Computer Command Control)
	Converter clutch apply valve stuck	Clean, service and/or replace valve body as required
	Check damaged converter	Replace torque converter
	Cup plug missing from pump release passage	Check and replace plug or pump assembly
	Turbine shaft end seal damaged or missing	Check and replace end seal or turbine shaft as required
	Hole not drilled through turbine shaft	Replace turbine shaft

FIGURE 9-1   (cont.)

system, and there is a narrative procedure in addition to the test chart itself.

If everything checks out okay upon completing a test chart sequence, you would probably return to the troubleshooting chart (the test chart might even direct you to do this) to select another possible cause and remedy. In this selection, try to consider all the observations you have made to this point in detecting and diagnosing this problem in this vehicle.

In your diagnostic approach, consider also the age, mileage, and general condition of the vehicle. For a new, low-mileage vehicle that appears to be well maintained, a complete, exhaustive diagnosis effort is worthwhile—you can be reasonably certain that the problem stems from one faulty part or assembly rather than overall wear. If, on an older, high-mileage car that has been poorly maintained, you find that there is an internal transmission problem, you are going to rebuild the transmission anyway, so you might just as well get to it rather than waste time on further diagnosis.

TESTING METHODS

Stall Testing

The **stall test** registers maximum rpm attainable with brakes locked, transmission in gear, and engine held *briefly* at W.O.T. It puts a lot of stress on all drive train components, as well as the rear brakes

and cooling system. Its critics point out that there is nothing in stall testing that cannot be revealed in a road test as well—and the latter is possibly safer to both parts and personnel.

But if the vehicle is not driveable, stall testing can be one way to detect clutch and band slippage. Here are the essential steps for stall testing:

Preparation

1. Bring engine to normal operating temperature.
2. Hook up tachometer to read the **stall speed** which is the maximum rpm attained during each test.
3. Arrange to keep people away from the front and rear of the vehicle during each test.
4. Block drive wheels *and* apply parking and service brakes.
5. Prepare to conduct test in Drive, manual low, and reverse only, cooling engine between each test by running in neutral at 1000 to 1500 rpm for about 1 minute.

Testing

6. Apply brakes, put transmission in gear, push throttle to floor, and hold for no more than 5 seconds.
(a) Note maximum rpm reached, and immediately release throttle.
(b) If rpm exceeds specified maximum, release throttle immediately.

CONDITION	POSSIBLE CAUSE	CORRECTION
Harsh Engagement of "R", "D", "2", "1"	Engine idle speed	Check setting and adjust
	Throttle linkage	Check for smooth travel; clean linkage pivot points as required, but do not lubricate them and then adjust
	Hydraulic pressure	Perform hydraulic pressure test; Repair hydraulic components as required; Check and correct throttle and line pressure settings
	Rear band	Check and adjust rear band
	Accumulator	Clean and inspect for broken seal rings, scratched bore or broken/collapsed spring; Check piston for cracks or evidence of it cocking in bore
	Valve body	Remove, disassemble, clean thoroughly and inspect valves and plugs for nicks, scratches, burrs and rounded edges on valve lands; Check bores for scratches, springs for collapsed coils, and all mating surfaces for nicks, burrs or warpage; Reassemble and install, tightening all screws to specification
	Front clutch	Clean and inspect all parts; Examine retainer and piston for scores and scratches; discs and plates for wear; return springs for collapsed coils; and seal rings for damage; vent check ball in retainer must operate freely
	Rear clutch	Inspect all rear clutch parts as outlined for front clutch
Slow to Engage "N", "R", "D", "2", "1"	Fluid level and condition	Fluid should be at "FULL" mark with engine at idle; replace fluid if "milky" and full of bubbles, or dark and smells burned
	Gearshift linkage	Check and adjust linkage
	Engine idle speed	Check setting and adjust
	Hydraulic pressure	Perform hydraulic pressure test; Repair hydraulic components as required; Check and correct throttle and line pressure settings
	Clogged oil filter	Inspect and replace filter
	Rear band	Check and adjust rear band
	Clutch and band operation	Remove valve body and perform air pressure test to apply clutches and bands to check operation
	Accumulator	Clean and inspect for broken seal rings, scratched bore or broken/collapsed spring; Check piston for cracks or evidence of it cocking in bore
	Valve body	Remove, disassemble, clean thoroughly and inspect valves and plugs for nicks, scratches, burrs and rounded edges on valve lands; Check bores for scratches, springs for collapsed coils, and all mating surfaces for nicks, burrs or warpage; Reassemble and install, tightening all screws to specification

FIGURE 9-2   Troubleshooting chart for AMC complete transmission assembly.

CONDITION	POSSIBLE CAUSE	CORRECTION
Slow to Engage "N", "R", "D", "2", "1" (Cont.)	Oil pump	Clean pump and check all clearances; Inspect rotors for scoring and seal and bushings for wear; Inspect pump housing and reaction shaft support mating surfaces for flatness
	Front clutch	Clean and inspect all parts; Examine retainer and piston for scores and scratches; discs and plates for wear; return springs for collapsed coils; and seal rings for damage; vent check ball in retainer must operate freely
	Rear clutch	Inspect all rear clutch parts as outlined for front clutch
	Seal Rings	Inspect seal rings on reaction shaft support and governor support for wear, cracks or breakage; Inspect ring grooves on both support assemblies for nicks, burrs or distortion; Inspect bores in front clutch retainer and output shaft support for nicks, grooves, wear, cracks, or scratches
No Upshift, Stuck in Low Gear	Fluid level and condition	Fluid should be at "FULL" mark with engine at idle; replace fluid if "milky" and full of bubbles, or dark and smells burned
	Throttle linkage	Check for smooth travel; clean linkage pivot points as required, but do not lubricate them and then adjust
	Gearshift linkage	Check and adjust linkage
	Hydraulic pressure	Perform hydraulic pressure test; Repair hydraulic components as required; Check and correct throttle and line pressure settings
	Governor valve	Clean and inspect all parts; Check weights, shaft and valve for burrs, nicks, scores or binding; Check spring for collapsed or distorted coils and snap rings for distortion; Check filter for dirt and debris; Inspect body for cracks or warpage; Check torque on governor and output shaft support bolts
	Valve body	Remove, disassemble, clean thoroughly and inspect valves and plugs for nicks, scratches, burrs and rounded edges on valve lands; Check bores for scratches, springs for collapsed coils, and all mating surfaces for nicks, burrs or warpage; Reassemble and install, tightening all screws to specification
	Front band	Check and adjust front band
	Front servo and linkage	Inspect piston for wear, cracks and worn or broken seal rings; Check springs for collapsed or broken coils; Check servo bore for scratches, nicks or wear; Check lever, strut and band for damage; Check lever shaft for wear, looseness in case, or for leaking "O" ring
	Clutch and band operation	Remove valve body and perform air pressure test to apply clutches and bands to check operation

FIGURE 9-2   (cont.)

CONDITION	POSSIBLE CAUSE	CORRECTION
No Upshift, Stuck in Low Gear (Cont.)	Oil pump	Clean and check all clearances; Inspect rotors for scoring and seal and bushings for wear; Inspect housing and reaction shaft support mating surfaces for flatness
	Front clutch	Clean and inspect all parts; Examine retainer and piston for scores and scratches; discs and plates for wear; return springs for collapsed coils; and seal rings for damage; vent check ball in retainer must operate freely
No Low Gear, Moves in 2nd or 3rd Gear	Governor valve	Clean and inspect all parts; Check weights, shaft and valve for burrs, nicks, scores or binding; Check spring for collapsed or distorted coils and snap rings for distortion; Check filter for dirt and debris; Inspect body for cracks or warpage; Check torque on governor and output shaft support bolts
	Valve body	Remove, disassemble, clean thoroughly and inspect valves and plugs for nicks, scratches, burrs and rounded edges on valve lands; Check bores for scratches, springs for collapsed coils, and all mating surfaces for nicks, burrs or warpage; Reassemble and install, tightening all screws to specification
No Kickdown or Normal Downshift	Fluid level and condition	Fluid should be at "FULL" mark with engine at idle; replace fluid if "milky" and full of bubbles, or dark and smells burned
	Throttle linkage	Check for smooth travel; clean linkage pivot points as required, but do not lubricate them and then adjust
	Gearshift linkage	Check and adjust linkage
	Front band	Check and adjust front band
	Hydraulic pressure	Perform hydraulic pressure test; Repair hydraulic components as required; Check and correct throttle and line pressure settings
	Governor valve	Clean and inspect all parts; Check weights, shaft and valve for burrs, nicks, scores or binding; Check spring for collapsed or distorted coils and snap rings for distortion; Check filter for dirt and debris; Inspect body for cracks or warpage; Check torque on governor and output shaft support bolts
	Valve body	Remove, disassemble, clean thoroughly and inspect valves and plugs for nicks, scratches, burrs and rounded edges on valve lands; Check bores for scratches, springs for collapsed coils, and all mating surfaces for nicks, burrs or warpage; Reassemble and install, tightening all screws to specification
	Front servo and linkage	Inspect piston for wear, cracks and worn or broken seal rings; Check springs for collapsed or broken coils; Check servo bore for scratches, nicks or wear; Check lever, strut and band for damage; Check lever shaft for wear, looseness in case, or for leaking "O" ring
	Clutch and band operation	Remove valve body and perform air pressure test to apply clutches and bands to check operation

FIGURE 9-2   (cont.)

CONDITION	POSSIBLE CAUSE	CORRECTION
Delayed Erratic Shifts – Harsh at Times	Fluid level and condition	Fluid should be at "FULL" mark with engine at idle; replace fluid if "milky" and full of bubbles, or dark and smells burned
	Throttle linkage	Check for smooth travel; clean linkage pivot points as required, but do not lubricate them and then adjust
	Gearshift linkage	Check and adjust linkage
	Hydraulic pressure	Perform hydraulic pressure test; Repair hydraulic components as required; Check and correct throttle and line pressure settings
	Front band	Check and adjust front band
	Governor valve	Clean and inspect all parts; Check weights, shaft and valve for burrs, nicks, scores or binding; Check spring for collapsed or distorted coils and snap rings for distortion; Check filter for dirt and debris; Inspect body for cracks or warpage; Check torque on governor and output shaft support bolts
	Clogged oil filter	Inspect and replace filter
	Valve body	Remove, disassemble, clean thoroughly and inspect valves and plugs for nicks, scratches, burrs and rounded edges on valve lands; Check bores for scratches, springs for collapsed coils, and all mating surfaces for nicks, burrs or warpage; Reassemble and install, tightening all screws to specification
	Front servo and linkage	Inspect piston for wear, cracks and worn or broken seal rings; Check springs for collapsed or broken coils; Check servo bore for scratches, nicks or wear; Check lever, strut and band for damage; Check lever shaft for wear, looseness in case, or for leaking "O" ring
	Rear servo and linkage	Inspect piston for wear, cracks, worn or broken seal ring, or damaged seal; Check springs for collapsed or broken coils; Check servo bore for scratches, nicks or wear; Check lever and band for damage; Check lever shaft for wear or looseness in case
	Oil pump	Clean pump and check all clearances; Inspect rotors for scoring and seal and bushings for wear; Inspect pump housing and reaction shaft support mating surfaces for flatness
Slips in Forward Drive Ranges	Fluid level and condition	Fluid should be at "FULL" mark with engine at idle; replace fluid if "milky" and full of bubbles, or dark and smells burned
	Throttle linkage	Check for smooth travel; clean linkage pivot points as required, but do not lubricate them and then adjust
	Gearshift linkage	Check and adjust linkage
	Hydraulic pressure	Perform hydraulic pressure test; Repair hydraulic components as required; Check and correct throttle and line pressure settings
	Front band	Check and adjust front band

FIGURE 9-2   (cont.)

CONDITION	POSSIBLE CAUSE	CORRECTION
Slips in Forward Drive Ranges (Cont.)	Valve body	Remove, disassemble, clean thoroughly and inspect valves and plugs for nicks, scratches, burrs and rounded edges on valve lands; Check bores for scratches, springs for collapsed coils, and all mating surfaces for nicks, burrs or warpage; Reassemble and install, tightening all screws to specification
	Front servo and linkage	Inspect piston for wear, cracks and worn or broken seal rings; Check springs for collapsed or broken coils; Check servo bore for scratches, nicks or wear; Check lever, strut and band for damage; Check lever shaft for wear, looseness in case, or for leaking "O" ring
	Rear servo and linkage	Inspect piston for wear, cracks, worn or broken seal ring, or damaged seal; Check springs for collapsed or broken coils; Check servo bore for scratches, nicks or wear; Check lever and band for damage; Check lever shaft for wear or looseness in case
	Accumulator	Clean and inspect for broken seal rings, scratched bore or broken/collapsed spring; Check piston for cracks or evidence of it cocking in bore
	Clutch and band operation	Remove valve body and perform air pressure test to apply clutches and bands to check operation
	Oil pump	Clean pump and check all clearances; Inspect rotors for scoring and seal and bushings for wear; Inspect pump housing and reaction shaft support mating surfaces for flatness
	Front clutch	Clean and inspect all parts; Examine retainer and piston for scores and scratches; discs and plates for wear; return springs for collapsed coils; and seal rings for damage; vent check ball in retainer must operate freely
	Rear clutch	Inspect all rear clutch parts as outlined for front clutch
	Rear band	Inspect band for wear and for good bonding of lining to band; Inspect lining for burn marks, glazing, uneven wear patterns, flaking or if band grooves are worn away at any portion of band; Replace band if any of these conditions are present
	Seal Rings	Inspect seal rings on reaction shaft support and governor support for wear, cracks or breakage; Inspect ring grooves on both support assemblies for nicks, burrs or distortion; Inspect bores in front clutch retainer and output shaft support for nicks, grooves, wear, cracks, or scratches
Slips in Reverse Only	Fluid level and condition	Fluid should be at "FULL" mark with engine at idle; replace fluid if "milky" and full of bubbles, or dark and smells burned
	Gearshift linkage	Check and adjust linkage

FIGURE 9-2   (cont.)

CONDITION	POSSIBLE CAUSE	CORRECTION
Slips in Reverse Only (Cont.)	Hydraulic pressure	Perform hydraulic pressure test; Repair hydraulic components as required; Check and correct throttle and line pressure settings
	Front band	Check and adjust front band
	Valve body	Remove, disassemble, clean thoroughly and inspect valves and plugs for nicks, scratches, burrs and rounded edges on valve lands; Check bores for scratches, springs for collapsed coils, and all mating surfaces for nicks, burrs or warpage; Reassemble and install, tightening all screws to specification
	Rear servo and linkage	Inspect piston for wear, cracks, worn or broken seal ring, or damaged seal; Check springs for collapsed or broken coils; Check servo bore for scratches, nicks or wear; Check lever and band for damage; Check lever shaft for wear or looseness in case
	Clutch and band operation	Remove valve body and perform air pressure test to apply clutches and bands to check operation
	Oil pump	Clean pump and check all clearances; Inspect rotors for scoring and seal and bushings for wear; Inspect pump housing and reaction shaft support mating surfaces for flatness
	Front clutch	Clean and inspect all parts; Examine retainer and piston for scores and scratches; discs and plates for wear; return springs for collapsed coils; and seal rings for damage; vent check ball in retainer must operate freely
	Rear band	Inspect band for wear and for good bonding of lining to band; Inspect lining for burn marks, glazing, uneven wear patterns, flaking or if band grooves are worn away at any portion of band; Replace band if any of these conditions are present
Will Not Move in Forward or Reverse	Fluid level and condition	Fluid should be at "FULL" mark with engine at idle; replace fluid if "milky" and full of bubbles, or dark and smells burned
	Gearshift linkage	Check and adjust linkage
	Hydraulic pressure	Perform hydraulic pressure test; Repair hydraulic components as required; Check and correct throttle and line pressure settings
	Clogged oil filter	Inspect and replace filter
	Valve body	Remove, disassemble, clean thoroughly and inspect valves and plugs for nicks, scratches, burrs and rounded edges on valve lands; Check bores for scratches, springs for collapsed coils, and all mating surfaces for nicks, burrs or warpage; Reassemble and install, tightening all screws to specification
	Clutch and band operation	Remove valve body and perform air pressure test to apply clutches and bands to check operation

FIGURE 9-2   (cont.)

CONDITION	POSSIBLE CAUSE	CORRECTION
Will Not Move in Forward or Reverse (Cont.)	Converter drive plate	Check plate for flatness, cracks at mounting bolt holes, loose attaching bolts or damaged ring gear teeth; A broken drive plate may indicate engine-to-transmission misalignment caused by loose, missing or misaligned dowels
	Oil pump	Clean pump and check all clearances; Inspect rotors for scoring and seal and bushings for wear; Inspect pump housing and reaction shaft support mating surfaces for flatness
	Planetary gear set	Clean and inspect annulus gear, planet pinion carrier assembly and sun gear for worn thrust washers, damaged gear teeth and excessive pinion end clearance; Examine bushings in sun gear for excessive wear
Slips in Low Gear "D" Only, But Not in "1"	Overrunning clutch	Clean and inspect clutch parts for brinelled clutch rollers or cam, or improperly assembled rollers or springs; Check for collapsed springs and bent spring retainer tabs
Reverse Okay, Will Not Move Forward in "D", "2", "1"	Gearshift linkage	Check and adjust linkage
	Hydraulic pressure	Perform hydraulic pressure test; Repair hydraulic components as required; Check and correct throttle and line pressure settings
	Valve body	Remove, disassemble, clean thoroughly and inspect valves and plugs for nicks, scratches, burrs and rounded edges on valve lands; Check bores for scratches, springs for collapsed coils, and all mating surfaces for nicks, burrs or warpage; Reassemble and install, tightening all screws to specification
	Clutch and band operation	Remove valve body and perform air pressure test to apply clutches and bands to check operation
	Rear clutch	Inspect all rear clutch parts as outlined for front clutch
No Reverse	Gearshift linkage	Check and adjust linkage
	Hydraulic pressure	Perform hydraulic pressure test; Repair hydraulic components as required; Check and correct throttle and line pressure settings
	Front band	Check and adjust front band
	Rear servo and linkage	Inspect piston for wear, cracks, worn or broken seal ring, or damaged seal; Check springs for collapsed or broken coils; Check servo bore for scratches, nicks or wear; Check lever and band for damage; Check lever shaft for wear or looseness in case
	Clutch and band operation	Remove valve body and perform air pressure test to apply clutches and bands to check operation
	Front clutch	Clean and inspect all parts; Examine retainer and piston for scores and scratches; discs and plates for wear; return springs for collapsed coils; and seal rings for damage; vent check ball in retainer must operate freely

FIGURE 9-2   (cont.)

CONDITION	POSSIBLE CAUSE	CORRECTION
No Reverse (Cont.)	Rear band	Inspect band for wear and for good bonding of lining to band; Inspect lining for burn marks, glazing, uneven wear patterns, flaking or if band grooves are worn away at any portion of band; Replace band if any of these conditions are present
Moves in Neutral Position (Creeps)	Gearshift linkage	Check and adjust linkage
	Valve body	Remove, disassemble, clean thoroughly and inspect valves and plugs for nicks, scratches, burrs and rounded edges on valve lands; Check bores for scratches, springs for collapsed coils, and all mating surfaces for nicks, burrs or warpage; Reassemble and install, tightening all screws to specification
	Rear clutch	Inspect all rear clutch parts as outlined for front clutch
Drags or Locks Up	Hydraulic pressure	Perform hydraulic pressure test; Repair hydraulic components as required; Check and correct throttle and line pressure settings
	Front band	Check and adjust front band
	Front band	Check and adjust front band
	Park lock	Check condition of lock rod, lock rod ball, sprag reaction plug, governor support, and sprag shaft; Replace parts as required
	Valve body	Remove, disassemble, clean thoroughly and inspect valves and plugs for nicks, scratches, burrs and rounded edges on valve lands; Check bores for scratches, springs for collapsed coils, and all mating surfaces for nicks, burrs or warpage; Reassemble and install, tightening all screws to specification
	Front servo and linkage	Inspect piston for wear, cracks and worn or broken seal rings; Check springs for collapsed or broken coils; Check servo bore for scratches, nicks or wear; Check lever, strut and band for damage; Check lever shaft for wear, looseness in case, or for leaking "O" ring
	Rear servo and linkage	Inspect piston for wear, cracks, worn or broken seal ring, or damaged seal; Check springs for collapsed or broken coils; Check servo bore for scratches, nicks or wear; Check lever and band for damage; Check lever shaft for wear or looseness in case
	Accumulator	Clean and inspect for broken seal rings, scratched bore or broken/collapsed spring; Check piston for cracks or evidence of it cocking in bore
	Front clutch	Clean and inspect all parts; Examine retainer and piston for scores and scratches; discs and plates for wear; return springs for collapsed coils; and seal rings for damage; vent check ball in retainer must operate freely
	Rear clutch	Inspect all rear clutch parts as outlined for front clutch

FIGURE 9-2   (cont.)

CONDITION	POSSIBLE CAUSE	CORRECTION
Drags or Locks Up (Cont.)	Planetary gear set	Clean and inspect annulus gear, planet pinion carrier assembly and sun gear for worn thrust washers, damaged gear teeth and excessive pinion end clearance; Examine bushings in sun gear for excessive wear
	Rear band	Inspect band for wear and for good bonding of lining to band; Inspect lining for burn marks, glazing, uneven wear patterns, flaking or if band grooves are worn away at any portion of band; Replace band if any of these conditions are present
	Overrunning clutch	Clean and inspect clutch parts for brinelled clutch rollers or cam, or improperly assembled rollers or springs; Check for collapsed springs and bent spring retainer tabs

TRANSMISSION NOISY

CONDITION	POSSIBLE CAUSE	CORRECTION
Grating, Growling or Scraping Noise	Fluid level and condition	Fluid should be at "FULL" mark with engine at idle; replace fluid if "milky" and full of bubbles, or dark and smells burned
	Park lock	Check condition of lock rod, lock rod ball, sprag reaction plug, governor support, and sprag shaft; Replace parts as required
	Output shaft bearing, bushing, or seal	Remove extension housing, inspect parts, and replace parts as required
	Clogged oil filter	Inspect and replace filter
	Converter drive plate	Check plate for flatness, cracks at mounting bolt holes, loose attaching bolts or damaged ring gear teeth; A broken drive plate may indicate engine-to-transmission misalignment caused by loose, missing or misaligned dowels
	Oil pump	Clean pump and check all clearances; Inspect rotors for scoring and seal and bushings for wear; Inspect pump housing and reaction shaft support mating surfaces for flatness
	Front clutch	Clean and inspect all parts; Examine retainer and piston for scores and scratches; discs and plates for wear; return springs for collapsed coils; and seal rings for damage; vent check ball in retainer must operate freely
	Planetary gear set	Clean and inspect annulus gear, planet pinion carrier assembly and sun gear for worn thrust washers, damaged gear teeth and excessive pinion end clearance; Examine bushings in sun gear for excessive wear
	Overrunning clutch	Clean and inspect clutch parts for brinelled clutch rollers or cam, or improperly assembled rollers or springs; Check for collapsed springs and bent spring retainer tabs
	Torque Converter	If converter hub seal surface or drive slots are damaged or if converter contains foreign material, burned-oxidized fluid or debris, replace converter; Do not attempt to clean or flush converter
Buzzing Noise	Fluid level and condition	Fluid should be at "FULL" mark with engine at idle; replace fluid if "milky" and full of bubbles, or dark and smells burned

FIGURE 9-2   (cont.)

CONDITION	POSSIBLE CAUSE	CORRECTION
TRANSMISSION NOISY (Cont.)		
Buzzing Noise (Cont.)	Governor valve	Clean and inspect all parts; Check weights, shaft and valve for burrs, nicks, scores or binding; Check spring for collapsed or distorted coils and snap rings for distortion; Check filter for dirt and debris; Inspect body for cracks or warpage; Check torque on governor and output shaft support bolts
	Valve body	Remove, disassemble, clean thoroughly and inspect valves and plugs for nicks, scratches, burrs and rounded edges on valve lands; Check bores for scratches, springs for collapsed coils, and all mating surfaces for nicks, burrs or warpage; Reassemble and install, tightening all screws to specification
	Clutch and band operation	Remove valve body and perform air pressure test to apply clutches and bands to check operation
	Oil pump	Clean pump and check all clearances; Inspect rotors for scoring and seal and bushings for wear; Inspect pump housing and reaction shaft support mating surfaces for flatness
	Torque Converter	If converter hub seal surface or drive slots are damaged or if converter contains foreign material, burned-oxidized fluid or debris, replace converter; Do not attempt to clean or flush converter
Oil Blows Out Filler Tube	Fluid level and condition	Fluid should be at "FULL" mark with engine at idle; replace fluid if "milky" and full of bubbles, or dark and smells burned
	Transmission Oil Cooler	Check lines and cooler for obstructions, or leaks (look for transmission fluid in radiator coolant, or milky-colored transmission fluid which indicates coolant in fluid)
	Clogged oil filter	Inspect and replace filter
	Valve body	Remove, disassemble, clean thoroughly and inspect valves and plugs for nicks, scratches, burrs and rounded edges on valve lands; Check bores for scratches, springs for collapsed coils, and all mating surfaces for nicks, burrs or warpage; Reassemble and install, tightening all screws to specification
	Oil pump	Clean pump and check all clearances; Inspect rotors for scoring and seal and bushings for wear; Inspect pump housing and reaction shaft support mating surfaces for flatness
	Transmission vent	Make sure vent is open and not obstructed
Transmission Overheats	Fluid level and condition	Fluid should be at "FULL" mark with engine at idle; replace fluid if "milky" and full of bubbles, or dark and smells burned
	Engine idle speed	Check setting and adjust
	Transmission Oil Cooler	Check lines and cooler for obstructions, or leaks (look for transmission fluid in radiator coolant, or milky-colored transmission fluid which indicates coolant in fluid)
	Front band	Check and adjust front band

FIGURE 9-2   (cont.)

CONDITION	POSSIBLE CAUSE	CORRECTION
	TRANSMISSION NOISY (Cont.)	
Transmission Overheats (Cont.)	Hydraulic pressure	Perform hydraulic pressure test; Repair hydraulic components as required; Check and correct throttle and line pressure settings
	Clogged oil filter	Inspect and replace filter
	Front band	Check and adjust front band
	Valve body	Remove, disassemble, clean thoroughly and inspect valves and plugs for nicks, scratches, burrs and rounded edges on valve lands; Check bores for scratches, springs for collapsed coils, and all mating surfaces for nicks, burrs or warpage; Reassemble and install, tightening all screws to specification
	Converter drive plate	Check plate for flatness, cracks at mounting bolt holes, loose attaching bolts or damaged ring gear teeth; A broken drive plate may indicate engine-to-transmission misalignment caused by loose, missing or misaligned dowels
Starter Will Not Operate in Neutral or Park	Gearshift linkage	Check and adjust linkage
	Neutral start switch	Check wires and connections; Test switch; See if valve body manual lever grounds switch in "P" and "N" positions; If not okay, check ground strip at valve body manual lever; If okay, check starting circuit
	Engine performance	Verify proper engine operation; Be sure compression meets specifications and that fuel and ignition systems are functioning properly
	Valve body	Remove, disassemble, clean thoroughly and inspect valves and plugs for nicks, scratches, burrs and rounded edges on valve lands; Check bores for scratches, springs for collapsed coils, and all mating surfaces for nicks, burrs or warpage; Reassemble and install, tightening all screws to specification
Sluggish Acceleration, Excessive Throttle Needed to Maintain Speed	Fluid level and condition	Fluid should be at "FULL" mark with engine at idle; replace fluid if "milky" and full of bubbles, or dark and smells burned
	Engine performance	Verify proper engine operation; Be sure compression meets specifications and that fuel and ignition systems are functioning properly
	Throttle linkage	Check for smooth travel; clean linkage pivot points as required, but do not lubricate them and then adjust
	Stall test	Perform stall test to check holding ability of converter and transmission clutches
	Hydraulic pressure	Perform hydraulic pressure test; Repair hydraulic components as required; Check and correct throttle and line pressure settings
	Torque Converter	If converter hub seal surface or drive slots are damaged or if converter contains foreign material, burned-oxidized fluid or debris, replace converter; Do not attempt to clean or flush converter

FIGURE 9-2   (cont.)

CONDITION	POSSIBLE CAUSE	CORRECTION
TRANSMISSION NOISY (Cont.)		
Sluggish Acceleration, Excessive Throttle Needed to Maintain Speed (Cont.)	Rear clutch	Inspect all rear clutch parts as outlined for front clutch
LOCK-UP CONVERTER DIAGNOSIS		
No Lock-Up	Faulty oil pump	Replace oil pump
	Sticking governor valve	Repair or replace as required
	Valve body malfunction Stuck switch valve Stuck lock-up valve Stuck fail-safe valve	Repair or replace valve body or its internal components as required
	Failed locking clutch	Replace torque converter
	Leaking turbine hub seal	Replace torque converter
	Faulty input shaft or seal ring	Repair or replace as required
Will Not Unlock	Sticking governor valve	Repair or replace as required
	Valve body malfunction Stuck switch valve Stuck lock-up valve Stuck fail-safe valve	Repair or replace valve body or its internal components as required
Stays Locked Up at Too Low a Speed in Direct	Sticking governor valve	Repair or replace as required
	Valve body malfunction Stuck switch valve Stuck lock-up valve Stuck fail-safe valve	Repair or replace valve body or its internal components as required
Locks Up or Drags in Low or Second	Faulty oil pump	Replace oil pump
	Valve body malfunction Stuck switch valve Stuck fail-safe valve	Repair or replace valve body or its internal components as required
Sluggish or Stalls in Reverse	Faulty oil pump	Replace oil pump
	Plugged cooler, cooler lines or fittings	Flush or replace cooler and flush lines and fittings
	Valve body malfunction Stuck switch valve Faulty input shaft or seal ring	Repair or replace valve body or its internal components as required
Loud Chatter During Lock-Up Engagement (Cold)	Faulty torque converter	Replace torque converter
	Failed locking clutch	Replace torque converter
	Leaking turbine hub seal	Replace torque converter
Vibration or Shudder During Lock-Up Engagement	Faulty oil pump	Repair or replace oil pump
	Valve body malfunction	Repair or replace valve body or its internal components as required
	Faulty torque converter	Replace torque converter
	Engine performance	Diagnose and tune engine
Vibration After Lock-Up Engagement	Faulty torque converter	Replace torque converter
	Exhaust system vibration	Align exhaust system
	Engine performance	Diagnose and tune engine

FIGURE 9-2   (cont.)

CONDITION	POSSIBLE CAUSE	CORRECTION
	LOCK-UP CONVERTER DIAGNOSIS (Cont.)	
Vibration After Lock-Up Engagement (Cont.)	Throttle linkage misadjusted	Check and adjust throttle linkage
Vibration When "Reved" in Neutral	Torque converter out of balance	Replace torque converter
Overheating: Oil Blows Out of Dipstick Tube or Pump Seal	Plugged cooler, cooler lines or fittings	Flush or replace cooler and flush lines and fittings
	Stuck switch valve	Repair switch valve in valve body or replace valve body
Shudder After Lock-Up Engagement	Faulty oil pump	Repair or replace oil pump
	Plugged cooler, cooler lines or fittings	Flush or replace cooler and flush lines and fittings
	Valve body malfunction	Repair or replace valve body or its internal components as required
	Faulty torque converter	Replace torque converter
	Faulty locking clutch	Replace torque converter
	Exhaust system vibration	Align exhaust system
	Engine performance	Diagnose and tune engine
	Throttle linkage misadjusted	Check and adjust throttle linkage

FIGURE 9-2   (cont.)

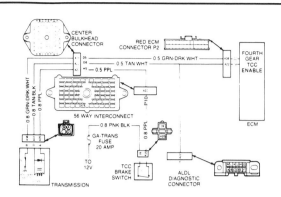

TORQUE CONVERTER CLUTCH (TCC) ELECTRICAL DIAGNOSIS (Chart One)

NOTE: Following procedure is designed to account for intermittent codes. If no malfunction is uncovered using this procedure, it will indicate that DFI system is okay at this time.

The ECM completes circuit for TCC solenoid by grounding circuit No. 422. Grounding this circuit allows solenoid to energize and supply oil pressure to torque converter clutch.

Code indicates that ECM is seeing engine speed at greater RPM than would be expected at 55 MPH with TCC engaged. Possible causes of this condition are: Defective TCC solenoid, defective TCC brake switch, defective wiring, terminals, etc., or ECM not able to process signals properly.

1) To begin diagnosis, connect test light to circuit No. 422 (pin F) on ALDL connector. With TCC disengaged (ECM not grounding circuit No. 422), test light should see 12 volts and light.

2) If test light lights, then power is being supplied through TCC brake switch. While in output cycling, circuit No. 422 should go between 12 volts and 0 volts every 3 seconds. If test light does not flash, transmission should be checked for short circuit. If resistance between pins A and D is less than 15 ohms, solenoid or wires are shorted and should be repaired. This low resistance through transmission may have damaged ECM, therefore, after repairs have been made, check output of ECM in output cycling.

If resistance is greater than 15 ohms, then circuit No. 422 should be checked for open to ECM. If wire is okay, check for faulty ECM connector or faulty ECM.

3) If test light goes on and off every 3 seconds, then ECM and wiring are okay. Fault could be mechanical problem in transmission, therefore, road test should be performed. When the 4th gear status light comes on, shift from Drive to manual 3rd. If no downshift occurs, verify that parameter ".1.2" is within 2 MPH of that shown on speedometer before continuing. Drive at 55 MPH with TCC solenoid energized (test light off), engine RPM is factor of driveline gear ratio if TCC is working properly. At 55 MPH, engine data parameter ".1.1" should be as shown in chart.

If RPM reading is greater than this limit, TCC has failed to engage and should be diagnosed.

4) If test light does not light on circuit No. 422, then there must be an open between ALDL connector and battery. First use switch tests to check TCC brake switch for proper operation. If there is no voltage on both sides of connector, either switch or circuit feeding switch is open.

5) If there is voltage on both sides of TCC brake switch, then voltage on circuit No. 420 should be checked at transmission. If test light does not light, circuit No. 420 is open. If test light between circuit Nos. 420 and 422 does not light with pin F jumpered to ground, then circuit No. 422 is open. If test light does light, then open must exist either at transmission connector terminals or inside transmission itself.

Note on Intermittents – If intermittent code is being set, it could be due to adjustment of brake switches. The ECM does not test for TCC code if it sees brake applied through cruise control brake signal on circuit No. 86. This is because TCC brake switch is also open under this condition. If TCC brake switch is adjusted such that it opens before cruise control brake switch, code could be set if operator were to keep brake pedal applied just enough to open TCC switch, but not cruise control switch.

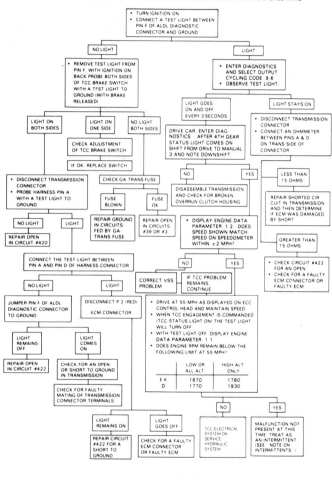

FIGURE 9-3 Test chart for General Motors' torque converter clutch (digital fuel injection).

A transmission and torque converter in good working order should produce stall speeds very nearly the same in each gear and within the range specified by the manufacturer. Not all manufacturers furnish stall speed specifications. In these cases, you can test only for a consistency in stall speed—a questionable return for the general risks taken in stall testing.

If stall speeds are exceeded in any gear, refer to the clutch and band application chart for the transmission you are testing. Comparing the gears in which specifications are met against those in which they are exceeded sometimes can pinpoint the slipping element. For example, suppose that you are testing a Ford AOXD, and either through a road test or a stall test you detect slipping in first gear (Drive). You look at the Clutch and Band Application Chart for that transmission (Table 9-3) and find that the Lo-Int Band, Fwd Clutch, and Low One-Way Clutch friction elements are applied in that gear. Which of those is slipping? Studying Table 9-3 further, you find that reverse gear uses two of these three. If reverse gear tests okay, then by process of elimination, you have isolated the problem as the low-intermediate band.

Aside from the effects of manufacturing tolerances and engine and/or transmission modifications, perhaps the biggest drawback to stall testing when compared to road testing is that you cannot check shift quality or slippage in intermediate or higher gears.

Vacuum Testing

Testing the vacuum system, like testing any other system, begins at the source—the intake manifold. A properly tuned engine will produce, or "pull," about 15 to 16 inches of vacuum at sealevel. If your vacuum gauge reads less, it is attributable to one or more of the following.

1. You are in Denver, or some other spot several thousand feet above sea level.
2. Intake manifold is cracked or has a leaking gasket.
3. Engine needs tune-up.
4. Excessive engine wear: Intake valves not seating well.

WHAT IS VACUUM?

We might want to think of vacuum as negative pressure, but there is really no such thing. The air we breathe and live in is exerting a pressure of 14.7 pounds per square inch (psi or lb/in.^{2}) at sea level. That pressure is referred to as **one atmosphere** and is equivalent to the pressure exerted by a 760-millimeter (mm) column of mercury (Hg), or about 29.6 in. Hg (see Chapter 2). The pressure lowers about 1 in. of mercury for each 1000 ft. above sea level.

Suppose that we begin to pump air out of an airtight container. We can start to detect vacuum with a gauge as soon as we begin to pump. This is because we are moving air out and not allowing it to be replaced. The air outside (atmosphere) now wants to rush in to replace the air we are pumping out. So by evacuating air from the container,

we have created a pressure differential or force and we can measure this with a vacuum gauge.

Notice that the face of the automotive vacuum gauge is labeled "vacuum" in the CW direction from zero and "fuel pump pressure" in the CCW direction. An automotive vacuum gauge is really a pressure gauge that registers pressure below 29.6 in. Hg (1 atm, 760 mm Hg, 14.7 lb/in.^{2}). All pressure gauges are, of course, under 1 atmosphere of pressure to start, but the designers of pressure gauges have found it to be more convenient to place the relative position of needle and face at 0 psi rather than 14.7 psi—and there is often a peg there to keep the needle from dropping below zero. But that is not the case with the automotive vacuum gauge. It is also under 1 atmosphere of pres-

sure to start, of course, and the relative position of its needle and face is set at zero. But it has no peg, and its face contains numbers in both CW and CCW directions from zero. The CCW-direction numbers signify pounds per square inch (psi), and the CW-direction numbers are for inches of mercury and are read as so many "inches of vacuum." So, unlike a pressure gauge, the vacuum gauge is able to measure pressures of less than 1 atm. (29.6 in. Hg) down to a perfect vacuum, which is no pressure at all.

Vacuum, then, is the result of a pressure differential caused by outside, or ambient, pressure being greater than pressure inside a container, and it is expressed in inches rather than pounds. In automobiles, vacuum is created by the intake stroke.

If engine vacuum tests okay at the manifold, it should test okay at each vacuum-operated unit—if there is no leak between the two.

But to test a vacuum system thoroughly, vacuum gauge readings should be taken at each connection as you follow its route from the source. The collective effect of small leaks at a number of connections can be significant. When you reach a tee or branching connector, disconnect and plug all branches except the one you want to test. After completing the test of that branch, plug it and test the others one by one. If a device on any branch is leaking, block it off by plugging the hose leading to it and continue with your testing. Loose slip-fit hose connections that you find can often be repaired as you move through the system. If the hose is long enough and still in good condition, cut back the damaged or distorted end until it is restored.

It is not always necessary to test the entire system. For example, if you want to check the modulator vacuum, check both the source and the hose end at the modulator connection; they both should read the same. If not, you will have to trace back through the circuit, testing each connection, branch, and device until the difference is eliminated. The modulator itself should be checked with a **vacuum pump** to detect a leaking diaphragm.

Electrical Testing

Electrical and/or electronic/electrical automatic transmission applications control hydraulic flow through the use of solenoid valves. When used for torque converter clutch control, the solenoid opens the direct or third gear circuit to the TCC spool valve, causing the spool valve to move to direct mainline pressure to apply the clutch. Several other switches are included in this circuit; among the most important are:

- *Governor Pressure Switch*: completes ground at speeds above 35 mph
- *Brake switch*: breaks circuit when brakes are applied
- *Vacuum regulator valve*: breaks circuit at full throttle
- *Low vacuum switch*: breaks circuit at full throttle

Others that might be included, depending on model, appear in the following list; all are pressure (including vacuum), temperature, or mechanically operated electrical switches:

- Cold inhibit switch ⎫ ⎧ These prevent TCC apply until engine is
- Thermal vacuum valve ⎭ ⎩ at operating temperature
- A/C high-pressure switch
- Third and/or fourth gear switch
- Low-vacuum switch
- TCC delay module
- Engine coolant for temperature switch

Electronic shifting is constructed similarly (see Chapter 7) and can be fine-tuned by the addition of various sensors, much the same way as in the torque converter clutch applications. Both can be computer controlled with sensor signals interpreted by the computer, which then times signals to the solenoids.

The first step in diagnosing any electrical problem is to make certain that connections are tight. Loose connections, even when clean, usually make only intermittent contact at best; they also corrode and collect foreign material which can prevent contact altogether.

Voltage checks are next. Voltage is measured with a **volt-meter** against specifications. A voltage measurement—like a hydraulic pressure measurement—can determine whether electricity is flowing in a circuit. The actual flow—the amount of electricity—is called **current** or **amperage**; it is measured by an **ammeter** in amperes, or "amps" for short. A voltage measurement can also determine whether an electrical device or subcircuit is operating correctly by the amount of **voltage drop**—the difference between the voltage readings at two points in a circuit. If the voltage drop exceeds specifications, it means that there is too much resistance in the circuit.

There is resistance to the flow of electricity in any circuit, and this is taken into account in electrical circuit design. In fact, a basic electrical device called a **potentiometer** provides the means to vary the amount of resistance. Examples are the volume control in a stereo set and the **throttle position sen-**

Application	Volts@Idle Throttle Position
Light Duty Trucks	
2.8L V6	.26V
4.3L V6	.25V
Calif. 5.0L & 5.7L V8	.41V
Passenger Vehicles	
2.8L V6	.30V
3.0L V6	.60V
3.8L V6 (VIN A)	.30V
5.0L V8 (VIN G & H)	.48V
5.0L V8 (VIN Y & 9)	.40V
5.7L (VIN 6)	.48V

FIGURE 9-4 Throttle position sensor voltage specifications.

sor used with computerized engine control. Figure 9-4 shows voltage specifications for the throttle position sensor on a number of General Motors models equipped with TCC. Notice that the voltage values given are for closed throttle, or idle position. Notice also that they are very small. This means that the potentiometer is designed to allow more and more voltage through as the throttle is opened.

Resistance can be measured directly using an **ohmmeter**. Unlike a voltmeter or ammeter, the ohmmeter provides its own electricity. So it can be used for a **continuity test**—that is, whether an electrical conductor such as wire or any electrical device can conduct electricity from one point to another. Brake switch operation can easily be checked by checking continuity. A closed switch shows continuity, an open one does not. A **test light** will also check continuity, but a source of electricity is needed, whereas the ohmmeter carries its own.

Both a voltmeter and an ohmmeter can be used to test a solenoid valve, but one of the easiest and quickest ways is to activate the solenoid (functional test) by applying voltage (electricity) directly to it from a source known to be good (like a **jumper wire** running directly from a charged battery). You cannot use an ohmmeter for this purpose, because its power supply is not strong enough (insufficient voltage and amperage).

In summary, the three electrical tests that you will conduct in diagnosing automatic transmission electrical problems are: voltage tests, continuity tests, and functional tests (solenoids).

Electronic and electrical testing in vehicles equipped with computer controls can be accomplished by diagnostic procedures that can be entered into the vehicle's computer (self-diagnos-

ing) and/or by plugging in manufacturer-furnished diagnostic units. Many manufacturers of vehicles with electronic control units furnish test procedures and charts requiring only the use of a test light.

Pressure Testing

There are two kinds of **pressure testing**: hydraulic and air. Air pressure tests make use of regulated (approximately 30 psi) shop air supply and are usually functional bench tests conducted on subassemblies; that is, they use air pressure in place of hydraulic pressure to actuate a particular mechanism. Some in-vehicle air pressure tests are discussed in Chapter 10.

Hydraulic pressure testing is done with a high-pressure [0 to 300 psi (0 to 21kg/cm^2)] gauge, a vacuum gauge (on transmissions that have a vacuum modulator), and a tachometer. The pressure gauge is connected to 1/4-in. hydraulic circuit taps in the transmission case. The vacuum gauge is T-connected to the vacuum modulator. (A vacuum pump may also be used to apply specified vacuum.) Some makes require pressure testing on the road, others with brakes applied, and still others with drive wheels suspended. In all cases the pressure gauge and vacuum gauge lines should be long enough to allow the gauges to be placed where they can be read easily.

Mainline, or control, pressure and governor pressure are the two most common pressure tests, although some manufacturers also specify servo pressures under different conditions. Tests are conducted at various vacuum readings or selected throttle valve positions; these must also be recorded with your pressure readings. Figures 9-5 and 9-6 are representative of the extremes in the number of **pressure taps** among transmission makes.

Low pressures in all gears indicate a plugged filter, a sticking oil pressure regulator valve, a worn pump, or anything that would affect the entire system—check the hydraulic circuit diagram. Low pressure in two gears might indicate a leak from one circuit to the other because of a leaking valve body gasket, loose bolts, or bolts torqued out of specification.

High pressure in all gears indicates a sticking pressure regulator valve, throttle valve or vacuum modulator problem, or a detent problem.

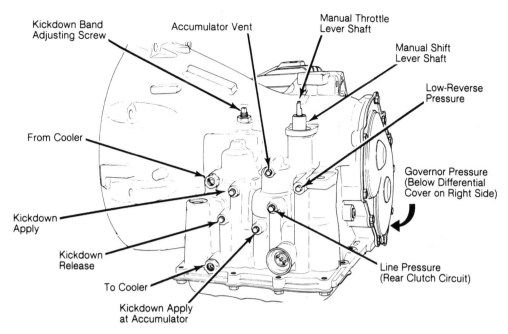

FIGURE 9-5   Pressure taps for Chrysler A-413/470.

Also check specific circuits in the hydraulic circuit diagram if low or high pressure is detected in one gear.

Pressure test procedures and specifications differ significantly from one transmission make to the next. Always follow the shop manual.

Pressure testing often is the last test because it can isolate internal transmission malfunctions to a particular circuit. There may be additional functional tests conducted with air pressure after the pan or complete transmission has been removed.

SPECIAL TOOLS

In addition to hand tools and essential equipment, such as vacuum pump, pressure gauges, timing light, and volt-ohmmeter, there is a group referred to as special tools. Within this group, there are three categories:

1. Truly special tools, without which a certain operation cannot be performed.

2. "Nice-to-have" tools that speed up an operation but without which standard tools will work—if you have the patience.

3. Duplicate tools (usually sold exclusively by the transmission manufacturer). These might look im-

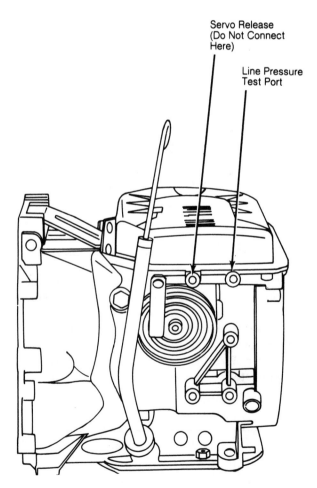

FIGURE 9-6   Pressure tap for Ford ATX.

DIGITAL VERSUS ANALOG METERS

You will find a lot of manufacturers' instructions calling for a digital volt-ohmmeter. If you have only analog (dial) voltmeter, ohmmeter, or combination, do not rush out to buy a digital one because your shop manual calls for it. The biggest advantage a digital has is that it can be read more easily from a greater distance. Just make sure that your meter can be read to the accuracy required by specifications for test circuits.

PACKAGED INSTRUMENT GROUPS

There are several devices on the market that consist of a vacuum gauge, tachometer, and pressure gauge mounted conveniently in a box with a carrying handle and some attaching device to clip to the partially open door glass. It is especially designed for transmission testing (long leads, etc.) and is dubbed "Automatic transmission tester," "automatic transmission analyzer," or some such. These are fine if you are going to be doing nothing but transmissions. However, the ordinary vacuum gauge, tachometer, and a 300-psi pressure gauge as separate units have no drawbacks, except, perhaps, that you need to grab three things instead of one.

pressive hanging on your shop wall, but they do nothing that a good set of hand tools, chains, wires, and two-by-fours won't do just as well and for a whole lot less money.

How do you know in which category a particular special tool fits? You don't. But being aware of the three categories will help you decide whether a special tool purchase you're considering is worth the cost. Alignment dowels, holding tools, and oil seal replacement tools tend to fall in the last category, but not always. Generally, a set of universal oil seal tools will do the job, but you will eventually run across particular needs for a specific special tool, depending on the type of work and the make of vehicle you work on most often. So be aware of what is available, and when you can, try out the tool before you buy it.

TRADE TERMS

Ammeter	One atmosphere	Test light
Branching diagram	Pressure tap	Throttle position
Continuity test	Pressure test	sensor
Customer contact	Road test	Troubleshooting
Flare-up	Shift speed	charts
Jumper Wire	Stall speed	Vacuum pump
Ohmmeter	Stall test	Visual checking
	Symptoms	Voltage drop
	Test charts	Voltmeter

REVIEW QUESTIONS

9-1. One of the most important parts of diagnosis is to _____ to your customer and help by asking the questions _____ _____ and _____.

9-2. The best way to listen is to tell your customer in your own words what he or she has just told you.   T   F

9-3. Diagnosis is:
   (a) A repair procedure.
   (b) A machine analysis.
   (c) A process of examination.
   (d) All of the above.

9-4. All but one of the following constitute the *first* steps in a well-planned detection and diagnosis procedure.
   (a) Listen to customer.
   (b) Check fluid level and condition.
   (c) Road test.
   (d) Conduct superficial check.
   (e) Ride with customer driving.

9-5. Visual checking begins with the easiest and most obvious.   T   F

9-6. The dipstick hot reading is always higher than the cool reading.   T   F

9-7. The ATF condition that indicates a cooler leak is:
   (a) Red or orange color.
   (b) Translucent.
   (c) Milky pink.
   (d) Opaque with burnt odor.

9-8. ATF leaks can be identified from engine oil leaks by _____ and _____ _____.

9-9. If a vacuum-modulated transmission consumes ATF but no leaks are evident:
   (a) Steam clean and check again for leaks.
   (b) Modulator diaphragm is likely to be broken.
   (c) Accumulator is collecting excess ATF.
   (d) None of the above.

9-10. A visual check is done without _____ _____.

9-11. It is good practice always to bring the customer with you on a road test.   T   F

9-12. Shift speed tests help evaluate _____ pressure, _____ pressure, and _____ _____ performance.

9-13. Which of the following can affect shift speed?
   (a) Final drive ratio.   (e) Governor.
   (b) Tire size.   (f) Computer
   (c) Manufacturing tolerances.   (g) All of the above.
   (d) Variations in throttle position.   (h) None of the above.

9-14. Slippage during shift and slippage after shift is completed are always caused by the same problem.   T   F

9-15. A seized stator will affect a vehicle's _____ _____.

9-16. _____ _____ charts and _____ charts are published by manufacturers especially to facilitate diagnosis.

9-17. Stall testing is the first test to be conducted on a malfunctioning transmission.   T   F

9-18. A stall test must not exceed _____ seconds.

9-19. Shift quality can be checked through both a stall test and a road test.   T   F

9-20. The measurement values of atmospheric pressure at sea level are _____lb/in.^{2}, _____ mm Hg, _____ in. Hg, and _____ atmosphere.

9-21. Atmospheric pressure lowers about _____ in. Hg for every _____ ft above sea level.

9-22. The three electrical tests associated with automatic transmission diagnosis are _____, _____ and _____ tests.

9-23. Either a test light or an ohmmeter can be used to check continuity in electrical conductors.   T   F

9-24. A pressure gauge to test any automatic transmission hydraulic pressure must have a capacity of at least:
   (a) 150 psi.
   (b) 200 psi.
   (c) 250 psi.
   (d) 300 psi.

9-25. Pressure tests are conducted at specific vacuum readings or throttle valve positions.   T   F

ESSAY QUESTIONS

9-1. Explain what you will do to elicit your customer's help in describing a specific problem.

9-2. How will you analyze ATF condition to help detect existing or potential transmission problems?

CHAPTER ACTIVITIES

9-1. Ask friends or relatives to tell you about a particular problem with their car. Be patient with their attempts to describe the problem. Help them by asking: What? When? Where? Listen to them. Tell them in your own words what you think they said.

9-2. Practice analyzing the condition of ATF by checking the transmission dipstick in different vehicles every chance you get.

9-3. In preparation for planning your own tool and equipment needs, ask practicing mechanics what special tools they value most, and why.

10

General Servicing and Repair

When you have completed this chapter, you should be able to:

- Assess the conditions under which a specific vehicle normally operates and apply this knowledge to your servicing and repair of that vehicle.
- Identify servicing and adjustments that can be done without transmission removal.
- State the general steps taken in preparation for, and removal of, an automatic transmission for overhaul.
- Describe cleaning and inspection methods for automatic transmission parts and subassemblies.
- Name three significant tasks that are never a part of removal and disassembly, but which always should be part of assembly and installation.
- Discuss the general steps and sequence of transmission/transaxle reassembly.

There are significant differences in transmission design from one make to another—and even from one model to another. There are also many similarities. In this chapter we focus on the similarities by discussing general servicing and adjustment guidelines followed by the basic sequence of transmission overhaul: removal, disassembly, cleaning and inspection, assembly, and installation.

If you have read and understood the preceding chapters, you have become familiar with the various automatic transmission systems and subassemblies. This chapter embodies the first detailed look at the automatic transmission as an assembly. So it serves as a bridge from the study of general fundamentals to the development of a familiarity with different makes and models—an opportunity for review as well as for application of the knowledge you have gained so far.

In the practice of your automotive career, there will be a number of technical manuals that you will use (Chapter 16). This general chapter together with the four that follow, covering representative transmissions and transaxles from specific manufacturers, will create a foundation on which you will build and refine your skills with automatic transmissions. Your particular skills may become highly developed with only a certain make of transmission and limited models, or you may become a generalist with respectable skills in several makes and models. No matter which the case might be, your expertise will be based on your understanding of fundamentals, the ability to recognize them in new automatic transmission applications, and the responsibility to refer to technical publications and specifications rather than relying solely on memory.

IN-VEHICLE SERVICING AND ADJUSTMENT

Automatic transmission maintenance includes a general visual inspection, lubrication, cooling inspection, cursory performance demonstration, and correct adjustments for specific operating conditions. In addition, knowing the conditions under which the vehicle usually operates can be very helpful in diagnosis, adjustments for optimum performance, and establishing service periods that will extend transmission life.

Conditions of Vehicle Operation

Ideal passenger car and light truck operating conditions are rarely experienced, but as a point of reference, they include the following:

- Trips of 30 minutes or more so that all assemblies reach operating temperature
- Ambient temperatures ranging from the high 40s and low 50s to the high 70s to low 80s (Fahrenheit)—the narrower the range, the better
- Moderate loads carried at medium speeds with very few stops and starts (light traffic)
- A driver who does not abuse the vehicle
- Correct level of clean, uncontaminated ATF

Under these **ideal operating conditions**, some domestic automatic transmission manufacturers recommend fluid and filter change at 100,000 miles; others omit any periodic service whatsoever, except the checking of ATF level whenever underhood maintenance is performed or leakage is detected. Foreign manufacturers generally recommend fluid and filter change every 30,000 miles. In both cases, however, follow the specific manufacturer's recommendations.

Extreme operating conditions include just about any variation from the ideal, among which are:

- Frequent starts and stops (delivery vehicles) and short trips (too short to reach operating temperature)
- Towing
- Carrying loads at or beyond maximum rating
- Operation at ambient temperature extremes—below the high 40s and above the low 80s (Fahrenheit)
- Operation in severe environmental conditions (dust, mud, water)
- Any abusive operation

Under any of these extreme conditions, domestic manufacturers recommend fluid and filter change at 15,000 to 30,000 miles. Obviously, a combination of two or more of the foregoing conditions would suggest more frequent attention. Again, this summary of vehicle operating conditions is intended to give you some insight into the establishment of service intervals and the basis for many of the manufacturers' recommendations.

In-Vehicle Servicing

A general visual inspection of the transmission includes checking for leaks and checking for loose wires, linkage, and mounting bolts. This should be done whenever work is performed under the vehicle—every engine oil change presents a good opportunity.

Perhaps the easiest in-vehicle servicing is checking ATF level—some drivers habitually check engine oil and ATF at every refueling. As a technician, however, you will not only check the level of ATF but also its condition, as covered in Chapter 9. Moreover, you will check it correctly (the driver may not know whether to check in park or neutral, hot or cold, or with the engine running or not). And you will be more aware of the need to use the recommended fluid type and the importance of proper fluid level.

When it is time for ATF and filter change, or if your assessment of fluid condition so indicates, the general procedure is to drain the transmission (and the torque converter, where possible) and remove the transmission sump pan for access to the filter.

Depending on make and model, automatic transmissions and transaxles are drained through either plugs in the pan or final drive, removal of the pan, or removal of the filler tube at the pan. Generally speaking, most foreign models have drain plugs, and most domestic models do not. (One reason for this is that it is a good way to encourage a filter change.)

Torque converters cannot be drained except those for Porsche, Mercedes-Benz, and Ford AOT, which have drain plugs.

General Motors has a procedure for drilling their torque converters to drain them, then plugging the drain hole with a closed-end pop rivet. This can be done only a few times because there are a limited number of places on the torque converter to do it. And it's tricky. You get only one chance to install the rivet so that it seals. If you drill it out, the end

remaining inside will damage the converter. The hole can be **tungsten inert gas (TIG) welded** though.

Fluid in a torque converter can be changed without draining, by disconnecting the return line at the cooler outlet and starting the engine, allowing the ATF to be pumped from the cooler outlet fitting through a hose to a drain pan. (If there are fiber particles in the cooler circuit, it can mean that the torque converter clutch is damaged if the vehicle is so equipped.) This is the preferred method. You should drain and refill the transmission with new ATF first, then run the engine until you see clean ATF being discharged—but do not run it for more than about 30 seconds without stopping to add a quart or so of ATF. Most converter and cooler circuits hold 6 quarts or more, which gives you an idea as to how much old ATF will discharge before you detect the new.

On models that do not have drain plugs and require transmission pan removal, the practice is to loosen the pan bolts and remove all but two or three along one side. Then, with a wide drain pan properly placed, the transmission pan seal can be broken, allowing the pan to drop an inch or so and spill into the drain pan. (Be careful, the oil is hot!)

Some models use **room-temperature vulcanizing (RTV) rubber** instead of a gasket. And some of these specify a special removal technique, instead of prying, to avoid transmission case flange damage (Figure 10-1). Another requires that the pan be replaced with a new one each time it is removed. So even with this seemingly simple operation, it will pay you to check the manufacturer's recommendations whenever you begin work on a transmission that is new to you.

The transmission pan will have some fluid left in it, so remove it carefully and slowly empty it, trying not to disturb any residue that might be in the bottom. Remember, this residue can tell you a lot about the condition of internal transmission parts (Chapter 9). If you detect a glistening from very, very small metallic flakes and/or a thin, fine, dark coating covering the bottom of the pan, you can attribute it to normal wear and tear, and the fluid and filter change is probably all that is needed. But if the flakes are really more like tiny pieces of metal and the dark material feels granular between your fingers—and if there is more than a thimblefull of

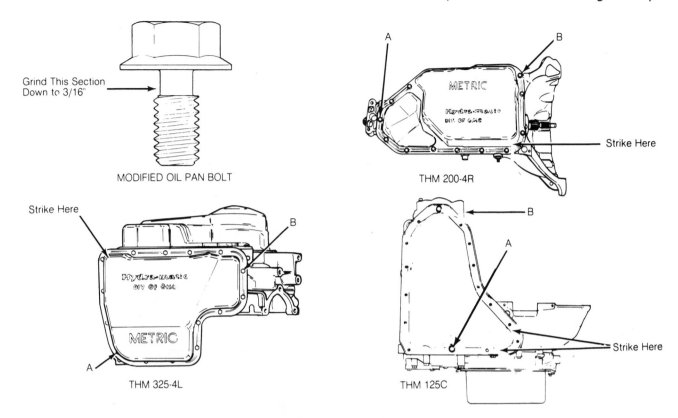

FIGURE 10-1 Recommended oil-pan removal procedure for one manufacturer's transmissions that use RTV sealant instead of a gasket. Replace bolt A with modified bolt; finger tighten; loosen bolt B four turns; strike corner of oil pan where indicated with rubber mallet to break seal; remove modified bolt to allow pan to drain.

it—the transmission is probably due for an overhaul.

During your visual inspection you will be checking transmission cooling system leaks as well. Also check for crimped cooler lines and places where the lines might be rubbing against another part and wearing thin—this can occur on higher-mileage vehicles which may have had substandard work done on them previously. Do not forget to check the auxiliary cooler if there is one, and blow out the bugs from the cooling fins on it and the radiator.

The **cursory performance demonstration** that is part of in-vehicle servicing is not necessarily a road test; it can be merely your observation of transmission operation under normal driving conditions. That is really all it need be unless the customer has complaints or your shop practice dictates otherwise. If you do detect abnormal operation, then—as part of your detection and diagnosis

(Chapter 9)—some in-vehicle service adjustments could restore normal operation.

Vacuum modulators and case-mounted governors can also be serviced without transmission removal; so can the valve body. These are covered in their respective sections under "In-Vehicle Adjustments" ("Vacuum modulator") and the section on cleaning and inspection under "Transmission Disassembly" ("Valve Body" and "Governor") later in this chapter.

In-Vehicle Adjustments

These include the rod or cable leading to the transmission throttle valve (or the vacuum modulator), the throttle position potentiometer, the shift linkage, the neutral start and backup light switch, the TCC/VCC brake switch, the kickdown or intermediate (front) band, and the low-reverse (rear) band.

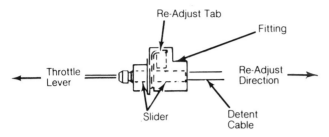

FIGURE 10-2 Self-adjusting or automatic-adjusting throttle valve cable needs your help.

Most of these are external linkage adjustments. But some models do require transmission pan removal or servo cover removal for band adjustment. Again, you must refer to a shop manual for manufacturer's recommended specifications and procedures.

The throttle valve is controlled by either a rod, cable, or vacuum modulator (vacuum diaphragm). Some cables are labeled "automatic adjusting" or "self-adjusting" (Figure 10-2). Do not assume that this means you can ignore them. Carefully check the manufacturer's service adjustment instructions for these. They do not work entirely by themselves.

Throttle linkage on some makes controls both the throttle valve and the kickdown valve. On others—those with vacuum modulators, for example—it controls only the kickdown valve. Still others with vacuum modulators have no linkage—in these, downshift valves are controlled entirely by vacuum and hydraulics.

Vacuum Modulator. Some OEM modulators are not adjustable. Those that are adjust spring tension by a screw located at the center of the modulator vacuum chamber. (On some makes the inlet part is also located here, and the adjusting screw is accessible through it.)

Modulators are relatively inexpensive items. It is easy to check for a broken diaphragm, but the test for spring tension requires the use of a scale for some (Figure 10-3) or a comparison gauge for measurement against a new unit for others. In the latter case, you might just as well use the new one—unless you are working at a dealer or some place that stocks parts—because the effort and time spent ordering the new part to check against, and returning it if the old one is found to be good, will probably exceed the cost of the modulator several times

FIGURE 10-3 Using a scale to check General Motors' vacuum modulator (Ford Vacuum diaphragm) spring tension against specifications furnished by Trans Go/Research, 2621 Merced Avenue, El Monte, CA 91733.

over. However, if it is quick and easy for you to put your hands on a new modulator, the comparison method recommended by General Motors can be used. The gauge can be made easily and is used as shown in Figure 10-4.

Throttle Position Sensors (Potentiometers). Some throttle position potentiometers are mechanically adjusted at their mounting according to voltage readings. Others cannot be adjusted but can be checked for continuity of operation through complete throttle movement, using an ohmmeter.

Shift Linkage. The length of shift linkage rod or cable is adjusted to allow the **shift gate** stops to match the **manual valve detents** (Figure 10-5). Adjustment is usually made by loosening or disconnecting the linkage at the manual valve lever (Figure 10-6), setting the selector lever against the drive or park gate, moving the manual valve lever to the corresponding position, then setting the linkage. Manufacturers' instructions are usually very specific on this relatively simple, but critical adjustment. Always check each gear position fol-

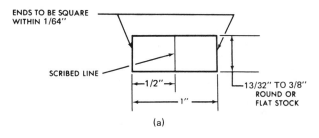

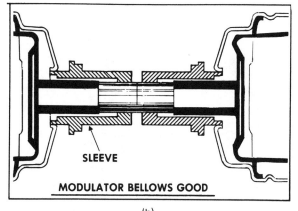

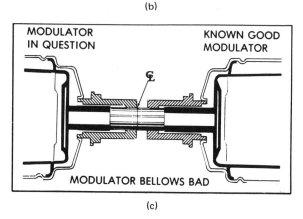

FIGURE 10-4 General Motors recommended procedures for checking vacuum modulator spring tension.

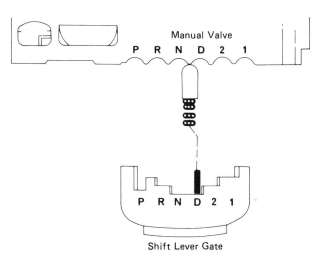

FIGURE 10-5 Condition requiring adjustment of shift linkage so that manual valve detents match shift lever gate stops.

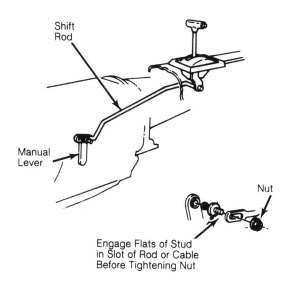

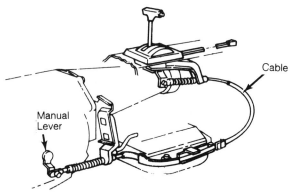

FIGURE 10-6 Shift linkage adjustment.

lowing an adjustment. Make sure that the neutral position is properly set by checking to see that the vehicle starts in neutral but not in drive.

Neutral Safety Switch. There are three types of neutral safety switch. One (usually a pluglike switch) mounts directly onto or into the transmission (Figure 10-7). Another is used most often with floor-shift models and mounts near the shift selector lever (Figure 10-8). The third is a mechanical interference type that allows the ignition key to be turned to the start position only when

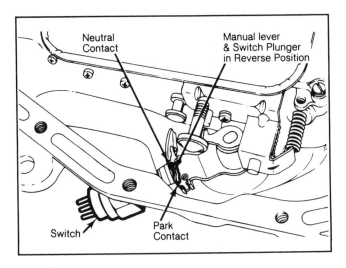

FIGURE 10-7 Combination plug-type neutral safety start switch and backup light switch mounted into transmission.

the transmission is in neutral or park. Generally speaking, the floor shift models have adjustable neutral start switches, the column shift models do not. The neutral start switch and the backup light switch often share the same housing, so adjusting one takes care of the other. A few also include a switch for the seat belt warning system.

Most neutral safety switches work by completing ground to the starting switch circuit, whereas the backup light switch completes the hot side of the circuit. Refer to the shop manual for electrical continuity tests. Never check or replace a neutral safety switch without first determining whether the shift linkage is adjusted correctly.

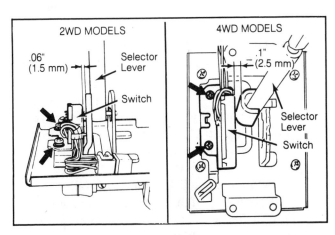

FIGURE 10-8 Representative neutral safety switch for floor shift transmissions.

Brake Switch. Some vehicle makes employing lock-up torque converters energize a spring-loaded solenoid valve to affect lock-up. Since a stopping vehicle must return to fluid coupling to prevent the engine from stalling, a simple switch activated by the brake pedal breaks the solenoid circuit, allowing the solenoid valve to close off hydraulic pressure to the lock-up valve.

Bands. Except for General Motors and Toyota, most makes have one or two band adjustments. Generally, the front (intermediate) band adjustment is accessible externally (Figure 10-9), whereas the pan must be removed to adjust the rear (low-reverse) band (Figure 10-10). There are a couple of makes that have externally adjusted rear

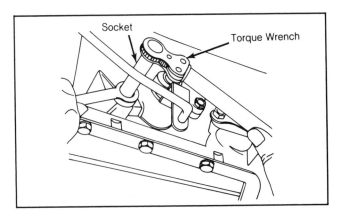

FIGURE 10-9 Front band adjustment.

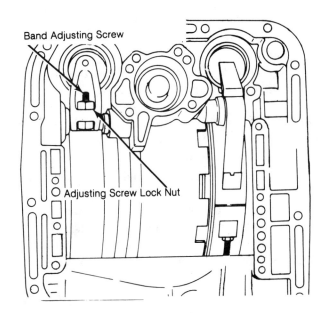

FIGURE 10-10 Low-reverse band adjustment.

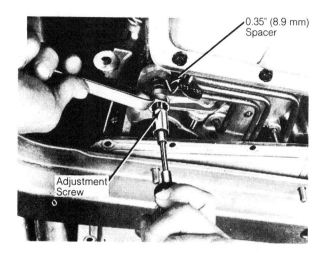

FIGURE 10-11 Front band adjustment using spacer.

bands, too, however. Basically, the adjustment is made by loosening a locknut, torquing to specification, and backing off a specific number of turns before locking. Some use a spacer to torque against (Figure 10-11). Shop manuals provide specific adjustment instructions, including torque and back-off specifications, and should be consulted.

TRANSMISSION REMOVAL

All transmissions are removed from under the vehicle, and most transaxles are lifted out (some with engine attached). A few domestic and foreign models require transaxle removal from underneath the vehicle.

Removal from underneath requires that the vehicle be raised high enough for the transmission or transaxle to clear. This should include enough room for a transmission jack or floor jack so you can roll rather than slide the transmission out from under the vehicle. If you are using a lift, you must have a lift-type transmission jack or plan to lower the vehicle for final removal so that a floor jack can be used.

Transaxles that are removed from the top will require hood removal and a suitable hoist.

Among the steps taken to remove automatic transmissions or transaxles are the following:

• Disconnect the battery at the negative post.

• Scribe the position of the hood hinges if the hood is to be removed. [Make it a habit to mark any major mating parts before disconnecting (e.g., converter-to-flex plate, output shaft-to-drive shaft-to-pinion shaft); spray paint or permanent marking pen is the easiest and most durable.]

• Remove distributor cap if located near firewall and any other items that might be damaged if engine drops somewhat during transmission removal.

• Drain transmission.

• Disconnect throttle cable/rod, dipstick tube, vacuum lines, and electrical connectors.

• Disconnect shift linkage and speedometer cable.

• Disconnect both oil cooler lines at transmission and drain.

• Remove starter.

• Remove converter pan or inspection plate, mark converter-to-flex plate, and remove three to six bolts. Engine will have to be turned to expose all bolts. (Do not turn engine backwards in belt-driven OHC designs.)

• Disconnect or remove exhaust pipes if they will interfere with transmission removal.

• Disconnect drive shaft (RWD) or drive axles (FWD).

• Support transmission and engine separately.

• Remove transmission mount and crossmember.

• Remove transmission-to-engine mounting bolts.

• Separate transmission from engine, making sure that torque converter stays with transmission.

• Secure torque converter to transmission with suitable holding device (safety wire or stout cord will do), and lower transmission to remove from beneath vehicle.

If you are using a lift, try to plan your removal procedure so that all of the under-the-hood work can be done first. Then you will not have to keep lowering and raising the vehicle.

During, or just after, transmission removal is a good time to flush the transmission cooler and lines. Hook up the solvent tank pump to the return line and let the transmission-to-cooler line lead back to the solvent tank drain to backflush the cooling system. If you use shop air to purge the cooling system, keep the pressure at 50 psi or less.

Check the alignment pins in the engine flywheel housing for damage or looseness, as well as their mating holes in the transmission housing.

Before removing the flex plate for cleaning and inspection, mark it and the crankshaft for reassembly reference.

TRANSMISSION DISASSEMBLY

Take the time to clean the outside of the transmission before disassembly. This starts you off on the right foot, keeps your work area clean, and helps in inspecting and organizing parts.

During disassembly, observe general conditions of seals, surfaces, springs, thrust washers, and bearings, noting any secondary condition that indicates primary wear or failure. Also check and record end play controlled by thrust washers during this disassembly for reference in selecting new washers for reassembly.

- Remove the torque converter, and measure input shaft end play (Figure 10-12). It should be at the low end of the manufacturer's specified range. If it is so loose that it is beyond specification, look not only for worn thrust washers and bearings but also worn rings and grooves.
- Remove the transmission pan and filter.
- Remove the valve body. (On some makes, this exposes ball check valves that are easily lost; on others, there is an auxiliary valve body also. So carefully review this section in your shop manual.)
- Remove accumulator and servo. (There may be other small parts and assemblies to be removed at this time to clear the path for clutch/band/gear/shaft removal later. Check your shop manual for specifics.)
- Remove speedometer gear and extension housing (except transaxle).
- Remove governor (with speedometer gear on many transaxles).
- Remove output shaft (only on some; others will be removed from the front of the transmission).
- Remove the bolts holding the pump to the case, and use a slide hammer with a commercial or home-made adapter to extract the pump body from the transmission housing (Figure 10-13).
- Remove clutches, gears, and band(s). These will be removed in assemblies along with shafts, bearings, and thrust washers.

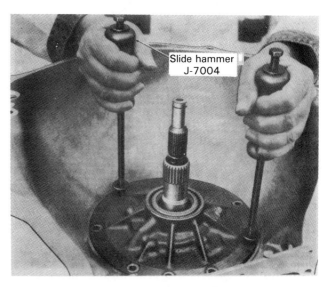

FIGURE 10-13 Pump body removal using slide hammers.

FIGURE 10-12 Measuring input shaft end play.

- Refer to manufacturer's specific instructions in your shop manuals for further disassembly. As you disassemble the transmission, keep the subassemblies separated, and lay out the parts in an organized fashion. This greatly helps your inspection as well as reassembly.

Cleaning and Inspection

Unless you are replacing all composition parts (e.g., some check balls and seals, bands, and clutch friction plates), avoid the use of solvents, degreasers, and detergents that will decompose the composition or bonding material. There are certain cleaning solvents (e.g., some carburetor cleaners) that can be used, or these parts can be cleaned with new transmission fluid.

Seals and Gaskets. It is good practice to replace all O-rings, seals and seal rings (metal as well as Teflon), and gaskets. But it also pays to inspect these anyway because their condition might indicate other problems or confirm the reason for those already identified. Be sure to check oil transfer-, seal-, and snap-ring grooves also for wear.

Thrust Washers and Bushings. Thrust washers are not included in overhaul kits because of the various thicknesses required to meet end-play specifications. They must be purchased separately.

Bushing wear can be checked visually as well as dimensionally, but the quickest check is to determine how the mated part fits—if there is lateral movement (i.e., if the part can be cocked), the bushing should be replaced. Pitted bushings should always be replaced—similarly with scored or pitted thrust washers. Under no circumstances should a bushing be used if a wire gauge of 0.006 in. or more can be inserted between the bushing and mating part.

Bearings and Shafts. A review of the bearing section in Chapter 3 will help you establish the best bearing inspection techniques. All bearings should be checked for roughness both before and after cleaning. Examine inner and outer races, balls, needles, and rollers for cracks, pitting or etching, and overheating.

If you use shop air in cleaning, resist the temptation to spin the bearings by air pressure. It can be dangerous, and besides that, it is a waste of time.

Inspect all shaft surfaces that mate with bushings, bearings, and seals. Check the splines for wear by fitting with mating splines. Blow out all oil passages to ensure that they are free from obstruction

Pump. Pump surfaces subject to the greatest wear are those bearing the greatest hydraulic pressure. For example, an IX gear pump (Figure 10-14) tends to greater wear at the following surfaces because of forces developed on the pump's pressure side:

- External gear-to-inside crescent surface on the suction side
- Internal gear-to-outside crescent surface on the suction side and to pump body on the pressure side
- Converter-hub-to-bushing on the suction side of the pump housing

FIGURE 10-14 Pump wear points.

Also check the pump body surfaces against which the sides of the IX gears bear. If they are scored, or if they do not fall within clearance specifications (Figure 10-15), the pump body should be replaced.

Carefully examine the external gear for cracks or damaged lugs caused by misalignment with torque converter hub drive slots.

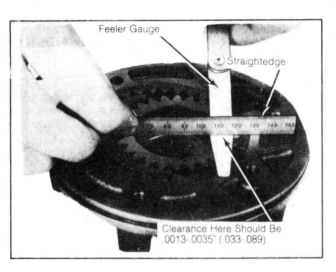

FIGURE 10-15 Pump body-to-gear or rotor clearance.

Do not forget to check the bushings in the stator support.

IX gear teeth can be checked by laying them on a flat surface, engaged, then pulling the external gear away from the engaged side. If the gears disengage, the teeth are worn excessively.

IX rotor pumps are inspected in a manner similar to that for IX gear pumps, except for checking rotor wear. Rotor wear is determined by measuring the tip clearance between inner and outer rotor teeth.

There are also some similarities in inspection of vane pumps. Rotors and slides for these pumps come in various thicknesses and must be ordered by part number according to pump measurement and selective pump rotor and slide replacement tables available in most shop manuals.

Sometimes the pump body contains lockup or pressure regulator valves. See "Valve Body" section later in this chapter.

Clutches. Seldom will the exploded views of clutch assemblies in shop manuals match exactly the number of clutch friction/steel plates you have—nor will they always match part for part, for that matter (Figure 10-16). Design variations for specific applications are too numerous to keep current. So it pays—as mentioned earlier—to lay out parts in an organized fashion, by assembly. Even if the parts are being replaced, the old, laid-out parts are a great help during reassembly.

Inspect bushings and seals as described previously. Coil springs should be compared for consistent length, and disc springs for cracks and distortion. Check piston groove for signs of scoring. Be certain that the check ball in the clutch piston or drum is free. Examine splines for wear.

Both clutch friction and steel plates are included in overhaul kits, so unless you are tearing down a relatively new transmission for a specific problem unrelated to the clutches, you might just as well replace them, even if the old ones are still serviceable.

Clutch friction and steel plates generally are still serviceable if

- They are flat—not distorted or coned.
- Steel plate surfaces are not scored.
- Friction plate surfaces are not pitted, glazed, or sloughing off—you should be able to see evidence of ATF soaked into the friction material on good plates by squeezing.

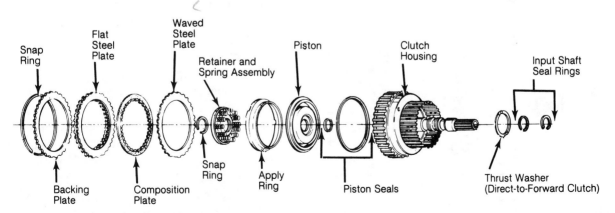

FIGURE 10-16 Subassembly illustrations do not always show exact number of multiple parts.

• They are kept in order and reassembled, surface for surface.

Never mix new plates with old ones—if only one is unserviceable, replace them all.

Bands. Friction surfaces on bands can be evaluated in much the same way as clutch friction plates. If the friction material is in good condition, and there is enough of it left so that the grooves are still evident, it is probably serviceable and can be adjusted or brought to specification by proper pin selection.

The drum surface is likely to be in good condition if the band is. Examine it closely for cracks, and if it is badly scored, both it and the band should be replaced.

Planetary Gearsets. In addition to the usual visual inspection for extreme wear or damage, such as cracked or chipped teeth, pitted bearing surfaces, and damaged splines, end-play measurements should be checked against specifications. On some Ravigneaux units, clearance must be measured at both ends of the long pinions (Figure 10-17).

One-Way Clutches. Sprag and roller clutches should be inspected in much the same way as bearings. Of course, they must turn in one direction and lock in the other. Look for broken or distorted springs as well.

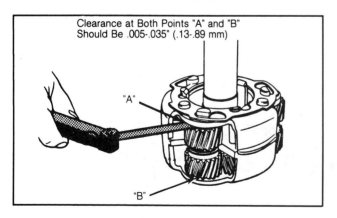

FIGURE 10-17 Checking planetary pinion end play.

Valve Body.   As mentioned earlier, it pays to disassemble and lay out parts in an organized fashion. This is especially true of valve body parts. Figure 10-18 is an example of a fairly complex valve body. Note the alternate pressure regulator/ boost valve, springs used on some models, not on others, and simple items such as the orificed plug used on only two out of about a dozen different models.

Inspect all spool valve bands and shoulders for burrs and nicks. Hairline scoring from a single dirt particle is generally acceptable, but if the damage is enough to allow significant bleed-by, then the assembly should be replaced. Generally speaking, damaged spool valves cannot be replaced individually; a new valve body assembly is required.

When cleaning up burred spool valves, use a very fine, flat stone or a fine **crocus cloth** laid out on a piece of plate glass or other level surface. This will ensure that the valve shoulders stay square so that one side of the valve is not opening or closing before the other.

Check each valve for free operation in its bore or bushing. The valve should slide smoothly in its bore under its own weight without lubrication.

The mating surfaces of the valve body, or valve body-to-transmission case, must be flat. Check for a warped body using a feeler gauge and straightedge. Close examination of the gasket patterns on the separator plate and on the old gaskets often indicate whether there is leakage from one passage to another because of valve body warpage or incorrect torquing.

Governor. Of the case-mounted governors, the checkball type is virtually service free; a check to make certain balls and springs are there and weights move freely is all that is needed. The spool valve type, however, is inspected similarly to any spool valve, and there are specifications for inlet and outlet openings (Figure 10-19). If the governor gear is loose or worn, replace it. Some case-mounted governors include the speedometer drive gear also. Except for these items, case mounted governors are serviced as a unit. A worn or bent spool valve means replacing the entire governor. Its case bushing can be replaced only if the corresponding surface on the governor sleeve is not worn. The

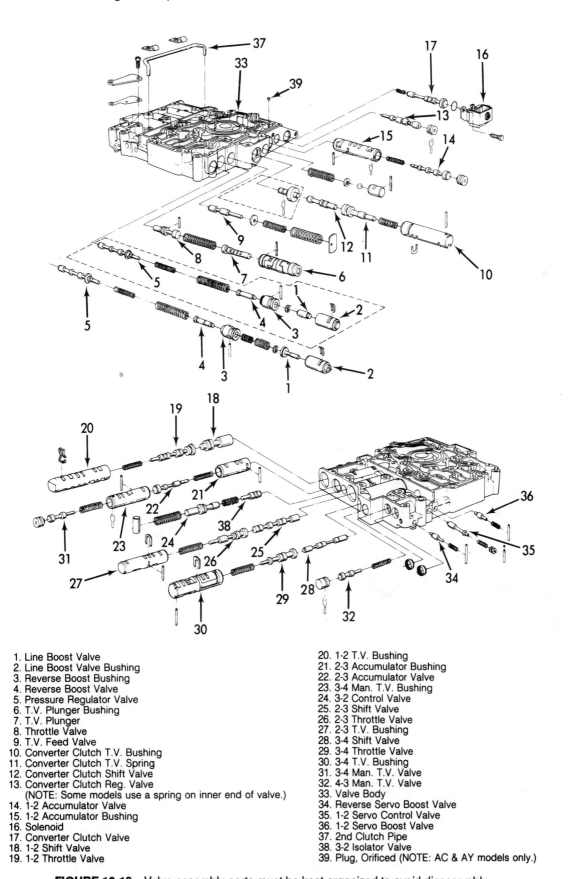

1. Line Boost Valve
2. Line Boost Valve Bushing
3. Reverse Boost Bushing
4. Reverse Boost Valve
5. Pressure Regulator Valve
6. T.V. Plunger Bushing
7. T.V. Plunger
8. Throttle Valve
9. T.V. Feed Valve
10. Converter Clutch T.V. Bushing
11. Converter Clutch T.V. Spring
12. Converter Clutch Shift Valve
13. Converter Clutch Reg. Valve
    (NOTE: Some models use a spring on inner end of valve.)
14. 1-2 Accumulator Valve
15. 1-2 Accumulator Bushing
16. Solenoid
17. Converter Clutch Valve
18. 1-2 Shift Valve
19. 1-2 Throttle Valve

20. 1-2 T.V. Bushing
21. 2-3 Accumulator Bushing
22. 2-3 Accumulator Valve
23. 3-4 Man. T.V. Bushing
24. 3-2 Control Valve
25. 2-3 Shift Valve
26. 2-3 Throttle Valve
27. 2-3 T.V. Bushing
28. 3-4 Shift Valve
29. 3-4 Throttle Valve
30. 3-4 T.V. Bushing
31. 3-4 Man. T.V. Valve
32. 4-3 Man. T.V. Valve
33. Valve Body
34. Reverse Servo Boost Valve
35. 1-2 Servo Control Valve
36. 1-2 Servo Boost Valve
37. 2nd Clutch Pipe
38. 3-2 Isolator Valve
39. Plug, Orificed (NOTE: AC & AY models only.)

FIGURE 10-18   Valve assembly parts must be kept organized to avoid disassembly.

(a)

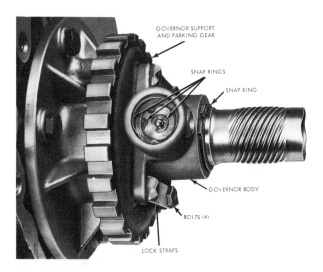

FIGURE 10-20   Shaft-mounted governor showing snap ring and valve-shaft "E" clip for removal (Courtesy of Chrysler Motors Corporation).

passes through the output shaft and must be removed before the governor can be slid off the shaft. The governor can then be disassembled, thoroughly cleaned, and inspected. Figure 10-21 shows an exploded view of an representative shaft-mounted governor.

(b)

FIGURE 10-19   Measuring (a) inlet and (b) outlet openings on case-mounted spool valve governor (courtesy of General Motors Corporation).

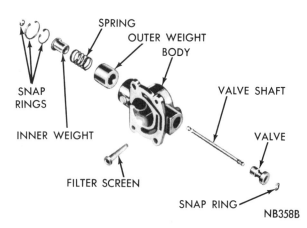

FIGURE 10-21   Exploded view of representative shaft-mounted governor (Courtesy of Chrysler Motors Corporation).

valve and sleeve can be dressed with crocus cloth to eliminate sticking from burrs.

Most Ford, Chrysler and foreign makes use output-shaft-mounted governors (Figure 10-20). These are not as readily accessible as case-mounted governors. The drive shaft and extension housing must be removed to expose the unit, which is held in place by a snap ring. The governor valve shaft

Flex Plate and Torque Converter.   The flex plate can be checked for runout with a dial gauge against specifications if the manufacturer provides them (usually not to exceed 0.060 in.). Even if runout is within specifications, the flex plate should be removed and inspected for cracks. These usually occur near the bolt holes. If cracks are found, or if the starter ring gear is damaged, replace the flex plate.

Before completely draining or cleaning the torque converter, several checks for internal wear should be made.

- Check the one-way roller clutch by engaging it with the stator support splines; a quick turn of the stator support clockwise should produce lock-up resistance and it should rotate freely in a counterclockwise direction. If it is free (or locked up) in both directions, the torque converter must be replaced.

- Using a pair of long-reach snap-ring pliers, reach into the hub and grasp the stator splines. If you can move the stator along its axis as much as 1/16 in., replace the torque converter—anything less than 1/16 in. is acceptable.

- Stator-to-turbine interference can be checked using the input shaft to turn the turbine with the torque converter sitting on a table. A scraping noise means that the torque converter must be replaced.

- Impeller-to-stator interference is checked using the stator support. It is placed on a table and the torque converter is then placed over it so that the support splines engage the stator. Again, replace the torque converter if scraping is detected when it is turned on the support shaft.

Before completing torque converter inspection, clean inside and out with solvent. If you notice foreign material in drained ATF or in the cleaning solvent, be aware that it is nearly impossible to clean the inside of a torque converter thoroughly, although there is flushing equipment designed to do the job. So if the ATF is badly contaminated and you are rebuilding an extremely worn transmission, it is probably wise to replace the torque converter—even if it checks out OK—to keep from contaminating the new transmission with residual dirt and metal particles from the transmission's condition before the rebuild.

Examine the outside of the torque converter for scoring on the hub, damaged oil pump drive lug slots from misalignment, cracks around the converter-to-flex plate bolt holes and weldnuts, miss-ing or loose balance weights, and damaged converter-to-crankshaft pilot. If any of these conditions are found and cannot be corrected, the torque converter must be replaced.

The clean converter can be inspected for leakage by fabricating a suitable plug device with an air valve in it to insert into the hub. The entire unit can then be submerged in a tank of water and pressurized to no more than 20 psi. Any leaks will be revealed by bubbles just like testing an inner tube. As a safety precaution, it is wise to bolt one end of a length of chain to one converter bolt, wind it once around the hub, and bolt it snugly to another converter bolt.

TRANSMISSION ASSEMBLY

To say that assembly is just reversing the disassembly procedure is really only partly true. Foremost among the differences are the fitting and proper mating of parts and correct nut and bolt **fastener** torquing. None of these is of immediate concern in disassembly, but they are critical in assembly.

Fitting is simply a quick check—before final assembly and fastening—of any replacement part against its mating parts and surfaces. Sometimes this needs to be done far ahead of final assembly. For example, suppose that you are replacing the torque converter—better to set the new one against the mounted flex plate to check pilot fit and mounting bolt alignment as soon as you get it rather than waiting until you have bolted the transmission to the engine and find that the holes do not match!

Mating requires care—some parts that look symmetrical fit together properly only one way. This is why marking mated parts before disassembly helps so much. Replacement parts can be mated while fitting and you can mark them for final assembly with your spray paint or other marking device. Properly mating parts saves time and assures that **broken-in** (slightly worn surfaces) and balanced parts are correctly assembled for greatest durability. Some parts (e.g., IX pump gears, Figure 10-22) are marked by the manufacturer for correct assembly. Manufacturer's instructions in your shop manual will identify the correct positioning with respect to these marks.

CODES FOR FASTENER STANDARDS

Many fasteners are marked and should never be replaced with ones of lesser strength. Metric bolts have numbers embossed on the heads, and **S.A.E.** (Society of Automotive Engineers) bolts use radial slashes; both increase in strength with increase in number or quantity of slashes. Metric nuts are similarly marked, whereas S.A.E. nuts use dots. Some studs are similarly marked, although some smaller ones use a geometric code stamped on one end. Bolt specifications usually include diameter, thread pitch, and length, in that order. The strength code is not always included. Diameter is the actual diameter of the shank before the threads are cut. Thread pitch is measured from one peak to the next for metric, but includes the number of peaks to the inch for S.A.E. fasteners. Length in both systems is always measured from the head bearing surface to the threaded end.

Fastener torque specifications are becoming more and more important. First, a great deal has been learned about the effect of stresses from shear, tensile, compression, and torsion forces on metal alloys and other materials. When you tighten a bolt you put a stretching force (**tensile**) and twisting force (**torsional**) on its shank, a **shear** force on its threads and on the female threads, and a **compression** force on the surfaces of the interfacing parts. The stress is also affected by temperature, part size, and external loads. Parts and fasteners are being designed to closer tolerances, so that tightening torque has become more critical than it used to be.

Often the manufacturer requires the use of new fasteners for reassembly. If you disregard these instructions, you are risking bolt or nut failure. Used bolts already have been stretched at their first torquing. Reuse means retorquing, and stretching, possibly beyond the elastic limit (the point at which the stretched bolt will not return to its original length

when loosened). The locking effect built into many nuts by slight thread distortion also "digs in" to the bolt threads—reuse never has the same locking effect as that of new fasteners.

In preparation for reassembly, always review the manufacturer's recommendation in your shop manual. Take note of the general assembly sequence and special tools and fixtures needed for positioning and holding parts and subassemblies during assembly. Often you can substitute for these, but you need to be aware of their purpose. Also note the parts and subassemblies for which the manufacturer provides specific instructions and clearance specifications, and the fasteners for which torque specifications are furnished. Then, as you proceed through the assembly process, you will have a better idea of when to refer to specifics in the manual.

When assembling parts and when installing subassemblies, take care not to nick mating surfaces or cut any seals. Use an assembling lubricant where recommended, and keep the assembly and work area clean and organized. Make certain that parts are completely seated before torquing fasteners.

Automatic transmission reassembly begins by mounting the transmission case in a holding fixture. If one is not available, the case can be stood on its end on a low bench or blocked horizontally on a workbench of standard height. If there are any worn bushings in the case, they should be replaced at this time.

Now is when the instruction "assemble in reverse order of disassembly" is helpful. But do not rely solely on your memory; besides providing critical clearance and tightening specifications, your

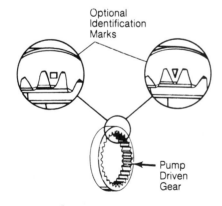

FIGURE 10-22 Example of oil pump IX gears marked by manufacturer for correct assembly.

shop manual is a very good guide and checklist for reassembly.

Assembling the transmission consists of installing numerous subassemblies. Some of these (e.g., governor, torque converter) are complete subassemblies; others may contain one complete subassembly and part of another (e.g., low-reverse clutch, one-way roller clutch, and rear planetary carrier). Again, the manufacturer's recommended assembly sequence helps a great deal, especially with the smaller parts (e.g., parking mechanism, manual shaft); it is easy to overlook these, and you might have to undo some pretty complex assembly work if you have missed the installation sequence.

The location and names of parts and subassemblies vary from one automatic transmission make to another. What General Motors calls a low-reverse clutch and locates in the rear of the case, Ford calls reverse and high and locates toward the front. There are even location differences from one model to another. Specific makes and models are discussed in the next four chapters, and specific questions or guidelines for particular transmission models are best answered by the appropriate section of your shop manual.

After you have installed any needed case bushings, install the new seals. Seals, and all parts, should be coated with ATF for ease of assembly and initial lubrication. Thrust washers or other small parts can be held in place with petroleum jelly; do not use white grease, it is incompatible with ATF.

A clutch and planetary assembly, sometimes with the output shaft, is usually the first to be installed in a transmission, whereas in a transaxle, it is usually the differential and final drive. In both cases, these are accompanied, of course, by bearings and thrust washers of thickness selected for correct end play. In some transaxles, especially, you will find tapered bearings that require shimming to meet specified torque requirements according to the manufacturer's instructions. The marking pawl and gear is located here, too. And some makes incorporate a band as well.

When assembling clutches, refer to clutchplate usage charts for the correct number of steel and composition plates for a particular model. Also, comply with any instructions concerning the location of clutch return springs (Figure 10-23). Some one-way clutches can be assembled and/or installed

Springs Must Be Installed In Pockets Marked X Only

FIGURE 10-23 Some clutches use less than a full complement of return springs and require specific locations for them.

so that they lock in the wrong direction; watch for this on those where one side is indistinguishable from the other. Following assembly, see that the composition clutch plates turn freely between the steel ones. Some makes furnish clearance specifications measured between the pressure plate and snap ring to check clutch clearance, and they furnish selective snap rings so that specifications can be met. Generally, minimum clearance for free clutch rotation is about 0.010 in. for each friction plate (four friction plates = 0.040 in. clearance). One eighth-inch clearance or more is too much and can be adjusted by adding more steel or composition clutch plates. Steels can be added next to steels without slipping since they are splined to the same rotating member. The friction material can be removed from one side of one plate or from the interfacing sides of two plates with the same results if a finer clearance adjustment is required.

Assembled clutches can be air checked to make sure that seals and rings are okay and that the piston applies and releases. Check with 30 psi—any more pressure could move the piston in spite of leaks that could show up later under normal hydraulic operating pressure, and more pressure could blow oil seals.

The ends of some bands are very similar in appearance, but one may be heavier than the other. Pay close attention to installing them properly to avoid broken band ends. Bands that have no adjusting screws require a pin of specific length between the servo piston and the apply end of the band. These are available in selected sizes.

KEEP IT LOOSE! _____

When tightening any fastener that directly or indirectly involves a rotating part or assembly (bushing or bearings), rotate that member during and after the tightening process to ensure that it is not binding.

_____

Continuing assembly to the front of the transmission includes much the same types of activity and parts. Some transmissions will incorporate a single Ravigneaux planetary rather than a Simpson, and others use additional planetaries for overdrive and final drive reduction. Still others may have more or less bands. As mentioned before, it is very important during this assembly to check end play where required. In fact, at least one manufacturer provides depth measurement specifications to ensure complete seating (engagement) of the direct and forward clutch assemblies before final torquing to avoid damaging or breaking parts.

Some valve bodies utilize part of the transmission case, others are complete units in themselves; still others consist of a main body with an auxiliary valve body, and some transaxles include the oil pump in the valve body.

Be certain that new gaskets match old ones, hole for hole. Do the same if you are replacing the separator plate.

Above all, carefully align the valve body, and tighten bolts in recommended sequence. Finger-tighten first, check for complete seating, then finish with a correctly set torque wrench. It is okay to use air tools but do not let them impact; it is too easy to overtorque, which can result in warped parts and unevenly compressed gaskets.

Manufacturer's instructions often illustrate valve body bolt locations as well as their sizes. Read these diagrams very carefully in conjunction with the torque specification description (auxiliary valve body, valve body-to-case cover, valve body-to-case) to be certain that you are reading the torque specifications for the assembly you intend to torque next—also take note of whether it is inch-pounds or foot-pounds.

Final assembly includes governor, servo, filter, pan, and torque converter. Put at least a quart of ATF into the torque converter before installing it. When slipping the torque converter over the stator support, rotate it until the lugs of the oil pump external gear or rotor engage the drive slots in the converter hub. Some manufacturers provide measurements to check that the torque converter is fully seated and engaged with the oil pump.

TRANSMISSION INSTALLATION

If you marked the flex plate during disassembly, rotate the engine to bring that mark into view; also rotate the torque converter to bring its mark to approximately the same position.

Mount the transmission on the jack, and slowly raise it to align with the engine. Carefully work the transmission forward and over the alignment pins until it is seated in place. Install the transmission case-to-engine bolts just snug for later torquing. (Some makes use studs in the torque converter, and these may have to be aligned with the flex plate simultaneously.) Slide the torque converter toward the engine and install fasteners. Snug-tighten these first to make sure the torque converter is seated against the flex plate. Now torque these and transmission-to-engine bolts to specification.

Install rear transmission mount, starter, transmission inspection plate, dipstick housing, electrical, mechanical, and vacuum linkage, and drive shaft or axles. Reconnect exhaust systems.

Now is a good time to put some ATF into the transmission through the filler tube—at least 2 quarts for small transmissions and 4 quarts for full-sized ones. Start the engine, and move the selector level through all the gears. Check ATF level and add fluid as necessary. Check for leaks. Allow the vehicle to run while you take care of any final assembly. By this time, the transmission is probably near operating temperature, and you can add fluid to bring the level between the add and full marks and then road test.

TRADE TERMS

Broken-in	Fastener	S.A.E.
Compression	Fitting	Shear
Crocus cloth	Ideal operating	Shift gate
Cursory	conditions	Tensile
performance	Manual valve detents	Torsional
demonstration	Mating	Tungsten inert gas
Extreme operating	Room-temperature	(TIG) weld
conditions	vulcanizing	
	(RTV) rubber	

REVIEW QUESTIONS

10-1. Knowing the conditions under which a vehicle most often operates helps in diagnosis, adjustments, and establishing _____ _____ that will extend transmission life.

10-2. There are only two sets of vehicle operating conditions: *ideal* and *extreme*.   T   F

10-3. A general visual inspection of the transmission:

(a) Includes checking for leaks.

(b) Includes checking for loose wires.

(c) Can be performed at each engine oil change.

(d) Includes checking linkage and mounting bolts.

(e) All of the above.

(f) None of the above.

(g) All but c above.

10-4. Automatic transmissions can be drained through:

(a) Plugs in the Pan.

(b) Plugs in the final drive.

(c) Removal of filler tube.

(d) Removal of the pan.

(e) All of the above.

(f) All but b above.

10-5. If you are changing converter fluid by disconnecting the cooling circuit you must:

(a) Keep the engine running until at least 6 quarts have been pumped out.

(b) Drain and refill the transmission with new ATF first.

(c) Run the engine at a fast idle.

(d) Allow ATF to cool first.

10-6. Some oil sump pans require special removal techniques.   T   F

10-7. When removing the oil sump pan, try to avoid disturbing any _____ in the bottom.

10-8. Which of the following conditions suggests that the transmission is ready for an overhaul?

(a) Dark ATF.

(b) Very small metallic flakes.

(c) Dark material that feels granular.

(d) All of the above.

10-9. All transmission bands have external adjustments.   T   F

10-10. Some cables are labeled "self-adjusting" or "automatic adjusting," which means that they adjust themselves totally.   T   F

10-11. Vacuum modulators are tested by the comparison method or by a scale reading against furnished specifications.   T   F

10-12. The length of the shift linkage rod or cable is adjusted to allow the _____ _____ stops to match the _____ _____ detents.

10-13. The neutral safety switch sometimes includes the _____ _____ switch and a switch for the _____ _____ warning system.

10-14. As a vehicle with a lock-up torque converter comes to a stop, its _____ _____ breaks the solenoid circuit to release the lock-up valve.

10-15. Some transaxles are removed with the engine attached.   T   F

10-16. The reason you mark parts before disassembly is to remember which part goes with which.   T   F

10-17. Before removing transmission mount, support _____ and _____ separately.

10-18. When separating transmission from engine, make sure that _____ _____ stays with transmission.

10-19. When using shop air for purging or testing, keep pressure at _____ psi, except _____ psi when testing torque converter for leaks.

10-20. End play is important. It should be checked and recorded during _____ _____ and checked against specifications during ____.

10-21. The output shaft is always removed out the rear of the transmission.   T   F

10-22. As you disassemble the transmission, keep the subassemblies _____, and lay out the parts in an _____ fashion.

10-23. Which of the following always should be replaced?
   (a) Seal rings.
   (b) Seals.
   (c) O-rings.
   (d) Gaskets.
   (e) None of the above.
   (f) All of the above.

10-24. Bushings should be replaced if the mating parts can be cocked or if a wire gauge of the following diameter can be inserted:
   (a) 0.060
   (b) 0.600 in.
   (c) 0.006 in.
   (d) None of the above.

10-25. IX gear pumps tend to wear on all but which of the following?
   (a) Inside and outside the crescent surface on the suction side.
   (b) Pump body on the pressure side.
   (c) Bushing toward the suction side.
   (d) Pump body on the suction side.

10-26. Wear in which of the following is measured with a feeler gauge?
   (a) IX rotor teeth.
   (b) IX gear teeth.

10-27. If one clutch plate needs replacing, replace _____.

10-28. Spool valves can be cleaned in _____ cleaner and deburred with _____ _____ .

10-29. Flex plate runout should generally not exceed:
   (a) 0.060 in.
   (b) 0.600 in.
   (c) 0.006 in.
   (d) None of the above.

10-30. The torque converter one-way roller clutch can be checked using the _____ _____ splines.

10-31. If you can move the stator along its axis as much as _____ _____ inch by grasping it with a pair of snap ring pliers, replace the torque converter.

10-32. Stator-to-turbine interference can be checked using the _____ shaft.

10-33. Impeller-to-stator interference can be checked using the _____ _____ .

10-34. _____, _____ and _____ are never a part of removal and disassembly, but always a part of assembly and installation.

10-35. During reassembly, do not use _____ _____ because it is incompatible with ATF.

10-36. Generally, minimum clearances for each friction plate is:
   (a) 0.100 in.
   (b) 0.010 in.
   (c) 0.001 in.
   (d) None of the above.

10-37. Planetary gearsets are also used in some overdrives and final drives.   T   F

10-38. Virtually all transmissions place the oil pump at the front of the transmission, but some transaxles locate the oil pump in the _____ _____ .

10-39. Gaskets and separator plates must match hole for hole.   T   F

10-40. Before adding transmission fluid, make sure that you have:
   (a) Inserted the drive shaft or axles.
   (b) Connected the speedometer cable.
   (c) Tightened the pan plug.
   (d) All of the above.

ESSAY QUESTIONS

10-1. What are the general steps you will take to prepare for removal and overhaul of an automatic transmission?

10-2. Discuss the three tasks that are never a part of removal and disassembly but always should be a part of reassembly and installation.

CHAPTER ACTIVITIES

10-1. Talk to a car owner in the presence of his car; if you are riding in the car at the time, all the better. Ask questions, and silently observe the driver's operation of the vehicle, to help determine on a scale of 1 to 10—ideal to extreme—the apparent conditions under which the car operates. Ask whether the owner has had the car since it was new; if not, how long? Ask what kinds of trips (long, short, stop-go, etc.) Observe to yourself the general condition by seeing, feeling, and hearing the vehicle operating.

10-2. In your workbook or shop manual, select a transmission model (the one in your own car or a car with which you are somewhat familiar is best) and preview the complete article as though you are preparing for the removal and overhaul of the transmission. Remember to look for general sequence, special instructions, special tools, and so on.

11

GENERAL MOTORS CORPORATION

―――――――――― **OBJECTIVES** ――――――――――

When you have completed this chapter, you should be able to:

- Recognize Turbo Hydra-Matic transmission and transaxle designations.
- Describe the normal power flow through a Simpson compound planetary gearset.
- Explain the significance of model identification codes in testing and ordering parts.
- Name the differentiating characteristics among General Motors transmissions and transaxles.

In 1908, the year Henry Ford's Model T first appeared, General Motors Company was incorporated in New Jersey. Although the 15 million Model T Fords manufactured between 1908 and 1927 all used a manually shifted (actually, foot-shifted) planetary gear transmission, it was General Motors that introduced the first fully automatic planetary

gear transmission in 1939. And General Motors was first on the market with a torque converter in its 1948 Buick Dynaflow—following by 10 years Chrysler's use of the fluid coupling.

General Motors Hydra-Matic Division produces over 10 different automatic transmission and transaxle models. All model numbers are preceded by three letters, **THM** for **Turbo Hydra-Matic**. Among the current designations are:

THM 180C, 200C, 350C, 400: three-speed, shaft-driven, RWD

THM 125C,: three-speed, transverse-mounted transaxle, FWD (and some RWD)

THM 200-4R, 700-R4: four-speed, automatic overdrive, shaft driven, RWD

THM 325-4L: four-speed, automatic overdrive transmission, FWD

THM 440-T4: four-speed, automatic overdrive, transverse-mounted transaxle

All models listed above, except the THM 400, can come equipped with torque converter clutches. Many of these transmission and transaxle models have a dozen or so alternates. (One has 30; another 45.) The alternates are designated by an alphanumeric code. These **model codes** signify that certain changes have been made to tailor this transmission to meet design and performance requirements of a particular combination of engine and final drive ratio option. The changes include such things as the number of clutch plates and the thickness of clutch backing plates as well as changes in pump and valve body circuits that affect control pressure specifications. So it is important to know which of the 18 versions of THM 440-T4, for example, you are working on when testing and ordering parts. Any good shop manual will list the codes and what vehicles they affect.

The sections remaining in this chapter each present a summary description of a particular Turbo Hydra-Matic transmission or transaxle model. The four selected—two FWD and two RWD—are typical of General Motors production passenger cars and light trucks.

TURBO HYDRA-MATIC 350C

Description and Identification

This is a three-speed, aluminum-cased transmission designed for shaft-driven, RWD vehicles. Initial identification, installed, is indicated by the pan

shape, the one-piece transmission case and bell housing, and the extension housing. The pan is nearly square except for the angled right rear corner. The bell housing portion of the case is completed by an inspection cover starting from the maximum diameter and angling down to the main part of the case. And there is an extension housing, which carries the speedometer-driven gear (Figure 11-1).

A cross section of the THM 350C is shown in Figure 11-2. This transmission utilizes a Simpson compound planetary gearset controlled by four multiple-disc clutch assemblies and a band to help effect second (intermediate) gear. Two one-way clutches are used in the main case: one in the low-reverse and the other in the intermediate mechanism. The torque converter clutch also incorporates a roller clutch with the stator and is hydraulically activated by a solenoid and spool valve located in the auxiliary valve body. An IX gear pump is driven by the converter hub.

There are several places that the model codes might be located on the THM 350: on a plate riveted to the case, or metal stamped on the side of the oil pan, the accumulator cover, or the governor cover. The code consists of a day and shift code, a two-letter (sometimes including one digit) model code, and a model year. **The Vehicle Identification Number (VIN)** is also metal-stamped onto the transmission case, but it is of no value in maintenance and repair; its only purpose is to identify the vehicle in which the transmission was originally installed.

Applications

The latest applications of the THM 350C are limited to Chevrolet and GMC trucks, although production was stopped after 1981. Early applications of the THM 350 were dominated by the developing manufacturers, Buick and Chevrolet.

History and Development

This transmission and its derivatives, the THM 250C and THM 375B, rank among the most popular ever made. It was originally developed by Buick and Chevrolet—independent of the Hydra-Matic Division—to replace the two-speed Buick Super Turbine 300 and the Chevrolet Powerglide.

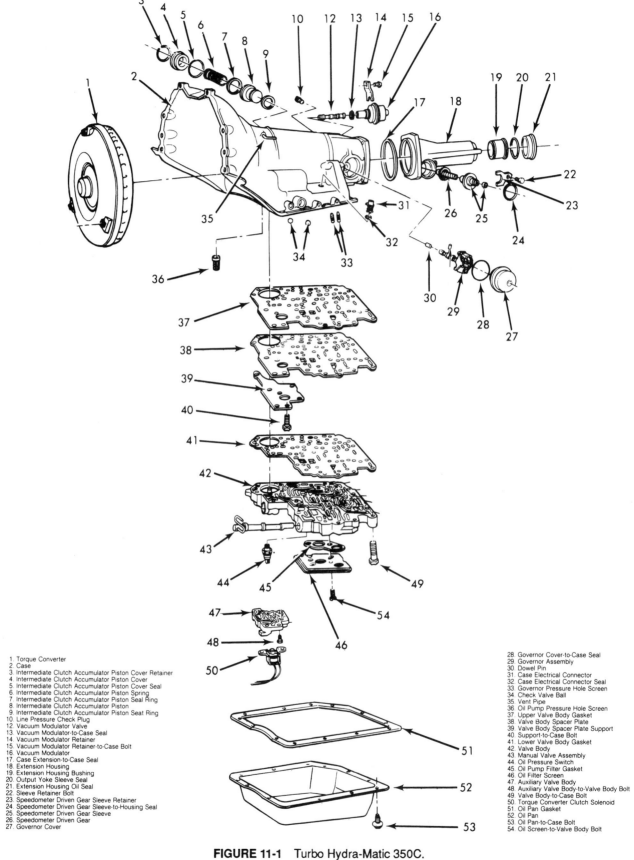

1. Torque Converter
2. Case
3. Intermediate Clutch Accumulator Piston Cover Retainer
4. Intermediate Clutch Accumulator Piston Cover
5. Intermediate Clutch Accumulator Piston Cover Seal
6. Intermediate Clutch Accumulator Piston Spring
7. Intermediate Clutch Accumulator Piston Seal Ring
8. Intermediate Clutch Accumulator Piston
9. Intermediate Clutch Accumulator Piston Seat Ring
10. Line Pressure Check Plug
12. Vacuum Modulator Valve
13. Vacuum Modulator-to-Case Seal
14. Vacuum Modulator Retainer
15. Vacuum Modulator Retainer-to-Case Bolt
16. Vacuum Modulator
17. Case Extension-to-Case Seal
18. Extension Housing
19. Extension Housing Bushing
20. Output Yoke Sleeve Seal
21. Extension Housing Oil Seal
22. Sleeve Retainer Bolt
23. Speedometer Driven Gear Sleeve Retainer
24. Speedometer Driven Gear Sleeve-to-Housing Seal
25. Speedometer Driven Gear Sleeve
26. Speedometer Driven Gear
27. Governor Cover

28. Governor Cover-to-Case Seal
29. Governor Assembly
30. Dowel Pin
31. Case Electrical Connector
32. Case Electrical Connector Seal
33. Governor Pressure Hole Screen
34. Check Valve Ball
35. Vent Pipe
36. Oil Pump Pressure Hole Screen
37. Upper Valve Body Gasket
38. Valve Body Spacer Plate
39. Valve Body Spacer Plate Support
40. Support-to-Case Bolt
41. Lower Valve Body Gasket
42. Valve Body
43. Manual Valve Assembly
44. Oil Pressure Switch
45. Oil Pump Filter Gasket
46. Oil Filter Screen
47. Auxiliary Valve Body
48. Auxiliary Valve Body-to-Valve Body Bolt
49. Valve Body-to-Case Bolt
50. Torque Converter Clutch Solenoid
51. Oil Pan Gasket
52. Oil Pan
53. Oil Pan-to-Case Bolt
54. Oil Screen-to-Valve Body Bolt

FIGURE 11-1   Turbo Hydra-Matic 350C.

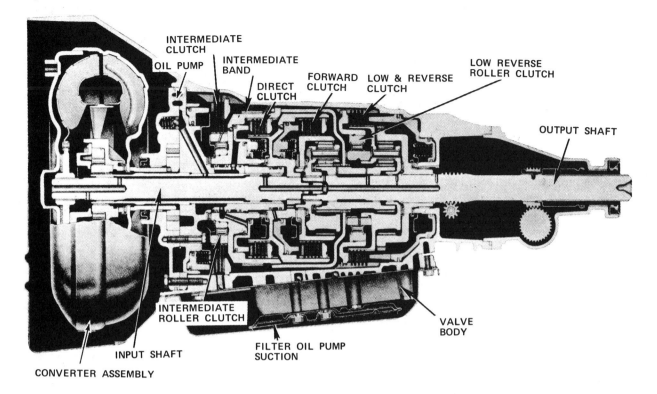

FIGURE 11-2 Turbo Hydra-Matic 350 cross section.

Power Flow

It helps in tracing power flow through the THM 350 to note the following (refer to Figure 11-2):

- The forward clutch is splined to the input shaft and engages the forward annulus gear.
- The front planet carrier is splined to the output shaft, as is the rear annulus.
- The intermediate clutch is anchored to the case and connected to the intermediate roller (one way) clutch, which is connected to the sun gear through the drive shell. When the clutch is released, the roller clutch is ineffective (turns both ways); when it is applied, the roller clutch holds the sun gear against CCW rotation.
- The intermediate band is anchored to the case and keeps the intermediate roller clutch from turning in its free direction, effectively locking it and, consequently, the sun gear.
- The **direct** (high-reverse) **clutch** is splined to the input shaft and engages the sun gear.

- The low-reverse clutch is anchored to the case and engages the rear (reaction) carrier.
- The low-reverse roller clutch holds the reaction carrier in one direction only.

The following paragraphs explaining power flow will be confusing if you try to read straight through them once—it may take two or more readings. And it will help if you hesitate every time there is an explanation of one part affecting or connected to another; try to envision those parts and what their relationship is. Referring to the power flow illustration or the cross section will also help.

The torque converter clutch is activated whenever the transmission is in third gear at a speed of 30 to 35 mph (but only in 2WD mode on 4WD vehicles). It is deactivated by the brake switch. In all other gears, it multiplies torque up to 2 1/4 times during vortex flow, then levels off at a little over 90% efficiency at full rotary flow.

Selector Lever in Drive. Under the usual driving conditions, power flow through the transmission begins in first gear when the selector lever is moved to Drive. This applies the forward clutch, which is splined to the input shaft, connecting the latter to the **input ring gear**, which is the forward annulus in this Simpson gearset. The planet carrier for this front part is splined to the output shaft and is referred to as the **output carrier**. The CW rotating ring gear then rotates the planet gears CW, and these drive the sun gear CCW because the output planet carrier is held by being splined to output shaft. The sun gear now turns the rear planet gears CW. At this point, the rear (reaction) planet carrier tries to turn CCW but the low roller (one-way) clutch stops it, and the planets then carry the torque through the output ring gear, CW. In summary, power comes in through the front ring gear and goes out through both the output carrier and the rear (output) ring gear, which are splined to the output shaft. The output carrier does not affect the gear ratio, however (Figure 11-3).

Power for drive second gear is also input through the input ring gear by application of the forward clutch, which locks it to the input shaft. But this time the intermediate clutch is applied, causing the intermediate roller (one-way) clutch to hold the sun gear against CCW rotation. With the sun gear held, torque is transferred through the planet gears to the carrier, which is splined to the output shaft. In summary, power comes in though the front ring gear and goes out through the front, or output, carrier. Only the front part of the Simpson gearset is used for second gear (Figure 11-4).

In third gear, power travels through both the input ring gear, which is coupled to the input shaft by the forward clutch, and the sun gear, which is coupled to the input shaft by the direct (high-reverse) clutch. Thus two of the three planetary members—sun gear and input ring gear—are locked together producing direct drive. The intermediate clutch remains applied to make the intermediate roller clutch effective, but this is not needed for direct drive. In summary, power is transmitted directly through the front planetary, which is

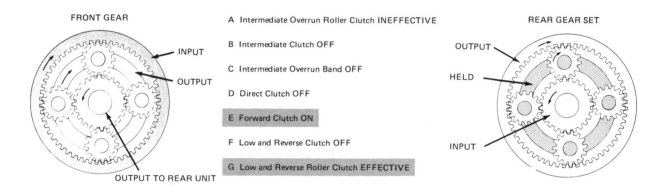

FRONT GEAR   INPUT   OUTPUT   OUTPUT TO REAR UNIT

A Intermediate Overrun Roller Clutch INEFFECTIVE

B Intermediate Clutch OFF

C Intermediate Overrun Band OFF

D Direct Clutch OFF

E Forward Clutch ON

F Low and Reverse Clutch OFF

G Low and Reverse Roller Clutch EFFECTIVE

REAR GEAR SET   OUTPUT   HELD   INPUT

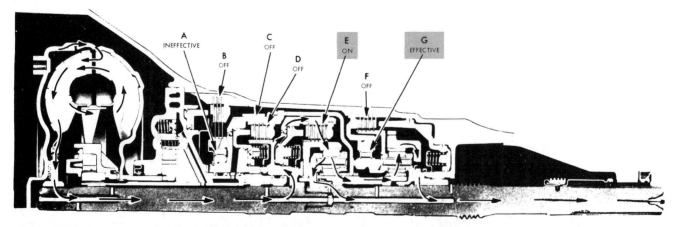

FIGURE 11-3   THM 350 power flow—direct low (Courtesy of General Motors Corporation).

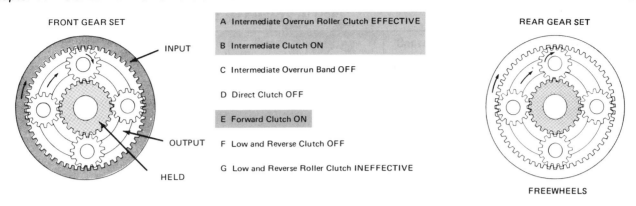

FRONT GEAR SET   REAR GEAR SET

INPUT

A Intermediate Overrun Roller Clutch EFFECTIVE

B Intermediate Clutch ON

C Intermediate Overrun Band OFF

D Direct Clutch OFF

E Forward Clutch ON

OUTPUT   F Low and Reverse Clutch OFF

G Low and Reverse Roller Clutch INEFFECTIVE

HELD

FREEWHEELS

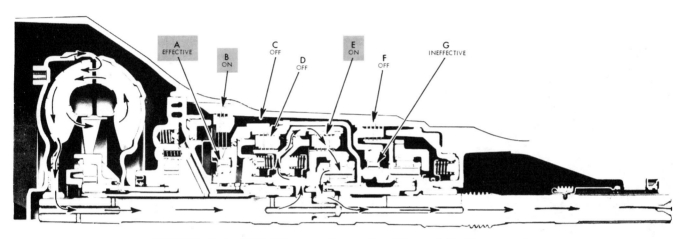

FIGURE 11-4   THM 350 power flow—drive intermediate (Courtesy of
General Motors Corporation).

rotating as a single unit (sun and annulus held to
input shaft), and through the output shaft, which is
splined to the front carrier (Figure 11-5).

Manual Selection Other Than Drive.   In
these shift positions, the power train remains fully
connected on deceleration, too, rather than just acceleration, which is the case in drive.

The transmission will shift automatically from
low to intermediate when the selector is set for
manual intermediate. All the same things happen
that happen in drive intermediate, but the intermediate overrun band is also applied, which keeps
the sun gear from turning CW during deceleration.
This prevents **freewheeling** (coasting) and the car
runs against engine compression. In summary,
power comes in through the front ring gear and goes
out through the front, or output, carrier. Power can
also flow the other way because the sun gear is held
in both directions (Figure 11-6).

In manual low as in drive low, the forward
clutch is applied, connecting the front, or input, ring
gear to the input shaft. The ring gear drives the
planet gears (whose carrier is held by the output
shaft), and the planets drive the sun gear, which
drives the rear planets, because the low roller (one-
way) clutch stops the rear (reaction) carrier from
turning CCW. Now, here is where manual low differs from drive low. In drive low, the low roller
clutch allows the reaction carrier to overrun (CW)
on deceleration, but it cannot in manual low because
the low-reverse clutch is applied, preventing CW
roller clutch rotation. So now the rear planet gears
drive the ring gear on deceleration. In summary, the
same power flow occurs in manual low as in drive
low, except that application of the low-reverse
clutch prevents the rear carrier from freewheeling
(Figure 11-7).

Reverse gear power flow goes from input shaft
to sun gear by application of the direct (high-
reverse) clutch. Although activated, the front

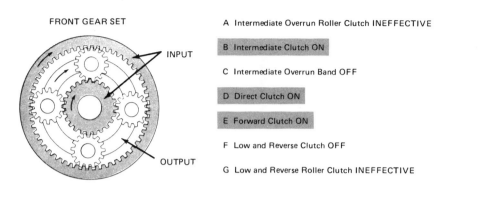

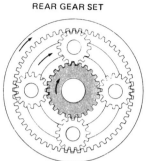

A Intermediate Overrun Roller Clutch INEFFECTIVE

B Intermediate Clutch ON

C Intermediate Overrun Band OFF

D Direct Clutch ON

E Forward Clutch ON

F Low and Reverse Clutch OFF

G Low and Reverse Roller Clutch INEFFECTIVE

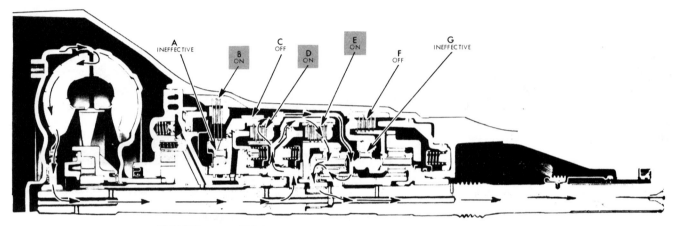

FIGURE 11-5   THM 350 power flow—drive direct (Courtesy of General Motors Corporation).

planetary is ineffective because the forward clutch is not applied. The sun gear turns the rear planets CCW, and they rotate the rear (output) ring gear CCW (the rear, or reaction, carrier is held by application of the low-reverse clutch). In summary, the high reverse (direct) and low-reverse clutches are applied to input power through the sun gear and hold the reaction carrier, respectively. Power is transmitted from the sun gear through the rear planetary only, because the forward clutch is not holding the forward (input) ring gear, rendering the

front planetary ineffective (no members held) (Figure 11-8).

Clutch and band application is summarized in the chart in Figure 11-9.

The THM 250 was derived from the 350 and used in production from 1974-1977. It is lighter and uses only a band for intermediate rather than the intermediate clutch, one-way clutch, and band combination of the 350.

The THM 375B is a heavier version of the 350 (see side bar below).

THM 375 AND THM 375B: NO RELATION

Only the 375B can claim any relation to the 350; it has more clutch plates and a longer output shaft and extension housing. It was used in the larger 1974-76 Buicks.

The 375 is a lighter version of the THM 400, but still heavier than the 375B.

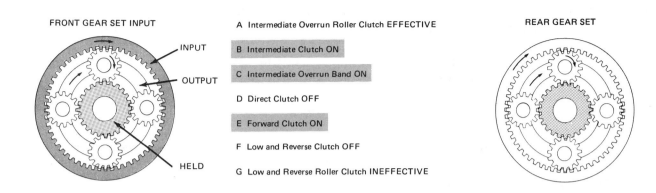

A Intermediate Overrun Roller Clutch EFFECTIVE

B Intermediate Clutch ON

C Intermediate Overrun Band ON

D Direct Clutch OFF

E Forward Clutch ON

F Low and Reverse Clutch OFF

G Low and Reverse Roller Clutch INEFFECTIVE

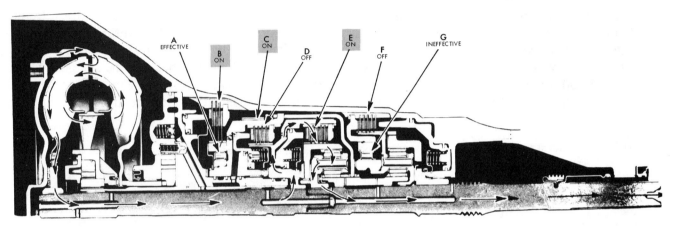

FIGURE 11-6 THM 350 power flow—manual intermediate (Courtesy of General Motors Corporation).

TURBO HYDRA-MATIC 200-4R

Description and Identification

This is a four-speed, or automatic overdrive, transmission for shaft-driven, RWD vehicles. It can be recognized by the unique shape of its pan (Figure 11-10).

A cross section of the THM 200-4R is shown in Figure 11-11. This transmission uses a Simpson compound planetary gearset and has added a simple planetary gearset for overdrive. These are controlled by five multiple-disc clutches, a band, and two roller clutches. The torque converter clutch incorporates a roller clutch with the stator and is hydraulically activated by a solenoid in the valve body. The vane pump is driven by the converter hub, and the pump body includes both the pressure regulator valve and converter clutch valve.

The model code appears on a plate at the right rear of the case near the modulator. There are over 15 variations.

Applications

Among the makes and models that may use the THM 200-4R are:

Buick LeSabre, Estate Wagon, Regal

Cadillac Fleetwood Brougham

Chevrolet Caballero, El Camino, Caprice, Impala, Malibu, Monte Carlo

Oldsmobile Cutlass, 88

Pontiac Bonneville, Grand Prix, Parisienne

History and Development

The THM 200-4R is remotely related to the THM 350 and 250 through the THM 200—the first metric transmission built by the General Motors Corp. The 200-4R, in addition to being metric, is one of several new transmissions and transaxles that includes **overdrive** as part of the usual shift sequence. The THM 200-4R has evolved as a result of the emphasis on operational economy.

Compensating for the lower torque developed by smaller engines can be accomplished through a combination of torque converter, transmission, and final drive ratios. Overdrive is not something new. The standard three-speed transmission in passenger cars of 40 years ago was often supplemented by a separate overdrive unit. Subsequently, overdrive was included as part of the transmission assembly, but not as part of the normal shift pattern. The four-speed units in many foreign makes (and later, domestic makes, as well) added reduction ratios only; fourth gear was direct drive. Now units such as the THM 200-4R incorporate an overdrive that can be utilized as part of the normal shift pattern.

Because of automatic overdrive, direct drive is internal to the shift pattern rather than being at one end of it. Final drive ratios now can be reduced slightly to give more torque at both extremes of the shift pattern.

Power Flow

The torque converter clutch is activated at 0 to 35 mph in third (direct) or fourth (overdrive). It is deactivated by the brake switch. In all other gears, it multiplies torque up to 2 1/4 times during vortex flow, then levels off at a little over 90% efficiency at full rotary flow (coupling phase).

The transmission input shaft is splined to the planet carrier of the simple (overdrive) gearset. A roller clutch between the sun gear and the carrier locks the two together (because the sun gear wants to turn faster than the carrier). This puts the simple (overdrive) gearset into direct drive, transmitting

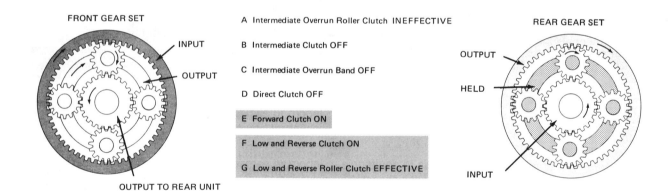

A Intermediate Overrun Roller Clutch INEFFECTIVE

B Intermediate Clutch OFF

C Intermediate Overrun Band OFF

D Direct Clutch OFF

E Forward Clutch ON

F Low and Reverse Clutch ON

G Low and Reverse Roller Clutch EFFECTIVE

FRONT GEAR SET — INPUT — OUTPUT — OUTPUT TO REAR UNIT

REAR GEAR SET — OUTPUT — HELD — INPUT

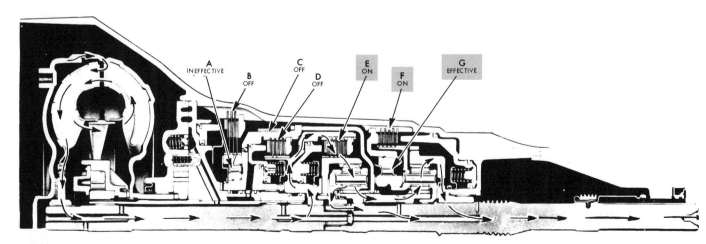

FIGURE 11-7   THM 350 power flow—manual low (Courtesy of General Motors Corporation).

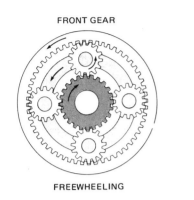

FRONT GEAR

FREEWHEELING

A Intermediate Overrun Roller Clutch INEFFECTIVE

B Intermediate Clutch OFF

C Intermediate Overrun Band OFF

D Direct Clutch ON

E Forward Clutch OFF

F Low and Reverse Clutch ON

G Low and Reverse Roller Clutch INEFFECTIVE

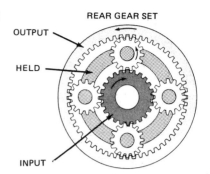

REAR GEAR SET

OUTPUT

HELD

INPUT

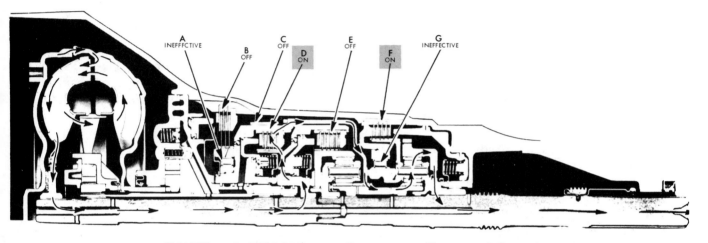

FIGURE 11-8 THM 350 power flow—reverse (Courtesy of General Motors Corporation).

Selector Lever Position	Intermed. Clutch	Direct Clutch	Forward Clutch	Low & Reverse Clutch	Intermed. Overrun Roller Clutch	Low & Reverse Roller Clutch	Intermed. Overrun Band
D – DRIVE							
First Gear			X			X	
Second Gear	X		X		X		
Third Gear	X	X	X				
2 – INTERMEDIATE							
Second Gear	X		X		X		X
1 – LOW (First)			X	X		X	
R – REVERSE		X		X			

NEUTRAL OR PARK – All clutches and bands released and/or ineffective.

FIGURE 11-9 Turbo Hydra-Matic 350 clutch and band application summary.

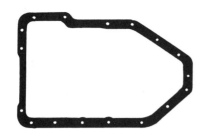

FIGURE 11-10 THM 200-4R is easily identified by its unique gasket shape.

power to the Simpson gearset through the forward clutch shaft. (Figure 11-12). The only time the simple (overdrive) gearset provides a gear ratio (anything other than direct) is in overdrive—but power for all gears is transmitted through it.

With the selector lever in drive, first gear input travels through the simple planetary as explained earlier. It then travels in the usual manner to the input ring gear because of forward clutch application. It continues as described previously (THM 350C) through the sun gear to the output (rear) ring gear, which is splined to the output shaft.

All other gears are effected in the same manner. That is, input is transmitted through the simple

(overdrive) gearset, which is locked for direct drive to the compound planetary. The compound planetary then provides drive first, drive second, drive third, reverse, and neutral in exactly the same fashion as it does for the THM 350C.

Manual first, second, and third is also achieved the same way, except that the overrun clutch is applied. This locks the overdrive roller clutch both ways to retain engine braking during deceleration.

Overdrive power flows through the input shaft to the simple (overdrive) carrier CW. The sun gear is held against turning CW by the overdrive roller clutch, the inner race of which is anchored to the case by the fourth clutch. This causes the planet gears to turn the overdrive ring gear, which is splined to the forward clutch shaft. The ratio of the carrier to the ring gear is 0.67:1, which means that the ring gear turns about one and one-half times to every one of the carrier. The compound gearset is in direct drive, so the overdrive ratio is carried directly through to the final drive.

Clutch and band application is summarized in the chart in Figure 11-13.

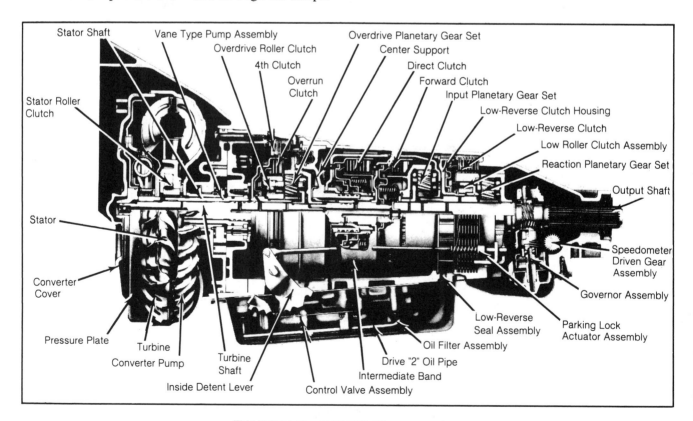

FIGURE 11-11 THM 200-4R cross section.

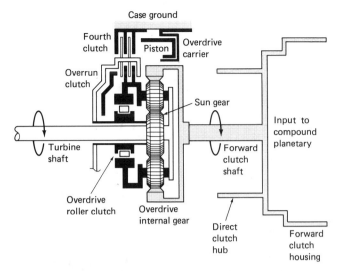

FIGURE 11-12 Schematic of single (overdrive) gearset used to transmit direct power to compound gearset.

TURBO HYDRA-MATIC 325-4L

Description and Identification

A quick glance might mislead you into thinking that this is a **transaxle**—a combined *trans*mission and drive *axle*. Technically it is not, but it is often referred to as a transaxle. It is a four-speed transmission designed for FWD vehicles with longitudinally mounted engines and a separate bevel gear, final drive/differential assembly.

A cross section of the THM 325-4L is shown in Figure 11-14. This transmission incorporates a Simpson compound planetary gearset and a simple planetary gearset. These are controlled by five multiple-disc clutches, a band, and two roller clutches. The torque converter clutch also incorporates a roller clutch for the stator, and it is hydraulically activated by a solenoid in the valve body. The IX gear pump is driven by the converter hub. The turbine ("input") shaft is splined to the simple (overdrive) planetary sun gear. The drive sprocket and the simple planetary ring gear comprise one limit. The carrier is splined to the overrun clutch discs and the plates spline to the overrun clutch housing. Power is transferred to the input shaft of the transmission through a drive link (chain) and drive sprocket (Figure 11-15).

The model code appears on a plate attached to the left side of the torque converter housing. There are a dozen variations of the THM 325-4L.

Applications

The makes and models that use the THM 325-4L are:

Buick Riviera
Cadillac El Dorado and Seville
Oldsmobile Toronado

CLUTCH AND BAND APPLICATION CHART (ELEMENTS IN USE)

Selector Lever Position	Overrun Clutch	Inter-mediate Band	Overdrive Roller Clutch	Direct Clutch	Low Roller Clutch	4th Clutch	Forward Clutch	Low-Reverse Clutch
D – DRIVE								
1st Gear			X		X		X	
2nd Gear		X	X				X	
3rd Gear			X	X			X	
Overdrive				X		X	X	
"3" – MANUAL 3rd	X			X			X	
"L2" – MANUAL 2nd	X	X	X				X	
"L1" – MANUAL LOW	X		X		X		X	X
"R" – REVERSE			X	X				X
NEUTRAL or PARK			X					

FIGURE 11-13 THM 200-4R and THM 325-4L clutch and band application summary.

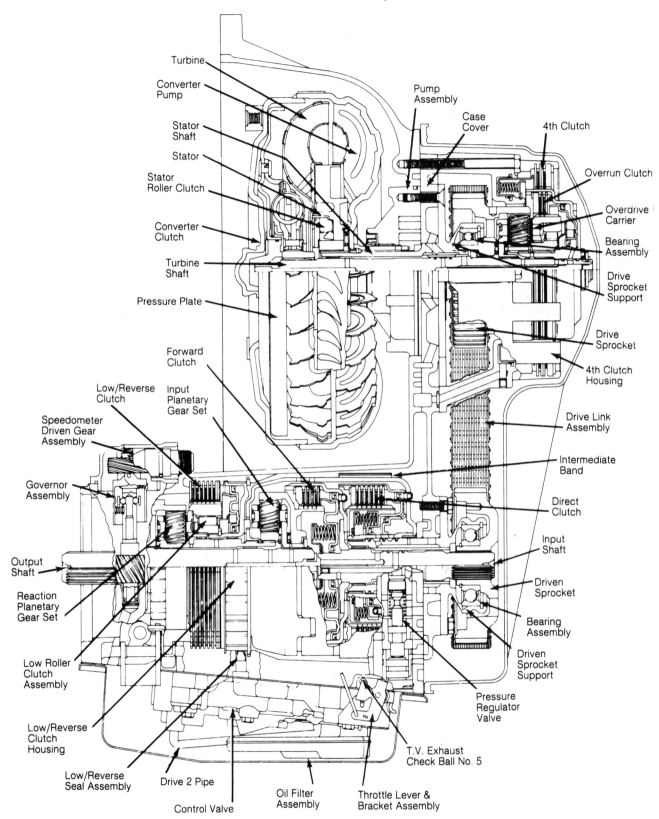

FIGURE 11-14   THM 325-4L cross section.

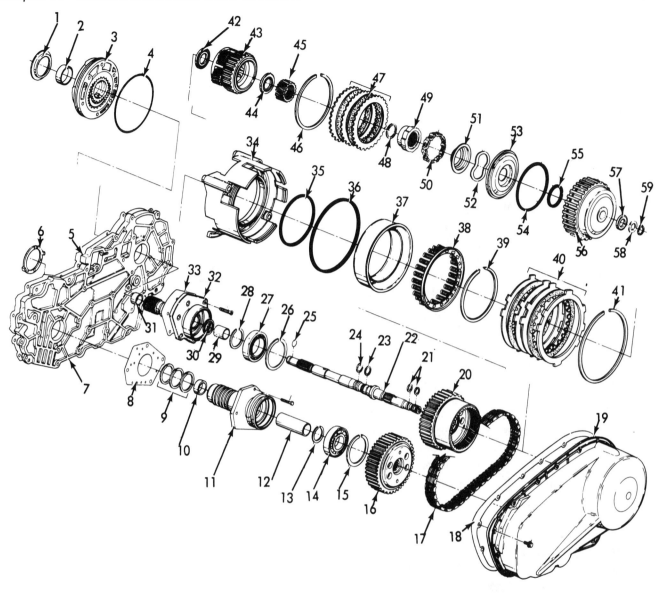

1. Converter Seal
2. Pump Bushing
3. Pump Body
4. Pump Seal Ring (Square Cut)
5. Gasket
6. Thrust Washer
7. Case Cover
8. Sprocket Support Gasket
9. Oil Seal Rings
10. Bushing
11. Driven Sprocket Support
12. Bushing
13. Snap Ring
14. Bearing
15. Snap Ring
16. Driven Sprocket
17. Drive Link
18. Sprocket Cover Gasket
19. Sprocket Cover
20. Drive Sprocket

21. Oil Seal Rings
22. Turbine Shaft
23. Oil Seal Ring
24. Oil Seal Ring
25. "O" Ring
26. Snap Ring
27. Bearing
28. Snap Ring
29. Bushing
30. Oil Seal
31. Bushing
32. Drive Sprocket Support
33. Sprocket Support Gasket
34. 4th Clutch Housing
35. Inner Seal Ring
36. Outer Seal Ring
37. Apply Ring
38. Release Springs & Retainer
39. Retaining Ring
40. 4th Clutch Plates

41. Retaining Ring
42. Thrust Bearing
43. Overdrive Carrier
44. Thrust Bearing
45. Overdrive Sun Gear
46. Snap Ring
47. Overrun Clutch Plates
48. Snap Ring
49. Roller Clutch Cam
50. Clutch Cam Rollers
51. Spring Retainer
52. Waved Release Spring
53. Overrun Clutch Piston
54. Outer Lip Seal
55. Inner Lip Seal
56. Overrun Clutch Housing
57. Thrust Bearing
58. Selective Washer
59. Snap Ring

FIGURE 11-15   T HM 325-4L exploded view of overdrive and drive link components.

History and Development

The THM 325-4L is a four speed, or automatic-overdrive, version of the THM-325, which was developed in 1979 as a reconfigured and heavier version of the THM-200. Its other configuration is the THM 200-4R.

Power Flow

The torque converter clutch is activated at 30 to 35 mph in third (direct) or fourth (overdrive). It is deactivated by the brake switch. In all other gears, it multiplies torque up to 2 1/4 times during vortex flow, then levels off at a little over 90% efficiency at full rotary flow (coupling phase).

Power flow is identical to the THM 200-4R, in that it travels through the simple (overdrive) planetary in all gears. Overdrive is achieved solely by the simple planetary while the compound planetary is in direct. All other gears are achieved solely by the compound planetary while the simple planetary is in direct. The change in transmission direction that is achieved by the drive link (chain) assembly, reverses pinion gear rotation with respect to that of a RWD vehicle, which drives the ring gear, axles, and wheels in the right direction.

See the clutch and band application chart in Figure 11-13.

TURBO HYDRA-MATIC 440-T4

Description and Identification

This four-speed, automatic overdrive, transverse-mounted transaxle is expected to be one of the most popular ever produced by General Motors. It is readily differentiated from the THM-125C by the bottom pan configuration and, of course, by its four speeds rather than three. The pans of the two are of similar shape, but the 440 is a little more complex (Figure 11-16). Other distinguishing features are a modulator, reverse servo and 1-2 servo. It is the first four speed, front-wheel-drive, automatic transaxle to be produced by a domestic automaker. The assembly mounts with the engine toward the passenger side and the axles to the rear of the engine and torque converter.

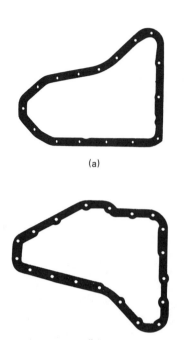

FIGURE 11-16 Gasket shape comparison: (a) THM 125C; (b) THM 440-T4.

A cross section of the THM 440-T4 is shown in Figure 11-17. This transaxle incorporates two simple planetary gearsets, certain elements of which are locked together: The front carrier (the one nearest the driven sprocket) is locked to the rear ring gear, and the front ring gear is locked to the rear carrier. The sun gears are separate, and there are two sets of pinions, each of which is affected by the carrier-to-ring gear union. Also, there is a third simple planetary that is used strictly for final drive. Unlike the 200-4R and 325-4L, it has nothing to do with overdrive. The 440-T4 has four multiple-disc clutches: *input, second, third,* and *fourth.* There are two bands and two one-way clutches, in addition to the stator clutch and lock-up clutch in the torque converter. One of the one-way clutches is a roller clutch and the other is a sprag. The final drive carrier and differential carrier are one integral unit (Figure 11-18). The pump body mounts over the valve body and contains a vane-type pump, with selective vanes, and is driven by its own shaft, which runs through the turbine shaft.

The model code tag is at the rear of the case and toward the right output shaft (Figure 11-19). There is also an ink stamp on top of the transmis-

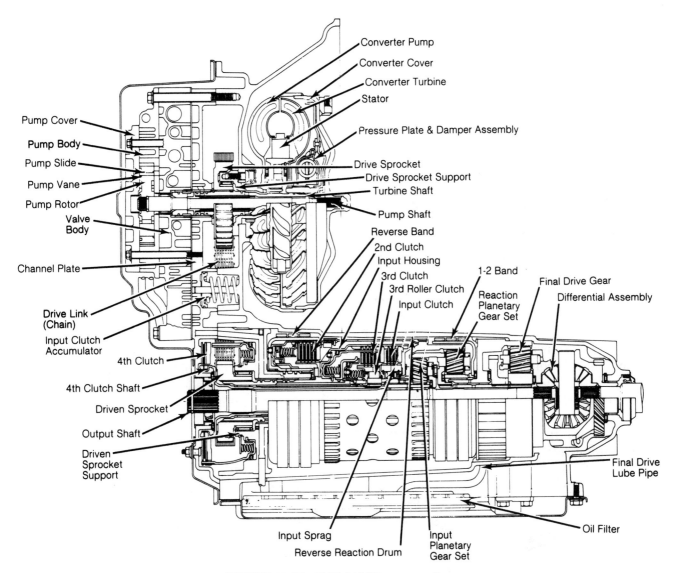

FIGURE 11-17 THM 440-T4 cross section.

sion near the bell housing. There are over 18 variations.

Applications

Among the makes and models that may use the THM 440-T4 are:

Buick Century, Electra
Cadillac DeVille, Fleetwood
Chevrolet Celebrity, Citation
Oldsmobile Cutlass, Ciera, 98
Pontiac 6000

History and Development

The THM 440-T4 uses the same general configuration as the metric THM 125 that was introduced in 1979 for the small (2.5- and 2.8- liter) engines in the first X-cars. Introduced in 1984, the 440-T4 was designed to incorporate all the latest developments, such as automatic overdrive and lock-up converters, in an elegantly engineered assembly for the entire size range of FWD passenger vehicles. Its design also reapplied use of a vacuum modulator—the first time that device has been used on a new transmission since the THM 350. [The modulator in the 440-

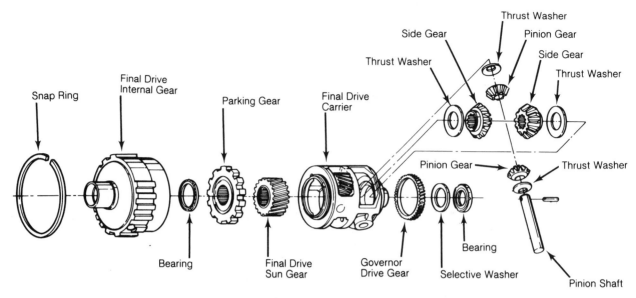

FIGURE 11-18   THM 440-T4 final drive planetary and differential assembly.

T4 controls line pressure (shift quality) only; up-shift/downshift is controlled by cable.]

Power Flow

The torque converter clutch is activated at 30 to 35 mph in third (direct) or fourth (overdrive). Cadillac

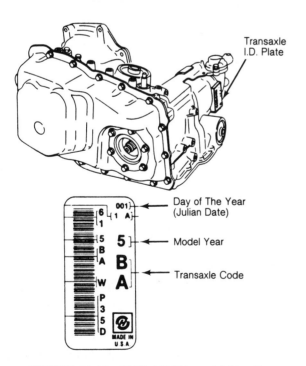

FIGURE 11-19   THM 440-T4 model identification plate and location.

DeVille and Fleetwood models using the 440-T4 with the 4.1 liter digital fuel-injected V8 engine use a viscous converter clutch (VCC) that engages at 20 to 30 mph in third or fourth gear under the proper conditions of throttle angle, ATF and coolant temperature, barometric temperature, and ambient temperature. It is deactivated by the brake switch.

All speeds, including overdrive, are achieved with the two tandem-operating, simple planetary gearsets. In first, input is through the front, or input, planetary sun gear, which drives the rear, or output, planetary ring gear because the two are connected. The rear sun gear is locked by the 1-2 band, so the rear carrier is driven by the rear ring gear at a reduced rate (2.92:1) for output.

Second gear input starts with the front carrier by application of the second clutch. This drives the rear ring gear at the same speed because the two are one integral part. The rear sun gear is anchored and output is through the rear carrier at a reduced rate (1.57:1).

Third, or direct, is input through the front sun gear (like first gear is achieved) by application of the third clutch. The second clutch is also still applied, which directs input through the front carrier. Since two of the three planetary elements are turning at the same speed (sun gear and carrier,—both input), the third (the ring gear) is turning with them. So the front planetary is locked together and turns the rear carrier at the same speed since the latter is

Selector Lever Position	4th Clutch	Reverse Band	2nd Clutch	3rd Clutch	3rd Roller Clutch	Input Clutch	Input Sprag	1-2 Band
D – DRIVE								
First Gear						X	[1]	X
Second Gear			X			[2]	[3]	X
Third Gear			X	X	[1]			
Overdrive	X		X	[2]	[3]			
3 – MANUAL THIRD			X	X	[1]	X	[1]	
2 – MANUAL SECOND			X			[2]	[3]	X
1 – MANUAL LOW				X	[1]	X	[1]	X
R – REVERSE		X				X	[1]	
NEUTRAL or PARK						[2]	[2]	

[1] – Holding.   [2] – Applied but not effective.   [3] – Overrunning.

FIGURE 11-20   THM 440-T4 clutch and band application summary.

integral with the front ring gear. The rear carrier is the output at 1:1.

Fourth gear, or overdrive, input is through the front carrier by application of the second clutch. The fourth clutch is also applied to anchor the front sun gear. Now the input carrier turns the input ring gear at increased speed; it is integral with the rear carrier for an overdrive of 0.70:1.

Reverse is achieved by locking the front carrier with the reverse band. CW input through the front sun gear turns the front ring gear CCW through the idling planetary pinions. The rear carrier also turns CCW for output since it is integral with the front ring gear. The ratio is 2.38:1.

Clutch and band application is summarized in the chart in Figure 11-20.

TRADE TERMS

Direct clutch	Output carrier	Vehicle identification
Freewheeling	Transaxle	number (VIN)
Input ring gear	Turbo Hydra-Matic (THM)	

REVIEW QUESTIONS

11-1. General Motors Corporation was the first to introduce an automatic _____ _____ transmission and a _____ _____ in production passenger cars.

11-2. All FWD vehicles use a transaxle.   T   F

11-3. Model identification numbers are important because they indicate differences in number of _____ _____ or changes in _____ circuits or _____ _____ circuits.

11-4. Recognizing the shape of the _____ is a quick way to identify an automatic transmission or transaxle model initially.

11-5. The General Motors units discussed in detail in this chapter all use the _____ compound planetary gearset.

11-6. The VIN stamped on the transmission is not useful when testing or ordering parts.   T F

11-7. The THM 250, 375, and 375B are all derivatives of THM 350.   T F

11-8. Except in the THM 440-T4, the _____ ___ is splined to the input shaft.

11-9. The front _____ and rear _____ are splined to the output shaft.

11-10. Another name for the front carrier is _____ _____.

11-11. Another name for the rear annulus is the _____ ring gear.

11-12. On most of its transmissions, General Motors calls the high-reverse clutch the ____ clutch.

11-13. The rear carrier is also called the _____ carrier.

11-14. The key difference in the effect of low and intermediate gears when selector is in Drive compared to manual positions is _____.

11-15. Sometimes, through application of multiple-disc clutches, roller clutches are locked in both directions.   T   F

11-16. The THM 250 is a lighter version of the 350 and uses only a _____ for intermediate.

11-17. Overdrive in the THM 200-4R is achieved by a _____ planetary gearset.

11-18. The THM 200 was the first _____ transmission built by General Motors Corporation.

11-19. The THM 325-4L is a transmission—not a transaxle—because its _____ _____ is located in a separate housing.

11-20. The THM 440-T4 uses a simple planetary gearset for overdrive.   T   F

ESSAY QUESTIONS

11-1. Explain why it is helpful to know the power flow—or be able to trace it—for a particular transmission when diagnosing performance problems.

11-2. Select and describe some of the major parts of General Motors automatic transmissions and transaxles.

CHAPTER ACTIVITIES

11-1. When you have the opportunity, compare an installed THM 440-T4 or THM 125C to an installed THM 325-L. In which one can you see the final drive?

11-2. Check out the installation of a 440-T4 mated to a V-8 engine—estimate the removal and installation time. How close was your estimate to book (flat rate) time?

11-3. If there are any THM 250s or THM 350s in your shop, an electrical connector on the left side of the case just above the oil pan flange means that the transmission is equipped with a torque converter clutch (included on most models since 1980). Check it out.

12

Ford Motor Company

OBJECTIVES

When you have completed this chapter, you should be able to:

- Recognize the three transmissions and two transaxles selected as representative in this chapter for Ford applications.
- Describe the normal power flow through a Ravigneaux compound planetary gearset.
- Describe the normal power flow through two tandem-operating simple planetary gearsets, such as that used in the Ford AXOD and the General Motors THM 440-T4.
- Describe the differentiating characteristics among Ford transmissions and transaxles.

Here's a company whose experience with planetary gear transmissions dates back to the beginning of the century. From 1908 to 1927, over 15 million Model-T Fords were driven off the assembly lines by pushing on a foot pedal that tightened a band on a planetary gearset. But the popularity of the sliding gear transmission won out, and it was to be over 25 years before Ford returned to the planetary with the advent of the automatic transmission.

Perhaps in pursuit of the "better idea," Ford is credited with some unique ideas in automatic transmission development. They were the first to incorporate automatic overdrive in an automatic transmission. In lock-up converter development, they have used not only the popular, hydraulically applied, clutch disc (A4LD), but a centrifugal clutch (C-5), a direct drive shaft (AOT), and a planetary splitter gear (ATX).

Ford has produced about a dozen automatic transmissions, among the more recent of which are the following:

C-3, C-5 and C-6: three-speed, shaft-driven RWD

AOT, A4LD: four speed, automatic overdrive, shaft-driven RWD

ATX: three speed, transverse-mounted transaxle, FWD

AXOD: four speed, automatic overdrive, transverse-mounted transaxle, FWD

It has been Ford's practice to include a transmission model code on the vehicle identification plate that is located on the driver's door or door frame. Some of those are as follows:

Transmission Model	*Code Letter*
C-3	V
C-5	C (pass. car)
C-5	W (truck)
C-6	K, G, U, Z
AOT	T (followed by a four-letter combination)
A4LD	T
ATX	B, O
AOXD	T (followed by a four-letter combination)

In addition to these model identification codes, however, there is a metal tag on one of the transmission bolts that contains further coding essential to ordering the right parts. Some include a serial number and/or an assembly part number and/or a transmission model number (Figure 12-1).

The balance of this chapter presents summary descriptions of three transmissions and two transaxles that are representative of Ford designs.

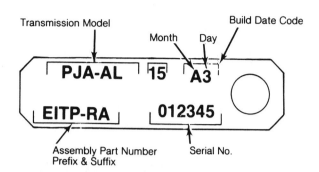

FIGURE 12-1   Typical Ford transmission identification tag.

FORD C-5 AUTOMATIC TRANSMISSION

Description and Identification

The **C-5** is a three-speed, aluminum-cased transmission designed for shaft-driven, RWD vehicles. It can be readily identified by its square pan (Figure 12-2). The vehicle identification label, located on the driver's door frame near the latch, will carry a "C" (passenger car) or "W" (truck) if the vehicle is equipped with the C-5 transmission

FIGURE 12-2   Ford C-5 pan gasket shape.

A cross section of the C-5 is shown in Figure 12-3 and an exploded view in Figure 12-4. This transmission incorporates a Simpson compound planetary gearset controlled by two multiple-disc clutches, two bands, and a one-way (roller) clutch. An IX gear pump is driven by the torque converter hub.

Torque converter lock-up is achieved by a centrifugal clutch. Weighted friction shoes are mounted around the edge of a damper-mounted disc that is splined to the input shaft. Return springs hold

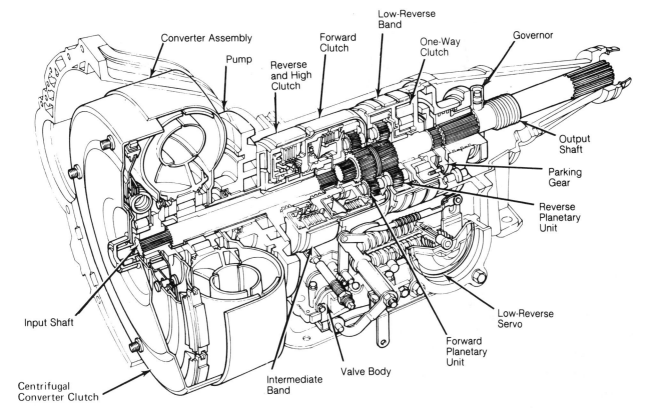

FIGURE 12-3   Ford C-5 cross section.

the shoes toward the center until input shaft rotation reaches 800 to 1000 rpm (depending on spring tension). Through centrifugal force (Chapter 2), the weight of the shoes overcomes the return spring tension and the shoes are thrown out against the inside of the converter cover. As the speed of rotation increases from the 800 rpm to the 1000 rpm range (vehicle speed about 15 mph in direct drive), the centrifugal force increases. So at lower speeds the clutch shoes slip, but the slippage decreases as input shaft speed increases until 100% lock-up (no slippage) is attained. The return spring tension determines at what input shaft speed the shoes will apply. The shoe weight and—to a lesser extent, by comparison—the friction material, together with vehicle load, determines at what input shaft speed 100% lock-up will occur. For all practical purposes, this occurs at normal highway speeds.

Applications

Among the models that may use the C-5 are:

Capri

Cougar

LTD

Marquis

Mustang

Thunderbird

E-150/350 Van

F-150/350 Pickup

Bronco

History and Development

The C-5 is one of a line of similarly designated transmissions: C-3, C-4, C-6, although the C-4 is no longer in production. Like the others, the C-5 is a three-speed unit using the Simpson planetary. It uses a low-reverse band like the C-3 and C-4 rather than a low-reverse clutch used by the C-6. The C-5, which was introduced in 1982, is the only one now using a lock-up torque converter.

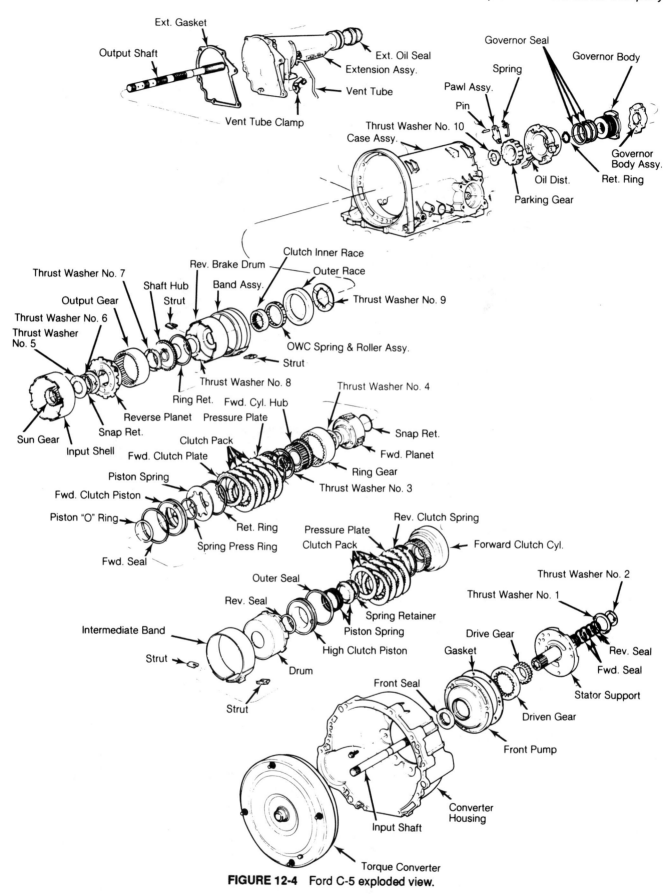

FIGURE 12-4 Ford C-5 exploded view.

Gear	Rev. & High Clutch	Forward Clutch	One-Way Clutch	Intermediate Band	Low-Reverse Band
1st (D Range)		Applied	Applied		
1st (1 Range)		Applied			Applied
2nd		Applied		Applied	
3rd	Applied	Applied			
Reverse	Applied				Applied

FIGURE 12-5   Ford C-5 clutch and band application summary.

Power Flow

Power flow through the C-5 is typical of the Simpson compound planetary. Input for all forward gears is effected by applying the forward clutch, which connects the forward (front) ring gear to the input shaft. First gear is a function of both the forward (front) and reverse (rear) planetaries. Second gear is achieved solely by the forward planetary. Third gear locks the planetary for direct drive by application of the forward clutch (ring gear-to-input shaft) and the reverse-high clutch (sun gear-to-input shaft). Clutch and band application is summarized in Figure 12-5.

FORD AUTOMATIC OVERDRIVE TRANSMISSION (AOT)

Description and Identification

The Ford **Automatic Overdrive Transmission (AOT)** is a four-speed automatic transmission for shaft-driven RWD vehicles, and the fourth speed is overdrive. Its pan shape is symmetrical (Figure 12-6). As with all Ford passenger cars and light trucks, the label on the driver's door or door frame will carry the transmission model code. "T" identifies this transmission. A metal tag on one of the transmission extension housing bolts will carry the transmission model number, serial number, and assembly part number.

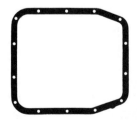

FIGURE 12-6   Ford AOT pan gasket shape.

Figures 12-7 and 12-8 present sectional and exploded views of the AOT. It incorporates a Ravigneaux compound planetary, four multiple-disc clutches, two bands, and two one-way (roller) clutches. The Ravigneaux provides reverse and all forward speeds, including overdrive. A direct drive shaft runs nearly the full length of the transmission inside the input (turbine) shaft and sun gear. It is splined, through a torsional vibration damper, to the converter cover at the forward end and to the direct clutch at the rear. The direct clutch is engaged in both third (direct) and fourth (overdrive). This transmission uses an IX gear pump driven by the torque converter hub.

Applications

This very popular Ford transmission can be found in many of the following models:

Capri
Crown Victoria
Continental
Cougar
Grand Marquis
LTD
Lincoln Mark VII
Mustang
Thunderbird
E 150/250 Van
F 150/250 Pickup

History and Development

The Automatic Overdrive Transmission is a major development, being the first automatic to include overdrive as part of the normal shift pattern. It is based on the **FMX** and its predecessors, which used the Ravigneaux compound planetary gearset. This

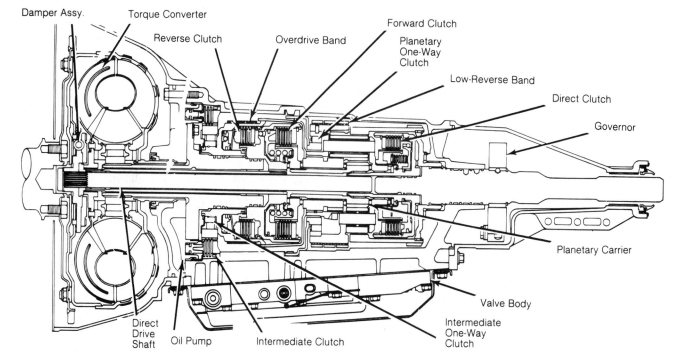

FIGURE 12-7   Ford AOT cross section.

line of transmissions dates back about 30 years and has been known by various names, perhaps the most popular of which as **Cruise-O-Matic**. The AOT adds the **overdrive band** and direct clutch, and replaces the front band with the multiple-disc intermediate clutch.

Power Flow

The equivalent of torque converter lock-up in the AOT is achieved by application of the direct clutch. In third (direct) 40% of the power is transmitted through the torque converter and input (turbine) shaft, and 60% is transmitted mechanically through the direct drive shaft. There is a small amount of slippage, as is explained below. In overdrive, all power is transmitted mechanically through the direct drive shaft, and there is no slippage.

Referring to Figure 12-9, you will see that the Ravigneaux compound planetary gearset includes one ring gear (6) two sun gears (1,5) and two sets of pinion gears (3,4) mounted on a common carrier (2). The left, upper quarter of Figure 12-9 shows a side-sectional and end-sectional view of the AOT Ravigneaux. Note that the forward sun gear (5) meshes only with the **short pinions** (4) and not with the ring gear (at least not directly). The short

pinions do mesh with the **long pinions** (3), which mesh with both the reverse sun gear (1) and ring (output) gear (6). So, in effect, we have a compound planetary made up of a simple planetary (reverse sun, long planet pinions, and ring) and a sun (forward) and short planet pinion set, all of which is connected by the long and short pinion mesh and a common carrier.

Reverse gear is achieved by applying the reverse clutch(10), which locks the input shaft to the reverse sun gear and by applying the low-reverse band (12), which grounds the planet carrier. Output is through the ring gear, which is splined to the output shaft.

Overdrive is achieved by locking the reverse sun gear by application of the overdrive band (9) and applying the direct clutch (14) to drive the planet carrier.

First gear is attained by input through the forward sun gear while the carrier is held by the planetary (low) one-way clutch (13) The sun gear is locked to the input (turbine) shaft by the forward clutch (11).

Second gear makes full use of the compound planetary. Input is directed through the forward sun gear by applying the forward clutch (11) CW. It drives the short pinions CCW, and they drive the

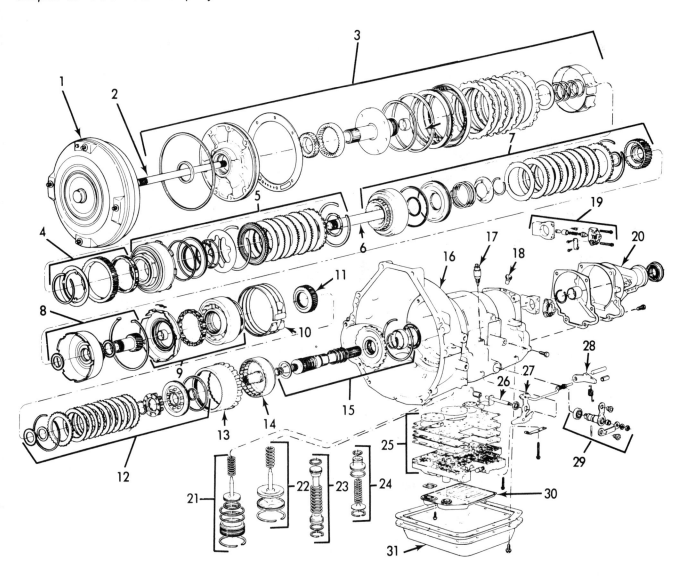

1. Torque Converter
2. Direct Drive Shaft
3. Oil Pump & Interm. Clutch Assy.
4. Interm. One-Way Clutch.
5. Reverse Clutch Assy.
6. Turbine Shaft
7. Forward Clutch Assy.
8. Sun Gear & Driving Shell.
9. Center Support & Planetary Assy.
10. Reverse Band
11. Direct Clutch Hub.
12. Direct Clutch Assy.
13. Ring Gear & Park Gear
14. Direct Clutch Cylinder
15. Output Shaft Assy.
16. Transmission Case

17. Neutral Start Switch
18. Vent Cap
19. Governor
20. Extension Housing
21. Overdrive Servo Assy.
22. Low-Reverse Servo Assy.
23. 3-4 Accumulator Assy.
24. 2-3 Accumulator Assy.
25. Valve Body Assy.
26. Inner Throttle Lever
27. Inner Manual Lever
28. Park Pawl
29. Outer Manual & Throttle Lever Assy.
30. Oil Filter
31. Oil Pan

FIGURE 12-8   Ford AOT exploded view.

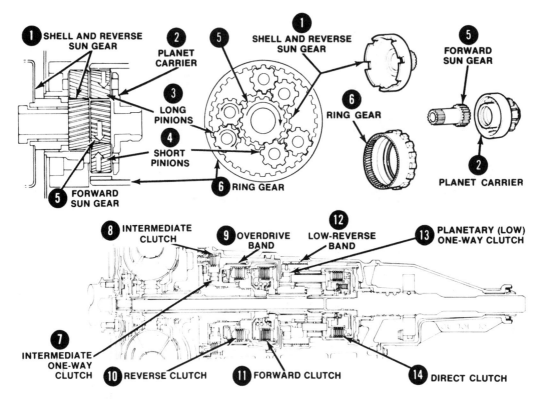

FIGURE 12-9   Ford AOT showing Ravigneaux planetary and friction drive links (Courtesy of Ford Motor Company).

long pinions CW, which in turn drives the ring gear and output shaft CW. The long pinions can not drive the reverse sun gear because it is held from turning CCW by the intermediate one-way clutch (7), which is grounded to the case by the intermediate multiple-disc clutch (8).

Third gear, or direct, has a **split-torque** power flow. The forward clutch (11) and direct clutch (14) lock two members of the planetary—the forward sun gear and the carrier, respectively. This, in effect, locks two out of the three planetary members, which always produces direct drive. But the sun gear is driven by the turbine, which is not 100% efficient like a mechanical hookup is. Even though the planet carrier is a 100% mechanical hookup, the small amount of slip in the torque converter does allow the sun gear to turn CCW very slowly, so that there is some loss in overall efficiency from input (engine) to output (transmission). But is not as much loss as would be experienced if the coupling were 100% fluid. Whatever the overall efficiency is, 60% of the deliverable torque is carried by the direct drive shaft (carrier), and 40% of it is delivered through the torque converter to the for-

ward sun gear. This percentage split is determined by the radius (torque arm) of the two planetary members. Even though the intermediate clutch is applied, it is not effective because the CW motion overrides the intermediate roller clutch.

Clutch and band application is summarized in the chart in Figure 12-10.

FORD A4LD AUTOMATIC TRANSMISSION

Description and Identification

This is also a four-speed automatic overdrive transmission designed for shaft-driven, RWD vehicles. Its pan shape is oblong, as shown by the gasket in Figure 12-11. The vehicle identification label on the driver's door or door frame will carry the code "T" to identify this transmission. A metal tag on one of the transmission housing extension bolts will carry the transmission model number, serial number, and assembly part number.

Figure 12-12 shows a sectioned view of the A4LD. It uses a Simpson compound planetary gear-

Selector Lever Position	Intermed. Clutch	Intermed. One-Way Clutch	Overdrive Band	Reverse Clutch	Forward Clutch	Planetary One-Way Clutch	Low-Reverse Band	Direct Clutch
O/D — OVERDRIVE								
First Gear					X	X		
Second Gear	X	X			X			
Third Gear	X				X			X
Fourth Gear	X		X					X
3 — OVERDRIVE LOCKOUT								
First Gear					X	X		
Second Gear	X	X			X			
Third Gear	X				X			X
1 — LOW								
First Gear					X	X	X	
Second Gear	X	X	X		X			
R — REVERSE				X			X	
P — PARK							X	

NEUTRAL — All clutches and bands released and/or ineffective.

FIGURE 12-10 Ford AOT clutch and band application summary.

set for all speeds except overdrive, which is achieved with a simple planetary at the front of the transmission. These are controlled by three multiple-disc clutches, two bands, and one-way clutch in addition to that for the stator. An IX gear pump gear is driven by the torque converter hub, and torque converter lock-up is achieved by a disc clutch applied against the inside of the converter cover. Torque converter clutch application is controlled electronically through the **Electronic Engine Control (EEC)** system. Release is achieved by a brake switch.

Applications

This transmission appears in Ford's lighter models:

Aerostar
Bronco II
Ranger

History and Development

The A4LD is a derivative of the Ford C-3. It was developed as a lighter counterpart to the AOT by incorporating the automatic overdrive concept and lock-up torque converter.

Power Flow

Power flow is similar to the C-3, except for overdrive. The overdrive clutch is used to lock the overdrive sun gear while input flows through the overdrive carrier. The carrier drives the ring gear for output through the locked-up (direct) Simpson gearset and output shaft.

Clutch and band application is summarized in Figure 12-13.

FORD AUTOMATIC TRANSAXLE (ATX)

Description and Identification

This is a three-speed transaxle design for FWD vehicles. It is essentially a one piece aluminum-alloy case with a stamped metal sump pan on the bottom and a stamped metal valve body cover on top. It is metric. The vehicle identification label on the driver's door or door frame carries a "B" or "O" on the lower line under "TR," for transmission/transaxle. Identification for testing and parts ordering should be taken from the metal tag attached to the transaxle case by one of the valve body cover bolts. The transaxle is mounted transversely on the driver's side of the engine compartment.

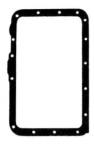

FIGURE 12-11   Ford A4LD pan gasket shape.

A cross section of the ATX is shown in Figure 12-14 and an exploded view in Figure 12-15. It uses a Ravigneaux compound planetary, which is controlled by three multiple-disc clutches, a band, a one-way clutch, in addition to that for the stator.

Torque converter lock-up is achieved by centrifugal clutches as in the C-5. But a simple planetary gear-set called a **splitter gear** has been added in the torque converter. It splits torque in second and third gears in a manner similar to the AOT in direct and overdrive. Also similar to the AOT is its pump drive shaft. Final drive consists of three helical cut gears: an input, an idler, and a final drive (output) gear that is fastened to the differential carrier.

Applications

This transmission may be used in any of the following models:

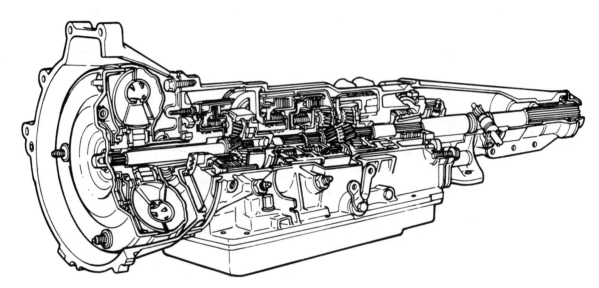

FIGURE 12-12   Ford A4LD sectioned view.

	Intermediate Band	Low-Reverse Clutch	Forward Clutch	Reverse-Direct Clutch	One-Way Clutch	Over-Drive Clutch
D — DRIVE First Second Third Overdrive	 X X X		 X X X X	 X X	 X	 X
2 — INTERMEDIATE Second	X		X			
1 — LOW First		 X	X			
R — REVERSE		X		X		
N — NEUTRAL						
P — PARK						

FIGURE 12-13   Ford A4LD clutch and band application summary.

Escort
EXP
Lynx
Tempo
Topaz
Taurus
Sable

History and Development

The ATX might be thought of as essentially an automatic transaxle version of the old FMX family of automatic transmissions in that it incorporates the Ravigneaux planetary. But it has utilized other technology, too, such as the centrifugal clutch of the C-5 and the split-torque power flow of the AOT.

Power Flow

Output is always through the carrier, but input can be through the reverse sun gear or the ring gear.

In drive low, input is through the reverse sun gear, which is locked to the turbine (input) shaft by the one-way roller clutch. Power then travels through the short pinions CCW, which drive the long pinion CW. The forward sun gear is held by the band, causing the carrier to rotate CW.

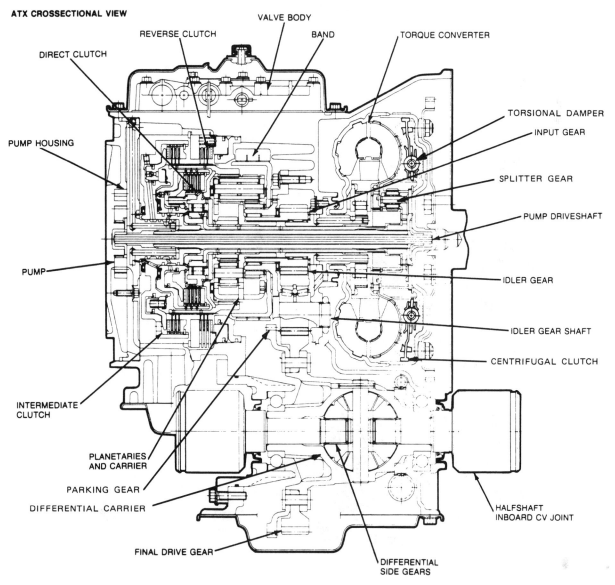

ATX CROSSECTIONAL VIEW

VALVE BODY

REVERSE CLUTCH   BAND   TORQUE CONVERTER

DIRECT CLUTCH

PUMP HOUSING

PUMP

INTERMEDIATE CLUTCH

PLANETARIES AND CARRIER

PARKING GEAR

DIFFERENTIAL CARRIER

FINAL DRIVE GEAR

TORSIONAL DAMPER

INPUT GEAR

SPLITTER GEAR

PUMP DRIVESHAFT

IDLER GEAR

IDLER GEAR SHAFT

CENTRIFUGAL CLUTCH

HALFSHAFT INBOARD CV JOINT

DIFFERENTIAL SIDE GEARS

FIGURE 12-14   Ford ATX cross section.

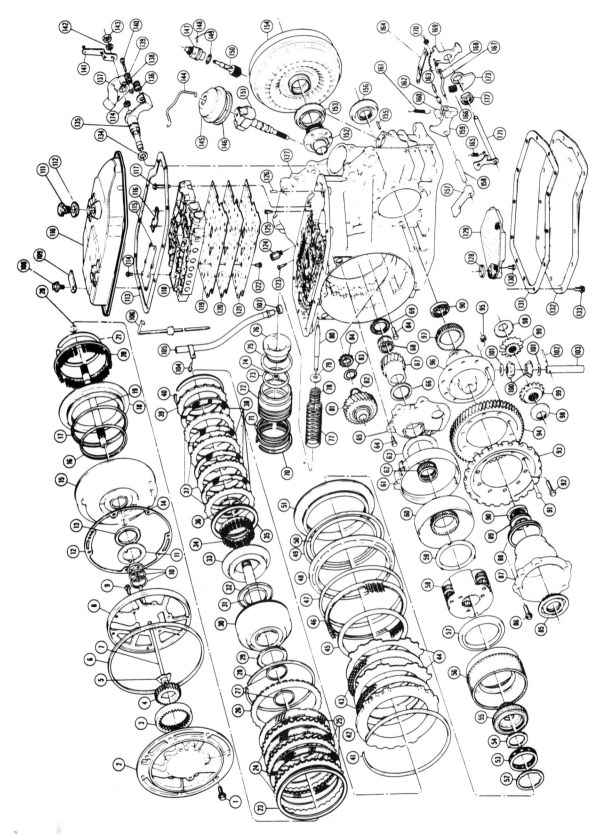

FIGURE 12-15 Ford ATX exploded view.

Parts list for FIGURE 12-15 (Cont.)

Item	Part No.	Description
1	N801003-S	BOLT & WSHR ASSY. (7A103 TO 7005) M8-1 X 40 (7 REQ'D.)
2	7F370	BODY & SLEEVE ASSY. — OIL PUMP
3	7C011	GEAR ASSY. — OIL PUMP DRIVEN
4	7C009	GEAR ASSY. — OIL PUMP DRIVE
5	7F402	INSERT — OIL PUMP DRIVE GEAR
6	7N266	SEAL — OIL PUMP
7	7B328	SHAFT — OIL PUMP DRIVE
8	7D043	SUPPORT & BSHG. ASSY. — OIL PUMP
9	N805772-S	BOLT (7A108 TO 7R370) M8-1 X 16MM LG. (5 REQ'D.)
10	7F425	SEAL — INTERM. CLUTCH — INNER (TEFLON)
11	7F367	OIL PUMP THRUST WASHER (SELECTIVE)
12	7A135	GASKET — OIL PUMP
13	7F374	BRG. ASSY. — INTERM. CLUTCH DRUM THRUST
14	N801009-S	RING — 17.0 RETAINING RD. WIRE EXTERNAL
15	7F369	CYLINDER — INTERM. CLUTCH
16	7F225	SEAL — INTERM. CLUTCH PISTON — INNER
17	7F224	SEAL — INTERM. CLUTCH PISTON — OUTER
18	7E005	PISTON — INTERM. CLUTCH
19	7F351	SHAFT — INTERM. CLUTCH
20	7F222	RET. & SPRING ASSY. — INTERM. CLUTCH
21	N805844-S	RING — 111.76MM RETAINING EXTERNAL
22	7F154	SPRING — REV. CLUTCH CUSHION
23	7F220	PLATE — INTERM. CL. EXT. SPLINE
24	7E312	PLATE ASSY. — INTERM. CL. INT. SPLINE
25	7F228	PLATE — INTERM. CLUTCH PRESSURE
26	7F424	SEAL — INTERM. CLUTCH — OUTER (TEFLON)
27	N806050-1-2-S	RING — RETAINING INT. (SELECTIVE)
28	7F373	BRG. ASSY. — DIRECT & INTERM. CLUTCH
29	7F380	CYL. SHAFT & RACE ASSY. — DIRECT CLUTCH
30	7F224	SEAL — DIRECT CL. PISTON — INNER
31	7C000	SEAL — DIRECT CL. PISTON OIL — OUTER
32	7C117	PISTON — DIRECT CLUTCH
33	7F235	RET. & SPRING ASSY. — DIRECT CLUTCH
34	7F408	SPRING — DIRECT CLUTCH CUSHION
35	N800943-S	RING — 50.5MM RETAINING, EXTERNAL
36	7B442	PLATE — DIRECT CLUTCH EXT. SPLINE (AS REQ'D.)
37	7D239	PLATE ASSY. — DIRECT CL. INT. SPLINE (AS REQ'D.)
38	7F477	PLATE — DIRECT CLUTCH PRESSURE
39	N800846-7-8-S	RING — RETAINING INT. (SELECTIVE)
40	N805054-S	RING — RETAINING INT.
41	7D408	PLATE — REVERSE CLUTCH PRESSURE
42	7E312	PLATE ASSY. — REV. CL. INT. SPLINE
43	7E315	PLATE — REV. CLUTCH EXT. SPLINE
45	7F154	SPRING — REV. CLUTCH CUSHION
46	7F153	SPRING & RET. ASSY. — REV. CLUTCH
47	N800633-S	SEAL — 196.0MM
48	7D042	PISTON — REVERSE CLUTCH
49	7D403	SEAL — REV. CL. PISTON — OUTER
50	7D404	SEAL — REV. CL. PISTON — INNER
51	7F341	CYLINDER — REVERSE CLUTCH
52	7A623	BEARING — ONE-WAY CLUTCH
53	7F366	SPRING & ROLLER ASSY. — ONE-WAY CLUTCH
54	7F369	WASHER — DIRECT CL. CYL. THRUST
55	7N107	GEAR ASSY. — 1ST-3RD REVERSE SPEED
56	7F348	GEAR ASSY. — INTER. & REV. CL. RG.
57	7F473	RACE & BRG. ASSY. — PLANT THRUST REAR
58	7A398	PLANE ASSEMBLY
59	7D423	WASHER — PLANETARY THRUST — FRONT
60	7F392	DRUM & SUN GEAR ASSY. — LOW INTERM.
61	7D034	BAND ASSY. —SLOW INTERM.
62	7F380	BEARING ASSY. — TRANSFER
63	7F366	WASHER — INTERM. SUN GR. THRUST
64	N805787-S100	BOLT — M8-1.25 X 25.0 HEX FLANGE HD. (5 REQ'D.)
65	7F334	HOUSING — FINAL DRIVE GEAR
66	7F405	BRG. ASSY. — FINAL DRIVE GEAR THRUST — REAR
67	7F342	GEAR — FINAL DRIVE INPUT
68	7F403	BRG. ASSY. — FINAL DRIVE INPUT GEAR
69	7F404	BRG. ASSY. — FINAL DRIVE GEAR THRUST — FRONT
70	N800645-S	RING — 103.5MM RET. FLAT INTERNAL
71	7F427	SEAL — LOW & INTERM. BAND SERVO PISTON COVER
72	7D027	COVER — LOW/INTERM. BAND SERVO
73	7D025	SEAL — LOW/INTERM. SERVO PISTON — SMALL
74	N853108-S	RING — 15.6MM RETAINING EXTERNAL
75	7D024	SEAL — LOW/INTERM. SERVO PISTON — LARGE
76	7D022	PISTON — LOW & INTERM. SERVO
77	7D028	SPRING — LOW/INTERM. SERVO PISTON
78	7D390	SPRING — SERVO PISTON CUSHION
79	N800640-S	WASHER — 9.7MM X 30 X 2.5 FLAT STEEL
80	7D023	ROD — LOW/INTERM. SERVO PISTON NOT AVAILABLE
81	7F475	GEAR & BRG. ASSY. — IDLER GEAR
82	7F358	SHAFT — IDLER GEAR
83	N800679-S	SEAL — 22.9 X 1.6 O-RING
84	N801216-S2	NUT — M25 X 1-12 POINT
85	1177	SEAL ASSY. — TRANSAXLE — DIFF.
86	N805788-S100	BOLT — M8-1.25 X 30 HEX FLANGE HD. (6 REQ'D.)
87	7F114	RETAINER — DIFF. BEARING
88		GASKET
89	4A451	SHIM — DIFF. BEARING (SELECTIVE)
90	4020	BALL BEARING — DIFF.
91	N47141B-S2	RIVET — M10 X 38 SOLID FLAT HD. (REF. ONLY — PRODUCTION)
92	N800746-S	BOLT — M10 X 1.5 X 40 HEX HD. (10 REQ'D.) SERVICE ONLY
93	7A233	GEAR — OUTPUT SHAFT PARK
94	7A343	GEAR — FINAL DRIVE OUTPUT
95	N800390-S	NUT — M10 X 1.5 HEX PLT. — (10 REQ'D.) SERVICE ONLY
96	4026	DIFF. ASSY. — TRANSAXLE
97	17285	GEAR — SPEEDO DRIVE
98	4228	WASHER — TRANSAXLE DIFF. SIDE GR. THRUST
99	4236	GEAR — TRANSAXLE DIFF. — SIDE
100	4215	PINION — TRANSAXLE DIFF.
101	4230	WASHER — TRANSAXLE DIFF. PINION THRUST
102	N800879-S2	PIN — 4.75MM X 38.1MM
103	4211	SHAFT — TRANSAXLE DIFF. PINION
104	N805570-S2	BOLT — M8-1 X 12 HEX FLANGE HD.
105	7A228	TUBE ASSY. — OIL FILTER
106	7A020	INDICATOR ASSY. — OIL LEVEL
107	7N243	GROMMET (SEAL FILLER TUBE TO CASE)
108	7B148	BOLT — M6-1 X 14MM LG (10 REQ'D.)
109		IDENTIFICATION TAG
110	7G004	COVER — MAIN CONTROL
111	7004	VENT ASSY. — MAIN CONTROL COVER
112	7G005	GROMMET — MAIN CONTROL COVER
113	7F396	GASKET — MAIN CONTROL COVER
114	N800671-S51M	BOLT — M8-1.0 X 45 HEX FLANGE HD. (7 REQ'D.)
115	7F422	PLATE — MAIN OIL PRESS. REG. EXH.
116	7E170	PLATE — TRANS.
117	N800670-S	BOLT — M8-1.0 X 40 HEX FLANGE HD. (20 REQ'D.)
118	7A100	CONTROL ASSY. — MAIN
119	7D100	GASKET — MAIN CONTROL (BET. 7A092 & 7A008)
120	7A008	PLATE — CONTROL VALVE BODY SEP.
121	7D100	GASKET — MAIN CONTROL (BET. 7A008 & 7006)
122	N805770-S2	BOLT — M6-1 X 12 HEX FLANGE HD. (2 REQ'D.)
123	7D007	PIN — TIMING (2.3L ONLY)
124	N802894-S100	COMM. ASSY. PUSH-IN
125	7E242	SCREEN ASSY. — GOV. OIL
126	N800673-S	PIN — 3.2MM X 25.65 DOWEL HRDN.
127	7F333	CASE & HSG. ASSY.
128	7B304	GASKET — OIL FILTER
129	7B155	FILTER ASSY. — OIL
130	N805771-S2	BOLT — M6-1 X 14MM LG (3 REQ'D.)
131	7A191	GASKET — OIL PAN
132	7A264	PAN — OIL
133	N805785-S2	BOLT — M9-1.25 X 16 HEX FLANGE (13 REQ'D.)
134	7F376	SEAL — MANUAL CONTROL LEVER
135	7A256	LEVER ASSY. — MANUAL CONTROL
136	7341	INSULATOR — GEAR SHIFT ARM
137	7A247	SWITCH ASSY. — NEUTRAL START
138	44717-S2	WASHER — #12 FLAT (2 REQ'D.)
139	N800723-S2	WASHER — 6.0MM HELICAL SPG. LK. (2 REQ'D.)
140	N800570-S2	BOLT — M8-1.0 X 70 HEX FLANGE HD. (2 REQ'D.)
141	7F291	LEVER ASSY. — THROTTLE VALVE — OUTER
142	N800173-S2	WASHER — 8MM LOCK
143	M820041-S2	NUT — M8 X 1.25 HEX
144	7F304	CLIP — GOV. COVER RETAINING
145	7A301	COVER — GOVERNOR
146	N801001-S	RETAINER — 77.9MM X 3.40 RECT. SECT.
147	N800874-S	RETAINER — SPEEDO DRIVEN GEAR
148	N800835-S	PIN — 3MM X 19.9 DOWEL HRDN.
149	1727I	SEAL — 25.06MM X 2.6 O-RING
150	7C053	GEAR — SPEEDO DRIVEN
151	7F383	GOVERNOR ASSEMBLY
152	7F-401	SUPPORT ASSY. — CONV. REACTOR
153	7902	SEAL ASSY. — CONV. IMP. HUB
154	N46525-S	CONVERTER ASSEMBLY
155	1177	PIN — SPEEDO RETAINING
156	7D430	SEAL ASSY. — TRANSAXLE — DIFF.
157	7D071	STRUT — LOW INTERM. BAND ANCHOR
158	7A441	SHAFT — PARKING PAWL
159	N802394-S	PAWL — PARKING BRAKE
160	7D070	PLUG — 12.0MM CUP
161	7D339	SPRING — PARK PAWL. RETURN
162	7D169	PIN — PARKING PAWL ROLLER
163	7E332	ROLLER — PARKING BRAKE
164	7F292	SPRING ASSY. — MANUAL VALVE DETENT
165	7A180	SPRING — THROTTLE VALVE CONTROL LEVER
166	7E333	SPRING — PARK PAWL. RATCHETING
167	N800695-S	ACTUATOR — MANUAL LEVER
168	7C494	WASHER
169	W823451-S1	LEVER — MANUAL VALVE DETENT — INNER
170	7F446	NUT — STAMPED
171	N800030-S	SHAFT ASSY. — TV LEVER ACTUATING
172	7A118	NUT — M20 X 1.5 HEX
173	7F337	LEVER — PARK PAWL ACTUATING
174		SEAL — THROTTLE CONTROL LEVER SHAFT

FIGURE 12-15 (Cont.)

Selector Lever Position	Band	Direct Clutch	Intermed. Clutch	Reverse Clutch	Intermed. One-Way Clutch
D — DRIVE					
First Gear	X				X
Second Gear	X		X		
Third Gear		X	X		
2 — INTERMEDIATE					
Second Gear	X		X		
1 — LOW					
First Gear	X	X			X
R — REVERSE		X		X	X
P — Park					X
N — Neutral					X

FIGURE 12-16   Ford ATX clutch and band application summary.

Manual low is achieved in the same way, except that the direct clutch is also applied. This keeps the one-way roller clutch from freewheeling, so the reverse sun gear now is locked both CW and CCW to the turbine (input) shaft, allowing the vehicle to decelerate against engine compression.

Drive second input takes place through the intermediate shaft, which is splined to the splitter gear carrier. The output end of the intermediate shaft is connected to the ring gear by the intermediate clutch. The band is still applied and holding the forward sun gear, so the ring gear drives the pinions and the carrier for output. Some of the torque is transmitted mechanically through the torque converter ring gear and carrier. The torque converter planetary pinions are turning against the sun gear, which is being driven by the turbine at greater torque efficiency during vortex flow. Thus 38% of the deliverable torque is transmitted hydraulically and 62% mechanically. There is deceleration against compression in both manual and drive second because the one-way roller clutch is not involved in the flow of power for either.

Third gear is achieved by simultaneous input through two of the three compound planetary members. This locks up the compound planetary to produce direct drive. The intermediate clutch connects the ring gear to the intermediate shaft, and the direct clutch connects the reverse sun gear to the turbine shaft. The torque converter is in full rotary flow (coupling phase), so that the hydraulically driven turbine shaft and the mechanically driven intermediate shaft, for all practical purposes, are turning at the same speed and sharing the input.

In reverse, as in low, input is through the reverse sun gear, which is connected to the turbine (input) shaft by application of the direct clutch for deceleration and by the locking action of the one-way roller clutch for acceleration. The reverse clutch holds the ring gear by grounding to the case. The CW-turning sun gear drives the short pinions CCW, and they drive the long pinions CW, which causes the carrier also to turn CW as the long pinions turn against the grounded ring gear.

Clutch and band application is summarized in Figure 12-16.

FORD AUTOMATIC OVERDRIVE TRANSAXLE (AXOD)

Description and Identification

The Ford **Automatic Overdrive Transaxle (AXOD)** is a four-speed automatic overdrive transaxle for RWD vehicles with transverse-mounted engines. It is metric, and fourth speed is overdrive. The pan configuration is shown in Figure 12-17. This and its four speeds easily differentiate it from the ATX. Transaxle model number, assembly num-

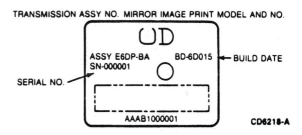

TRANSMISSION ASSY NO. MIRROR IMAGE PRINT MODEL AND NO.

FIGURE 12-18   Ford AXOD identification tag.

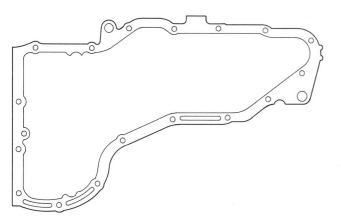

FIGURE 12-17   Ford AXOD pan gasket shape.

ber, and serial number appear on a tag on top of the converter housing (Figure 12-18).

Figures 12-19 and 12-20 present cross section and exploded views, respectively, of the AXOD. It uses two simple planetary gearsets that operate in tandem; each of the carriers is locked to the other's ring gear. Each has its own sun gear and set of planetary pinions. These gearsets are controlled by four multiple-disc clutches, two bands, and two one-way roller clutches. This transaxle also uses a simple planetary gearset for its final drive. The torque converter and transmission are linked by a chain and sprocket drive. Torque converter lock-up is achieved by a torsional damper-mounted piston plate clutch that mechanically links the turbine and torque converter cover in third (direct) and fourth (overdrive), under control of the Electronic Engine Control (EEC) system. This transaxle uses a variable displacement/vane type of rotary pump. It is driven by the torque converter cover through its own splined shaft. The valve body is located between the oil pump and drive sprocket.

Applications

This is a newly developed transaxle that was introduced in the Ford Taurus and Mercury Sable. But it is destined to find broad application among future Ford models.

History and Development

There is nothing in the Ford transmission lineage that ties directly to the AXOD, but its similarity to the General Motors THM 440-T4 is apparent. Both use tandem-operating, simple planetary gearsets rather than a Simpson or Ravigneaux, and their general configuration is the same.

Power Flow

All speeds, including overdrive, are achieved with the two tandem-operating, simple planetary gearsets.

Output is through the rear carrier—and front ring gear, since the two are attached. Input is through either the front sun gear or the front carrier—and rear ring gear, since these two are attached. The low/intermediate band holds the rear sun gear. The overdrive band holds the front sun gear. The reverse clutch holds the front carrier and rear ring gear. The direct clutch locks the gear train so that the vehicle will run against engine compression on deceleration.

In drive low, the low/intermediate band holds the rear sun gear. The front sun gear is the input and is connected to the turbine (input) shaft by the forward clutch. It drives the front pinions, carrier, and rear ring gear, which drives the rear carrier for output.

Intermediate (second) gets its input through the front carrier and rear ring gear by application of the intermediate clutch, which connects the latter to the turbine (input) shaft. The rear sun gear is held by the low/intermediate band. Output is through the rear carrier, which is driven by the rear ring gear through the rear pinion gears.

Third gear (direct) is achieved by application of the intermediate clutch and forward clutch, which connect both the front carrier and the front sun gear, respectively, to the turbine (input) shaft. The rear sun gear is held from turning CCW by the direct one-way clutch. Thus all elements of the tandem gearset are turning as one for direct (1:1) output by the rear carrier.

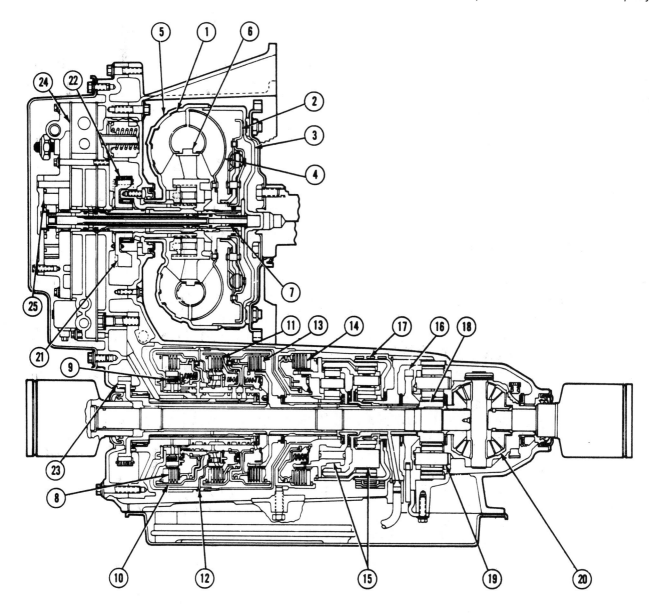

FIGURE 12-19 Ford AXOD cross section.

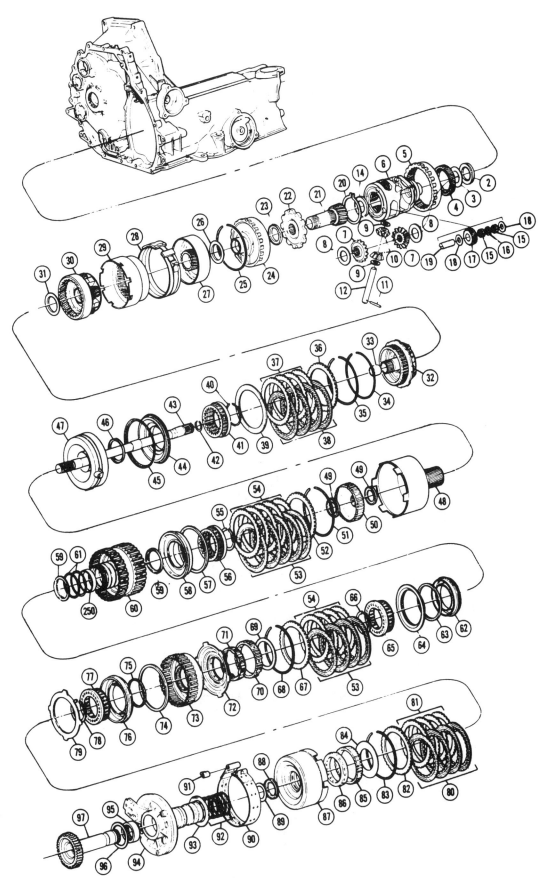

FIGURE 12-20 Ford AXOD exploded view.

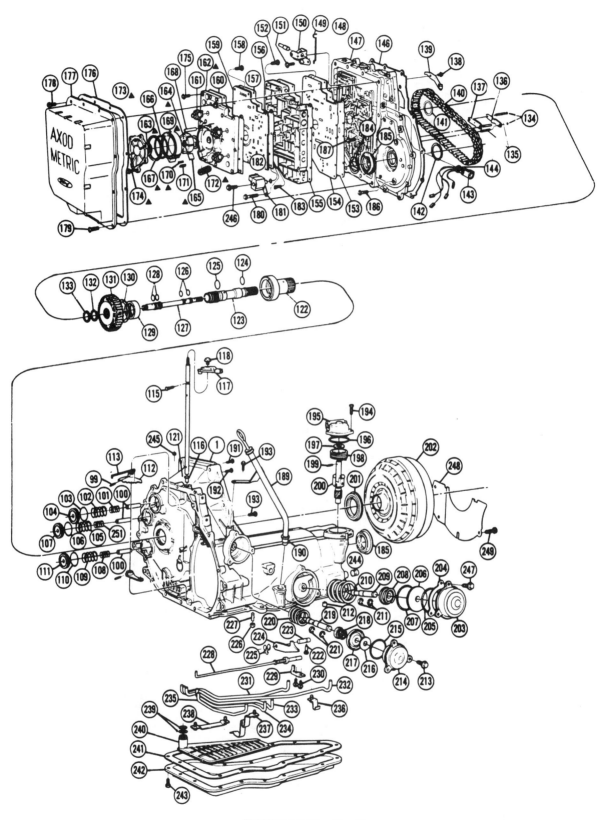

FIGURE 12-20 (Cont.)

LEGEND:

1. CASE ASSY
2. BRG & RACE ASSY — DIFF CARRIER THRUST (#19)
3. WASHER — DIFF CARRIER THRUST (#18 — SEL FIT
4. GEAR — GOVERNOR DRIVE
5. GEAR — FINAL DRIVE RING
6. CASE — TRANSAXLE DIFF GEAR
7. GEAR — DIFF SIDE (2 REQ'D)
8. WASHER — DIFF SIDE GEAR THRUST (2 REQ'D)
9. WASHER — RR AXLE DIFF PINION THRUST (2 REQ'D)
10. PINION — REAR AXLE DIFF (2 REQ'D)
11. PIN — COILED SPRING (RETAINS DIFF PINION SHAFT)
12. SHAFT — DIFF PINION
13.
14. BRG & RACE ASSY — FINAL DRIVE CARRIER (#17)
15. BRG — FINAL DRIVE PLANET GEAR NEEDLE (168 REQ'D)
16. SPACER — FINAL DRIVE PLANETARY GEAR (4 REQ'D)
17. GEAR — FINAL DRIVE PLANET (4 REQ'D)
18. WASHER — FINAL DRIVE PLANETARY GEAR THRUST (8 REQ'D)
19. SHAFT — FINAL DRIVE PINION (4 REQ'D)
20. RING — 77.3 RET EXT (RETAIN PINION SHAFTS INTO CARIER)
21. GEAR ASSY — FINAL DRIVE SUN
22. GEAR — PARKING
23. BRG & RACE ASSY — FINAL DRIVE GEAR THRUST (#16)
24. SUPPORT ASSY — PLANET REAR
25. RING — 150.7 RET INT (USED AS REAR SUPPORT RET RING)
26. BRG & RACE ASSY — SUN GEAR THRUST — RR (#15)
27. GEAR & DRUM ASSY — RR SUN
28. BAND ASSY — LOW & INTERM
29. GEAR — REAR RING
30. GEAR ASSY — PLANET REAR
31. BRG. & RACE ASSY — PLANET THRUST — CENTER (#13)
32. PLANET ASSY — FRONT
33. BUSHING — FRT PLT GR CARRIER
34. RETAINING RING — SHELL — REAR
35. RING — 153.9 RET INT (RETAIN REV CL PRESS PLATE TO CYL) — SEL FIT
36. PLATE — REV CLUTCH PRESSURE
37. PLATE ASSY — REV CL INT SPLINE (FRICTION) 4 REQ'D
38. PLATE — REV CL EXT SPLINE (STEEL) 4 REQ'D
39. SPRING — REV CLUTCH CUSHION
40. RING — 67.0 RET TYPE SU EXT (RET REV CL SPG & RET TO CYL)
41. SUPT & SPRING ASSY — REV CLUTCH
42. RING — 27.0MM RET EXT (RET DIFF CARRIER OUTPUT SHAFT)
43. SHAFT — DIFF OUTPUT
44. PISTON — REVERSE CLUTCH
45. SEAL — REV CLUTCH PISTON — OUTER
46. SEAL — REV CLUTCH PISTON — INNER
47. CYLINDER — REV CLUTCH
48. GEAR & SHELL ASSY — FRT SUN
49. BRG & RACE ASSY — FRT SUN GR THRUST (#10 & #11) — 2 REQ'D
50. HUB — INTERM CLUTCH

51. RING P INTERM CLUTCH PLATE (SEL FIT)
52. PLATE — CLUTCH PRESSURE (INTERM)
53. PLATE ASSY — CL INT SPLINE (USED IN INTERM & DIRECT CLUTCH) AS REQ'D
54. PLATE — CLUTCH EXT SPLINE (USED IN INTERM & DIRECT CLUTCH) AS REQ'D
55. RING — 72.0 RET STYLE SU EXT (RET INTERM CL SPG & RET TO CYL)
56. SUPT & SPRING ASSY — INTERM CLUTCH
57. SEAL — INTERM CLUTCH — OUTER
58. PISTON — INTERM CLUTCH
59. SEAL — INTERM/DIR CL INNER (2 REQ'D)
60. CYLINDER ASSY — DIR/INTERM CLUTCH
61. SEAL — INTERM & DIR CL HUB 2 REQ'D
62. PISTON ASSY — DIRECT CLUTCH
63. SEAL — DIRECT CLUTCH — OUTER
64. RING — DIRECT CLUTCH (PISTON)
65. SUPT & SPRING ASSY — DIRECT CLUTCH
66. RING — 77.0 RET STYLE SU EXT (RET DIR CL SPG & RET TO CYL)
67. PLATE — CLUTCH PRESSURE (DIRECT)
68. RING — DIR CL PLATE (SEL FIT)
69. RING — 152.26 RET INT (RET DIR CL PRESS PLATE TO CYL)
70. WASHER — DIR CLUTCH THRUST (#7)
71. RACE — DIR ONE-WAY CL — OUTER
72. CLUTCH ASSY — DIRECT ONE-WAY
73. RACE & BSHG ASSY — DIR OWC — INNER
74. CYLINDER ASSY — FWD CLUTCH
75. SEAL — FWD CLUTCH — OUTER
76. SEAL — FWD CLUTCH — INNER
77. PISTON — FORWARD CLUTCH
78. SUPT & SPRING ASSY — FWD CLUTCH
79. RING — 85.0 RET TYPE SU EXT (RET FWD CL SPG & RET TO CYL)
80. SPRING — FORWARD CLUTCH WAVE
81. PLATE ASSY — FWD CL INT SPLINE (FRICTION) AS REQ'D
82. PLATE — FWD CL EXT SPLINE (STEEL) AS REQ'D
83. PLATE — FWD CL PRESSURE
84. RING — 152.26 RET INT (FWD) SEL FIT (RET FWD CL PRESS PLT)
85. WASHER — FWD CLUTCH THRUST (#6)
86. RACE — LOW OWC — OUTER
87. CLUTCH ASSY — LOW ONE-WAY
88. DRUM ASSY — OVERDRIVE
89. BRG & RACE ASSY — DIR CL HUB (#9)
90. WASHER — DRIVEN SPROCKET SUPT THRUST — RR (#8) SEL FIT
91. BAND ASSY — OVERDRIVE
92. RETAINER — 0/D BAND
93. SEAL — FWD CLUTCH CYL (5 REQ'D)
94. WASHER — SUPPORT THRUST — FRT (#5) SEL FIT
95. SUPPORT ASSY — DRIVEN SPROCKET
96. BRG ASSY — DRIVEN SPROCKET
97. WASHER — DRIVEN SPROCKET THRUST (#4)
98. SPROCKET ASSY — DRIVEN
99. LEVER ASSY — MANUAL CONTROL

FIGURE 12-20 (Cont.)

99.   PIN — 4MM X 20 SPG COILED STD (2-USED AS MAN CNTL SHFT PIN)
100.   SHAFT — SHIFT ACCUM PISTON (3 REQ'D)
101.   SPRING — 1-2 SHIFT ACCUM — INNER
102.   SPRING — 1-2 SHIFT ACCUM — OUTER
103.   SEAL — 1-2 SHIFT ACCUM — PISTON
104.   PISTON — 1-2 SHIFT ACCUM
105.   SPRING — 3-4 SHIFT ACCUM
106.   SEAL — 3-4 SHIFT ACCUM — PISTON
107.   PISTON — 3-4 SHIFT ACCUM
108.   SPRING — DRIVE SHIFT ACCUM — INNER
109.   SPRING — DRIVE SHIFT ACCUM — OUTER
110.   SEAL — DRIVE SHIFT ACCUM — PISTON
111.   PISTON — DRIVE SHIFT ACCUM
112.   LEVER ASSY — MANUAL DETENT
113.   ROD — MAN CONTROL VALVE ACTU
114.   SHAFT — MANUAL CONTROL
115.   PIN — SHAFT RET (USED AS MAN LVR SHAFT RET PIN)
116.   SEAL ASSY — MAN CONTROL SHAFT
117.   SWITCH ASSY — GR SHIFT NEUTRAL
118.   BOLT — M6 — 1.0 X 28 HEX FLG HD (2-NEUT START SWITCH TO CASE)
119.   LEVER — MANUAL CONTROL — OUTER
120.   INSULATOR — GEAR SHIFT ARM
121.   TAG — IDENTIFICATION
122.   SUPPORT ASSY — STATOR
123.   SHAFT — TURBINE
124.   SEAL — O'RING (FRT TURBINE SHAFT TO DRIVE SPRKT)
125.   SEAL — TURBINE SHAFT — REAR
126.   SEAL — PUMP SHAFT — REAR (2 REQ'D)
127.   SHAFT ASSY — OIL PUMP DRIVE
128.   SEAL — PUMP SHAFT — FRONT
129.   BRG ASSY — DRIVE SPROCKET
130.   WASHER — DRIVE SPROCKET THRUST (#2)
131.   SPROCKET ASSY — DRIVE
132.   RING — 26.36 RET STY SU EXT (RET TURB SHAFT TO DRIVE SPRKT)
133.   SEAL — TURBINE SHAFT — FRONT (METAL)
134.   COLLAR — OIL LEVEL THERMO RETAIN
135.   PIN — 4MM X 22 COILED (LOCATING BY-METAL ELEMENT; (3) REG)
136.   ELEMENT — OIL LEVEL THERMOSTATIC
137.   PLATE — OIL LEVEL THERMOSTAT — VALVE
138.   BOLT — M6 X 16 HEX FLG HD (ATT DET SPRING ASSY TO CHAIN coVER)
139.   SPRING ASSY — MAN VLV DETENT
140.   CHAIN ASSY — DRIVE
141.   WASHER — DRIVE SPROCKET THRUST (#1)
142.   WASHER — CHAIN COVER THRUST (#3)
143.   BULKHEAD ASSY — WIRING CONN
144.   SEAL — 17.12 X 2.62 O'RING (WIRE HARNESS TO CASE)
145.   VENT ASSY — CASE
146.   GASKET — CHAIN COVER
147.   COVER ASSY — CHAIN
148.   CONN ASSY — 5/16 TUBE X 1/4 EX PIPE PLUG (2 REQ'D)
149.   LINK — THROTTLE CONTROL LEVER

150.   LEVER ASSY — THROTTLE CONTROL
151.   BOLT — M6-1.0 X 14 HEX FLG HD (2-ATT T.V. LVR ASSY TO CHAIN COVER)
152.   SCREW — M6 X 1.0 X 14 PAN HD (2-ATT VLV BDY SEP PLT TO VLV BDY)
153.   GASKET — CONTROL ASSY
154.   PLATE ASSY — VALVE BODY SEP
155.   GASKET — CNTL VLV BODY SEP PLATE
156.   CONTROL ASSY — MAIN
157.   GASKET — PUMP ASSY
158.   SCREW — M6 X 1.0 X 14 PAN HD. (3 — PUMP SEP PLATE TO PUMP BODY)
159.   PLATE — OIL PUMP BODY SEP
160.   GASKET — OIL PUMP BODY SEP PLATE
161.   SWITCH ASSY — OIL PRESSURE (3 REQ'D)
162.   BODY BRG & SEAL ASSY — OIL PUMP
163.   RING — OIL PUMP VANE SUPPORT (2 REQ'D)
164.   ROTOR — OIL PUMP
165.   VANE — OIL PUMP (7 REQ'D)
166.   SEAL — OIL PUMP BORE RING SIDE
167.   SUPPORT — OIL PUMP BORE RING SIDE SEAL
168.   PIN — 8MM X 37.7 STRAIGHT HRDN
169.   RING — OIL PUMP BODY
170.   SUPPORT — OIL PUMP BORE RING RADIAL SEAL
171.   SEAL — OIL PUMP BORE RING RADIAL
172.   SPRING — OIL PUMP BORE RING
173.   COVER & SLEEVE ASSY — OIL PUMP
174.   BOLT — M6 X 1.0 X 20 HEP FLG PLT (6 REQ'D) ATT PUMP COVER TO PUMP BODY
175.   BOLT — HEX FLG HD (22-ATT PUMP BODY & MAIN CONTR TO CHAIN COVER)
176.   GASKET — MAIN CONTROL COVER
177.   COVER — MAIN CONTROL
178.   BOLT — M8-35.0 HEX FLG HD (12-ATT CHAIN COVER TO CASE)
179.   BOLT — M8-1.25 X 25 HEX FLG HD (12-ATT MAIN CTL CVR TO CHN CVR)
180.   BOLT — M6-1.00 X 40 HEX FG HD (3-ATT VLV BDY TO CHN CVR&SOL ASSY)
181.   SOLENOID ASSY — BY-PASS CLUTCH
182.   SEAL — 6.07 X 1.79 O'RING (BY-PASS SOLENOID SEAL)
183.   SCREEN ASSY — BY-PASS CLUTCH SOLENOID
184.   CIRCLE CLIP — OUTPUT SHAFT RE-TAINER (RETAINS CV JOINT)
185.   SEAL ASSY — DIFF (2 REQ'D)
186.   BOLT — M8-1.25 X 45 HEX FLG HD (2-ATT VLV BDY TO CHN CVR&SOL ASY)
187.   BOLT — M10-1.50 X 45 HEX (ATT CHAIN COVER TO DRIVEN SUPPORT)
188.   INDICATOR ASSY — OIL LEVEL
189.   TUBE ASSY — OIL FILLER
190.   GROMMET — OIL FILLER
191.   BOLT — M10-1.50 X 45 HEX (ATT CHAIN COVER TO DRIVEN SUPPORT)
192.   BOLT — M6 X 1.00 X 30 HEX FLG HD (4-ATT CASE TO CHAIN COVER)
193.   SCREW — M6-1.0 X 20 PAN HD (6-ATT CASE TO STATOR SUPPORT)
194.   BOLT — (2-GOVERNOR COVER TO CASE)

FIGURE 12-20   (Cont.)

195.	COVER — GOVERNOR	223.	SHAFT — PARK PAWL
196.	SEAL — 63.2 X 1.80 O'RING (USED AS GOV. COVER SEAL)	224.	PAWL — PARKING BRAKE
197.	BRG & RACE ASSY — GOV THRUST	225.	SPRING — PARK PAWL RETURN
198.	GEAR — SPEEDO DRIVE (7TLH)	226.	SCREW — M12 X 1.75MM SET HD SCKET (REV CL ASSY LOCATOR BLT)
199.	PIN — 3.3 X 22 SPG SLOT HVY (USED AS SPEEDO GEAR DRIVE PIN)	227.	NUT — M12 X 1.75 HEX (REV CL ASSY LOCATOR BOLT)
200.	GOVERNOR ASSEMBLY	228.	ROD ASSY — PARK PAWL ACTUATING
201.	SEAL ASSY — CONV IMP HUB	229.	ABUTMENT — PARK PAWL ACTUATING
202.	CONVERTER ASSY — 10-1/4	230.	BOLT — M8-1.25 X 25 HEX FLG HD (2-ATT ABUTMENT ASSY TO CASE)
203.	COVER — LOW/INTERM BAND SERVO	231.	TUBE — REAR LUBE OIL TRANSFER
204.	GASKET — LOW/INTERM BAND SERVO	232.	TUBE — GOV FEED OIL TRANSFER
205.	SEAL — LOW/INTERM SERVO PISTON COVER	233.	TUBE — SERVO APPLY OIL TRANSFER
206.	PISTON — LOW/INTERM bAND SERVO	234.	TUBE — SERVO REL OIL TRANSFER
207.	SEAL — LOW/INTERM BAND SERVO PISTON	235.	TUBE — REV CL APPLY OIL TRANSFER
208.	RETAINER & SPRING ASSY — LOW/INTERM SERVO	236.	BRKT ASSY — TUBE SUPPORT — GOV FEED
209.	ROD — LOW/INTERM SERVO PISTON (SEL FIT)	237.	BRKT ASSY — TUBE SUPPORT — REV CLUTCH
210.	SPRING — LOW/INTERM SERVO PISTON	238.	BRKT ASSY — TUBE SUPPORT MAIN
211.	RING — 11MM RET TYPE RB EXT (2-ATT L/I SERVO PISTON)	239.	SEAL — 23.46 X 2.62 O'RING (2-USED ON OIL FILTER)
212.	SEAL ASSY — RR LUBE TRANSFER TUBE	240.	FILTER ASSY — OIL
213.	BOLT — (3-ATT O/D SERVO COVER TO CASE)	241.	GASKET — OIL PAN
		242.	PAN OIL
214.	COVER — O/D BAND SERVO	243.	BOLT — M8-1.25 X 14 HEX FLG HD (17-ATT OIL PAN TO CASE)
215.	SEAL — O/D SERVO COVER	244.	PLUG — 13.9MM CUP
216.	RETAINER — O/D SERVO PISTON	245.	NUT — 1/4 SPRING (RETAIN I.D. TAG)
217.	PISTON & SEAL ASSY — O/D SERVO	246.	BOLT — M6 X 16 HEX HD (ATT SOLENOID ASSY TO VLV BODY)
218.	RETAINER & CUSHION SPRING ASSY — O/D SERVO	247.	BOLT — (3-ATT L/I SERVO COVER TO CASE)
219.	ROD — O/D SERVO PISTON (SEL FIT)	248.	COVER — CONV HSG LOWER
220.	SPRING — O/D SERVO RETURN	249.	BOLT — (ATT CONV HSG CUR TO CASE)
221.	RING — RET EXT ROD O/D SERVO (2 USED ON O/D SERVO ROD)	250.	BUSHING — DIR/INTERM CLUTCH CYLINDER
222.	PIN — SHAFT RETAINER (USED AS PARK PAWL SHAFT RETURN PIN)	251.	SPRING — 3-4 SHIFT ACCUM-INNER

FIGURE 12-20   (Cont.)

Fourth gear (overdrive) is input through the front carrier and rear ring gear, which are locked together; these are connected to the turbine shaft by the intermediate clutch. The overdrive band holds the front sun gear so that the pinions, turning against it, drive the front ring and rear carrier faster (overdrive output) than the front carrier is turning. The direct one-way clutch overruns and the direct clutch is applied to prevent freewheeling on deceleration.

For reverse, the forward clutch connects the front sun gear to the turbine shaft for input. The reverse clutch holds the front carrier, which drives the front ring gear and rear carrier CCW for output.

Figure 12-21 summarizes clutch and band application for the AXOD.

TRADE TERMS

Automatic overdrive transaxle (AXOD)	C-5	Long pinions
Automatic Overdrive Transmission	Cruise-O-Matic	Overdrive band
AOT	Electronic Engine Control (EEC)	Short pinions
	FMX	Splitter gear
		Split torque

	Fwd Clutch	Lo/Intermed. One-Way	O. D. Band	Direct Clutch	Direct One-Way	Intermed. Clutch	Reverse Clutch	Lo/Intermed. Band
Drive 1.	X	X						X
2.	X					X		X
3.	X			X	X	X		
4.			X	X	X			
Manual	X	X		X				X
Reverse	X	X					X	

FIGURE 12-21   Ford AXOD clutch and band application summary.

REVIEW QUESTIONS

12-1. Ford Motor Company was the first to introduce the _____ _____ transmission, the _____ clutch for torque converter lock-up, and the application of a simple planetary gearset in the torque converter, which is called a _____ gear.

12-2. The Ford transmissions and transaxles discussed in this chapter use:

(a) Simpson planetary gearset

(b) Ravigneaux planetary gearset

(c) Tandem-operating simple planetary gearsets.

(d) All of the above.

12-3. Torque converter lock-up for the C-5 transmission is achieved by a _____ _____.

12-4. The C-5 uses a _____ compound planetary, as does the C-3, C-4, and C-6.

12-5. Input for the C-5 is through the _____ ring gear by application of the _____ clutch.

12-6. The FMX is an old Ford Transaxle.   T   F

12-7. Match the terms in the first column with those in the second.

(a) AOT.

(b) A4LD.

(c) AXOD.

(d) ATX.

(1) Tandem-operating planetaries.

(2) "Splitter" gear.

(3) Ravigneaux planetary.

(4) C-3 derivative.

12-8. In a Ravigneaux compound planetary, which two of the three major members are common to the gearset?

(a) Carrier.

(b) Sun gear.

(c) Ring gear.

(d) All of the above.

(e) None of the above.

12-9. The split-torque concept is not a true 100% lock-up because the mechanical connection (100% efficient) runs against a torque converter connection (something less than 100% efficient).   T   F

12-10. The percentage split between mechanical and deliverable hydraulic torque is determined by the torque arm, or _____ of each of the two planetary members.

12-11. The Ford A4LD is a four-speed automatic overdrive transmission for light, shaft-driven, RWD vehicles.   T   F

12-12. All four forward speeds in the A4LD are achieved with a Simpson compound planetary gearset.   T   F

12-13. The ATX in second and third gears is similar to the AOT in third and fourth in that it ____ torque.

12-14. The AXOD final drive uses three _____ _____, whereas the ATX uses a _____ ___.

12-15. AXOD output is through the _____ _____ and _____ _____ _____, since the two are attached.

12-16. In the ATX, output is always through the _____ , but input can be through the reverse _____ gear or the _____ gear.

12-17. The EEC-controlled torque converter clutch is common to both the _____ transmission and the _____ transaxles.

12-18. A _____ type of rotary pump is used in the AXOD.

12-19. The Ford _____ and General Motors ____ are very similar transaxles.

12-20. Overdrive output through the rear carrier of the AXOD is possible because the rear carrier is locked to the _____ _____ _____ .

E S S A Y   Q U E S T I O N S

12-1. Describe the major differences between the Simpson gearset, Ravigneaux gearset, and the gearset used in the Ford AXOD (and General Motors THM 440-T4).

12-2. Select and describe some of the major parts of Ford Motor Company automatic transmissions and transaxles.

C H A P T E R   A C T I V I T I E S

12-1. Compare the Ford AXOD and General Motors THM 440-T4 if both are available in your shop. If they are not available, use the section views and other information in this chapter.

12-2. Check the door frame vehicle identification plates on Ford vehicles to identify the transmission model used.

13

Chrysler Corporation

_____ **OBJECTIVES** _____

When you have completed this chapter, you should be able to:

- Discuss the major design characteristics of Chrysler automatic transmissions and transaxles.
- Describe the normal power control and power flow through the Chrysler automatic transmissions and transaxles.
- State the reason the Chrysler transmission or transaxle part number is so important.

By comparison to other large automotive manufacturers, we might say that Chrysler has kept it simple. They make a three-speed transmission and a three-speed transaxle, both among the most reliable in the industry. There are four variations on the transmission and two on the transaxle. Among those, there are differences in torque converter sizes, in the quantity of certain clutch discs, and in band types to accommodate different engine–vehicle combinations. Each transmission has a seven-digit part num-

ber that must be noted when testing, ordering parts, and assembling. The number is stamped on the left side of the transmission case oil pan flange or bell housing.

AMC/Jeep (now Chrysler), as well as International Harvester (now Navistar), also use Chrysler transmissions with bell housing and extensions designed to fit the engine and drive shaft interfaces in their vehicles. There are also some internal changes (clutches, bands, pressures) to accommodate the various combinations of vehicle weight, engine torque, axle ratio, and so on.

Chrysler does use an imported four-speed automatic overdrive, designated KM148 (AW372) and manufactured by Aisin-Warner, in its D-50 vehicles (Raider, Ram 50), which started with the 1987 models.

TRANSMISSION

Identification

The **Torqueflite** A-904 (Torqueflite 6) and the A-727 (Torqueflite 8) are the two basic, regular- and heavy-duty designs, respectively. The two can be readily identified by the differences in their pan shape (Figure 13-1). Variations of these basic trans-

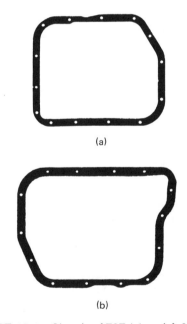

(a)

(b)

FIGURE 13-1 Chrysler A727 (a) and A-904 (b)

missions are designated **Torque Command** 727, 904, and 998 (AMC), A-998 and 999 (Chrysler), and T-407 for the A-727 Torqueflite used by International Harvester (see Figures 13-2 and 13-3).

Description

These transmissions use the Simpson compound planetary controlled by two multiple-disc clutches,

an **overrunning** (one-way roller) **clutch**, and two bands. The **kickdown band** is single wrap and the low-reverse band is double wrap. Most incorporate a lock-up converter of the piston/disc type. They use an IX rotor pump that is driven in the conventional manner by the torque converter hub.

History and Development

Chrysler was the first to use the Simpson compound planetary gearset. It was used in the original Torqueflite (A-466), which was introduced in 1956.

Both the A-904 and A-727 Torqueflite transmissions were introduced in the early 1960s. They replaced the earlier cast-iron, two-speed **Powerflite** and three-speed Torqueflite and were the first to have the transmission case and bell housing produced as a single casting. By 1978, they also incorporated lock-up converters.

Power Control and Power Flow

Earlier in this book (Chapter 6), we presented a detailed description of the hydraulic power flow from the pump, through the valve body for specific gear selector positions. Also, in other chapters, we have described the power flow from the turbine through the input shaft, clutches, bands, and planetaries to the output shaft. Here, for the Torqueflite, we combine the two so that you can follow both the control system path and the power flow path as the vehicle moves through the automatic shifting sequence in Drive. Figures 13-4 through 13-8 illustrate the power control sequence, and by now, you should be able to picture power flow through the Simpson compound planetary gearset.

Input and Output. Output for Torqueflite transmissions is through the front carrier or rear ring gear, both of which are splined to the output shaft. Input can be through the front ring gear or the sun gear by application of the rear clutch, or the front clutch, respectively.

Neutral. In neutral (Figure 13-4) the manual valve is positioned so that it connects line pressure from the pump right back to the regulator balance valve. Line pressure also passes through the regulator valve and goes directly to a control

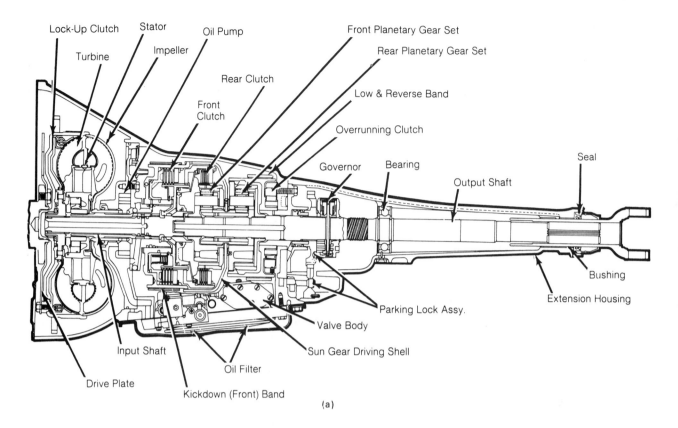

(a)

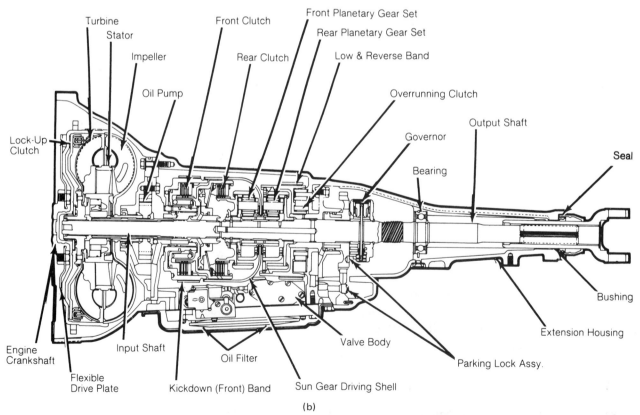

(b)

FIGURE 13-2   Basic Chrysler transmissions: (a) heavy-duty (Torqueflite 727); (b) regular duty (Torqueflite 904).

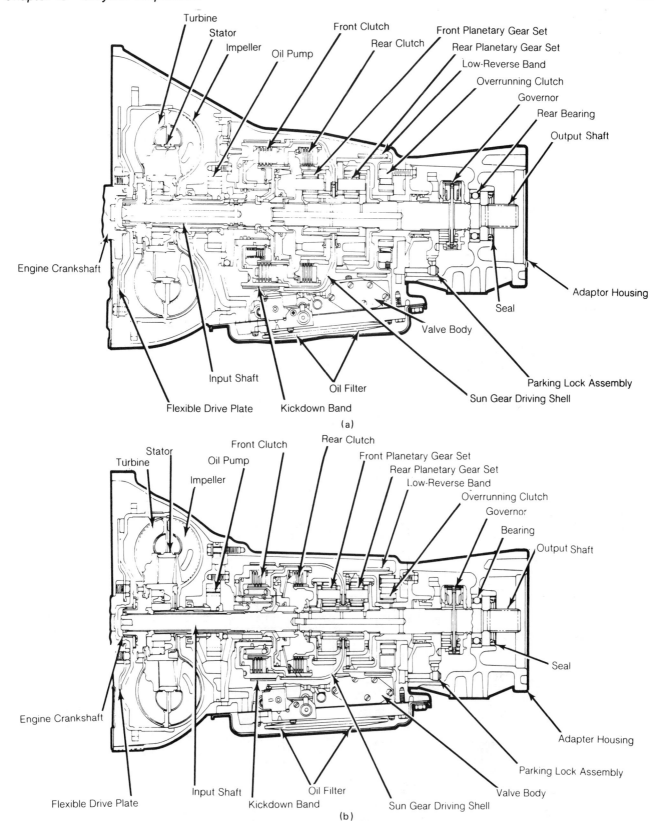

FIGURE 13-3 AMC/Jeep variations of Chrysler 727 and 904: (a) Torque Command 727; (b) Torque Command 904.

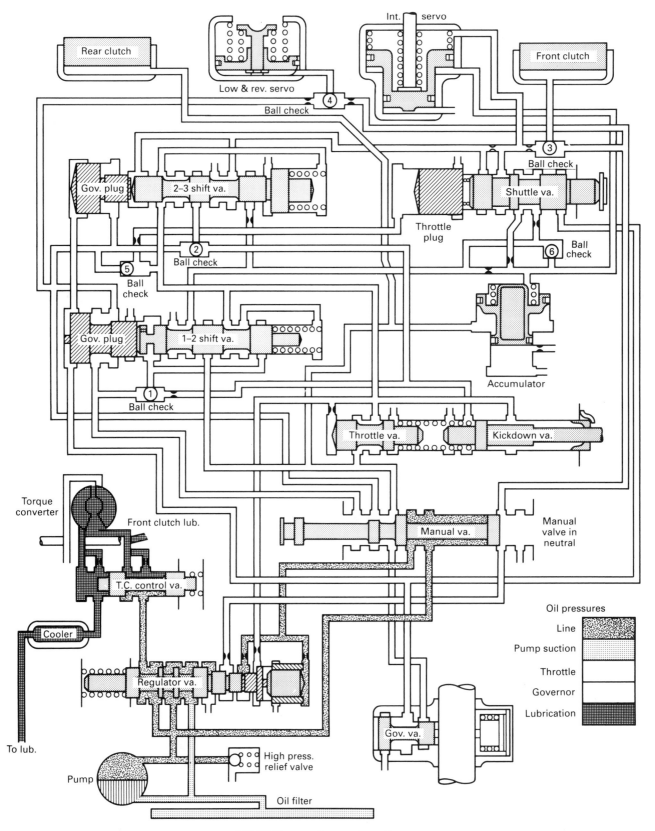

FIGURE 13-4 Torqueflite—neutral.

valve that regulates flow to the cooling and lubrication circuits. In this position the manual valve blocks pressure to any of the apply circuits so that no planetary element is held and no power is transmitted.

Drive Low. In Drive low (Figure 13-5), the manual valve is positioned to connect line pressure with the regulator valve and torque converter as with neutral, but it also allows line pressure to pass to (1) the governor, (2) the 1-2 shift valve, and (3) the rear (forward) clutch, and on the way, the accumulator.

The result of this hydraulic control sequence, application of the rear clutch, connects the front ring gear to the turbine (input) shaft. The CW rotating ring gear drives the front planet pinions clockwise, which drive the sun gear CCW. This turns the rear planet pinions CW, and the rear carrier is kept from moving CCW by the overrunning (one-way roller) clutch. So the rear pinions drive the rear ring gear and output shaft clockwise at a greatly reduced rate.

In manual low, the low-reverse band holds the rear carrier from turning in either direction so that the vehicle runs against engine compression during deceleration—that is, it prevents freewheeling.

Note also in Figure 13-5 that as vehicle speed increases, the governor valve opens to create governor pressure from the line pressure source. It can vary from zero to full line pressure, depending on how far the valve opens, which depends on how fast the governor is turning. Governor pressure is routed to the shuttle valve and to the two shift valves, where it opposes throttle pressure.

Throttle pressure is created at the throttle valve from line pressure, depending on how far the throttle is opened by the driver. Throttle pressure is routed to (1) the kickdown valve: (2) the throttle valve itself, to oppose throttle valve spring tension and linkage pressure; (3) the regulator balance valve; and (4) both shift valves to oppose governor pressure, and to the shuttle valve to do the same. Notice that the 1-2 shift valve has not moved yet because governor pressure and throttle pressure paired with 1-2 shift valve spring tension are in equilibrium, that is, one is exerting no more force than the other.

Drive Intermediate. Now as vehicle speed increases, the governor turns faster, which causes the governor valve to open wider, increasing governor pressure. In Figure 13-6 we can see the effect that the increased governor pressure has had on the 1-2 shift valve: it has overcome the combined force of throttle pressure and spring tension, moving the valve to the right. Now line pressure is allowed to pass to (1) the 2-3 shift valve to be ready when that shift occurs, (2) the shuttle valve to act against throttle pressure, and (3) the intermediate (or kickdown) servo.

With the rear clutch still applied and connecting the front ring gear to the turbine shaft, activation of the intermediate servo tightens the intermediate band, which anchors the sun gear. The CW-rotating front ring gear turns the front pinions CW around the stationary sun gear. This causes the front carrier—which is splined to the output shaft—to turn CW at a reduced rate. There is no application of the low-reverse band, or any other device, to prevent freewheeling in either gear.

In manual second, the vehicle starts in low, then shifts to second, but will not shift to third (direct).

As acceleration continues in drive second, or intermediate, governor pressure continues to build.

Drive Direct. In Figure 13-7 we can see that governor pressure has increased enough to overcome the spring tension and throttle pressure acting against it at the 2-3 shift valve. This causes the valve to move to the right, allowing line pressure to reach the front (high-reverse) clutch. Observe that with but one very significant exception, little else has changed from the condition of drive intermediate. The significant exception is that line pressure has also been routed to the release side of the intermediate servo. This quickly moves the servo piston to a release position (the piston's surface on that side is larger and its movement is assisted by the spring), unlocking the sun gear, which takes the transmission out of intermediate.

With the front clutch now engaged, the sun gear is connected to the input shaft. The rear clutch is still engaged, connecting the front ring gear also to the input shaft. Thus with two of the three major planetary members locked together to the same shaft, the forward planetary turns as a unit, driving the forward carrier and output shaft CW at the same speed as the input shaft is turning.

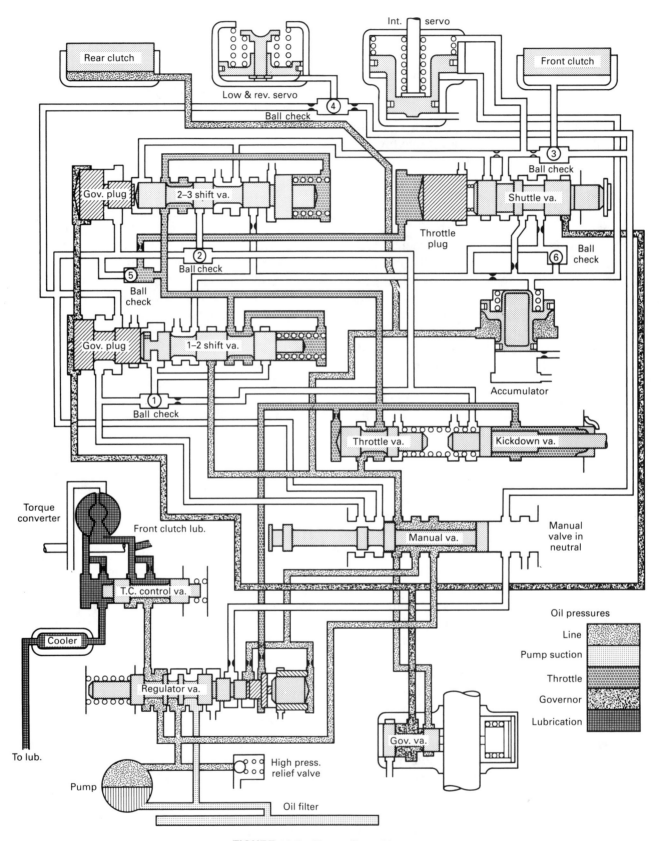

FIGURE 13-5 Torqueflite—drive low.

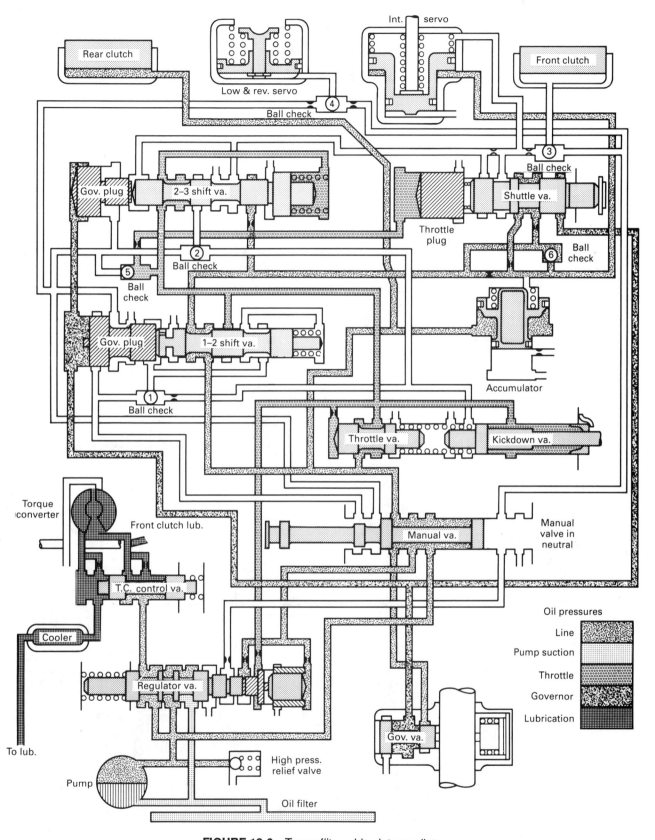

FIGURE 13-6 Torqueflite—drive intermediate.

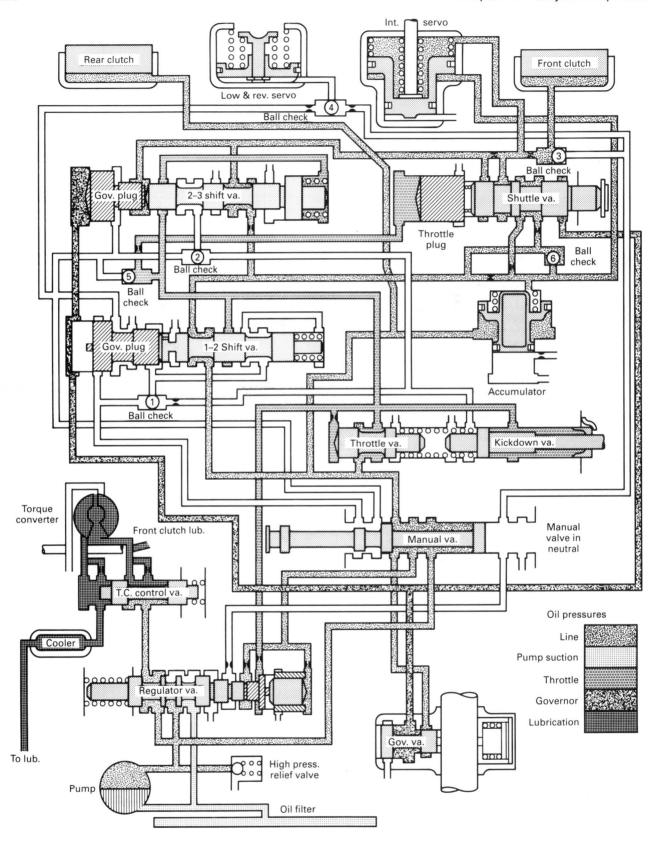

FIGURE 13-7 Torqueflite—drive direct.

Shuttle Valve. Throttle pressure usually holds the shuttle valve in a position that opens a bypass circuit for line pressure to the intermediate servo. When the servo piston and accumulator piston reach full stroke, line pressure builds in the shuttle valve, quickly countering the decreased throttle pressure that occurs should the driver lift his foot from the accelerator during a 2-3 upshift. The bypass is then closed and fluid is rerouted through orificed circuits to cushion the 2-3 upshift.

Reverse. In reverse the manual valve is moved by the driver to the reverse position. As you can see in Figure 13-8, this blocks line pressure from all but the front clutch, low-reverse servo, and the regulator balance valve. It is a simple circuit. Notice that check valves 3 and 4 are moved from their usual alternate positions for drive direct and manual low, respectively, to block feedback to those circuits.

The front clutch connects the sun gear to the turbine shaft for input. The CW rotating sun gear drives the rear pinions CCW, but the rear carrier is anchored by the low-reverse servo, so the rear pinions drive the rear ring gear and output shaft CCW.

Clutch and band application is summarized in Figure 13-9.

TRANSAXLE

Identification

The A-413 and A-470 transaxles appear from the outside to be identical. Generally speaking, the A-470 is for the heavier-duty applications. The differences are primarily internal, involving torque converter size, final drive ratio, quantity of clutch plates and driving discs, and variations in valve body springs and orifices. As with the Chrysler transmissions, it is equally important to note the seven-digit transmission part number when testing, ordering parts, and assembling. It is stamped on the oil pan flange at the rear.

Description

Figure 13-10 is a cross section representative of the A-413 and A-470 transaxles. The sketch in Figure 13-11 shows the various external adjustments, control and line connections, and pressure taps.

These transaxles use a Simpson compound planetary gearset for three forward speeds and reverse. They are controlled by two multiple-disc clutches, two bands, and an overrunning (one-way roller) clutch. Two helical gears are used—rather than sprockets and chain—for power transfer, and the two final drive gears are also helical cut. The oil pump is an IX gear design, driven by the torque converter hub.

History and Development

The first Chrysler automatic transaxle was developed in the late 1970s for the Dodge Omni and Plymouth Horizon. It was called the Omni/Horizon A-404 and drew heavily on the three-speed Torqueflite transmission power train. The A-413 and A-470, introduced in 1981, are modifications of the A-404.

Power Flow

Power flow up to the output shaft for the transaxles is identical to that for the transmissions, which is summarized in Figure 13-9. The transaxle output shaft is fitted with a helical cut gear that meshes with one just like it at one end of the transfer shaft. The other end of the transfer shaft contains the final drive pinion, which meshes with the ring gear to provide the final drive ratio. The transfer shaft serves to restore output shaft direction of rotation to the final drive. The ring gear is bolted to the differential carrier, and the axles are splined to the differential side gears.

TRADE TERMS

Kickdown band	**Powerflite**	**Torque Command**
	Overrunning clutch	**Torqueflite**

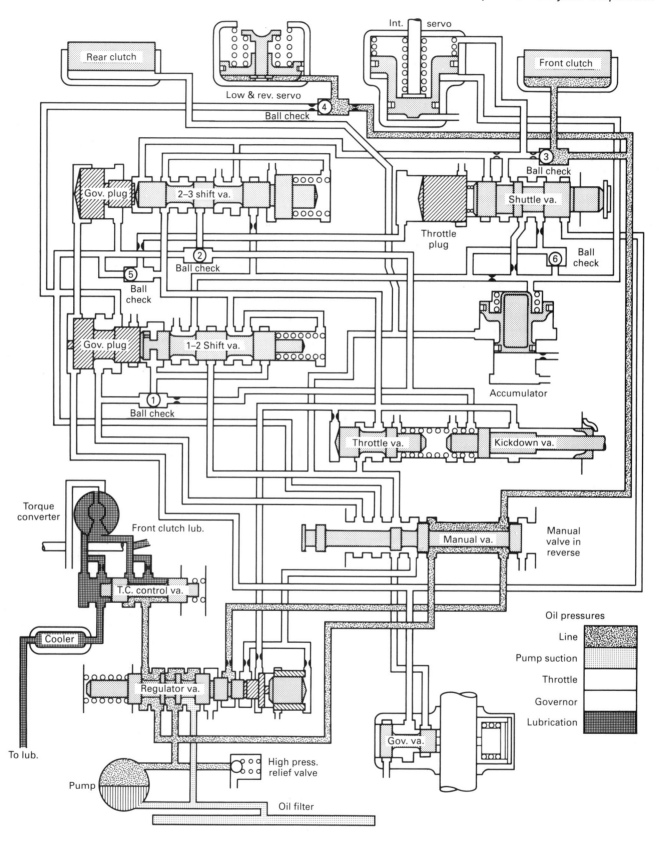

FIGURE 13-8   Torqueflite—reverse.

CLUTCH & BAND APPLICATION CHART (ELEMENTS IN USE)

Selector Lever Position	Front (High-Reverse) Clutch	Rear (Forward) Clutch	Over-running Clutch	Converter Lock-up Clutch	Intermediate (Kickdown) Band	Low-Reverse Band
D – DRIVE						
First		X	X			
Second		X			X	
Third	X	X		X	X	
2 – SECOND						
First		X	X			
Second		X			X	
1 – LOW (First)		X				X
R – REVERSE	X					X

NEUTRAL or PARK – All clutches and bands released and/or ineffective.

FIGURE 13-9   Chrysler Torqueflite clutch and band application summary.

REVIEW QUESTIONS

13-1. Chrysler automatic transmissions were the first to use the _____ compound planetary gearset.

13-2. They were also the first to produce a single casting for the _____ housing and _____ housing.

13-3. The final drive in the Chrysler transaxle is:
(a) Sprocket and chain.
(b) Bevel ring and pinion gearset.
(c) Helical ring and pinion gearset.
(d) Simple planetary gearset.

13-4. All Chrysler transmissions and transaxles use lock-up torque converters.   T   F

13-5. Chrysler also sells transmissions to _____ and _____.

13-6. The A-904 and A-727 have identical pan shapes.   T   F

13-7. The name that Chrysler uses for the intermediate band is the _____ band.

13-8. Input for Chrysler transmissions and transaxles is through the front _____ _____ or _____ _____.

13-9. All Chrysler transmissions use an IX rotor oil pump, whereas all their transaxles use an IX gear type.   T   F

13-10. The first Chrysler three-speed automatic transmissions and transaxles were designated _____ and _____, respectively.

13-11. In neutral, the Torqueflite transmission ____ valve blocks pressure to any of the _____ circuits so that no planetary element is held.

13-12. Chrysler calls the forward clutch the _____ clutch and the high-reverse clutch the ____ clutch.

13-13. Which of the following does not receive line pressure with the manual valve in drive low?
(a) Governor.
(b) 1-2 shift valve.
(c) Accumulator.
(d) Low-reverse servo.

13-14. In the Torqueflite, the front planetary ring gear can be connected to the turbine shaft by application of the _____ clutch.

13-15. The overrunning clutch in the Torqueflite acts to keep the rear carrier from turning CCW in _____ gear.

13-16. In manual low, the Torqueflite's low-reverse band locks the rear carrier. What is its effect on the transmission?

13-17. Governor pressure depends on governor __ ____.

13-18. Throttle pressure is controlled by the _____ valve, which is ultimately controlled by what? _____ _____

13-19. The front clutch of the Torqueflite serves to connect the _____ gear to the _____ shaft.

13-20. In reverse, the Torqueflite's CW-rotating sun gear drives the rear pinions CCW. How does it achieve reverse from that point?

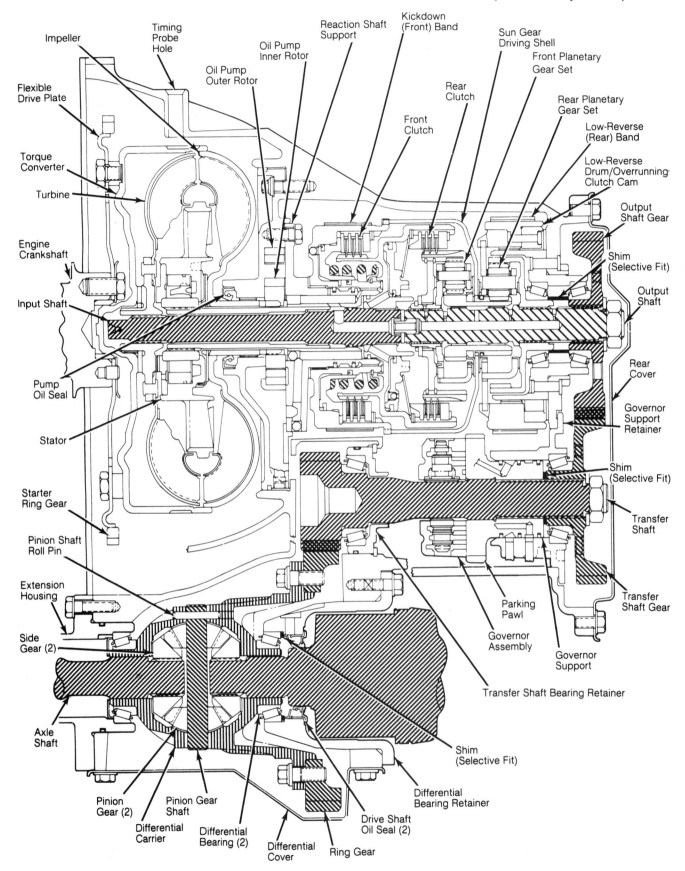

FIGURE 13-10 Chrysler automatic transaxle.

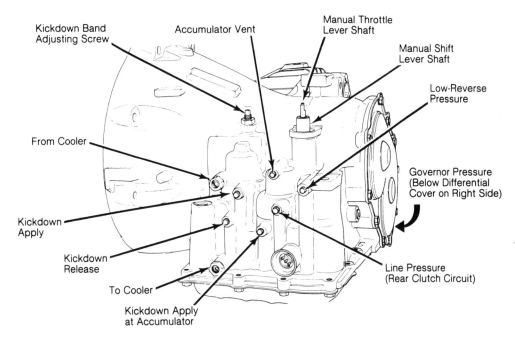

Kickdown Band Adjusting Screw

Accumulator Vent

Manual Throttle Lever Shaft

Manual Shift Lever Shaft

Low-Reverse Pressure

From Cooler

Governor Pressure (Below Differential Cover on Right Side)

Kickdown Apply

Kickdown Release

To Cooler

Kickdown Apply at Accumulator

Line Pressure (Rear Clutch Circuit)

FIGURE 13-11   Chrysler transaxle external adjustments and connections.

ESSAY QUESTIONS

13-1. Discuss Chrysler transmissions with respect to who uses them and how the various models are differentiated.

13-2. Select and describe some of the major parts of the Chrysler automatic transaxle—especially with respect to those comparable parts typical of General Motors and Ford transaxles.

CHAPTER ACTIVITIES

13-1. If there is an IX rotor pump in your shop, determine whether it is excessively worn by measuring IX rotor tip clearance (0.005 to 0.010 in.), outer rotor circumference-to-pump body bore (0.004 to 0.008 in.) and rotor face-to-pump body face, using a straight edge, (0.001 to 0.0025 in.).

13-2. Study the pump rotor assembly, especially the position of the inner rotor. Can you detect a possible problem when it comes to installing the torque converter? There is a special tool, C-3756 for the A-904-LA, that can alleviate any problem.

13-3. Trace through the hydraulic circuit diagrams in this chapter for drive low and drive intermediate to see if you can see how they would change for manual low and manual intermediate, respectively.

14

Foreign Manufacturers

OBJECTIVES

When you have completed this chapter, you should be able to:

• Recognize the names or model designations of three foreign-manufactured transmissions and describe their major characteristics.

• Recognize the names or model designations of six foreign-manufactured transaxles and describe their major characteristics.

• Identify other foreign and/or domestic vehicle models using transmissions or transaxles manufactured by Chrysler, JATCO, Aisin-Warner/Borg-Warner, and Mitsubishi.

Well over half of all transmission shops now handle foreign transmissions in addition to domestic. This chapter contains a representative sampling of transmissions and transaxles produced by foreign manufacturers.

JATCO AUTOMATIC TRANSMISSIONS

The basic design for this automatic transmission was developed cooperatively for Ford and the Japanese Automatic Transmission Company

(JATCO) in the early 1970s. Variations have been used in Ford, Chrysler, Mazda, Nissan/Datsun, and Mitsubishi passenger cars and light trucks. They are aluminum-cased, metric units with bolt-on bell and extension housings. Current models are summarized in Table 14-1.

Model identification is stamped on a metal plate attached to the transmission case. Exploded views are presented in Figures 14-1 (three-speed) and 14-2 (four speed). Note that they tend to follow Chrysler **nomenclature** (part and assembly names), referring to the high-reverse clutch as the front clutch and the forward clutch as the rear clutch. They all use an IX gear pump driven by the torque converter hub.

Both four-speed units (L4N71B and E4N71B) have electronically controlled torque converter lock-up. The electronic control unit (ECU) senses vehicle speed from governor input and activates the lock-up solenoid under preprogrammed conditions.

The third/overdrive shift on the L4N71B can be blocked by a switch controlled by the driver. In the *Off* position the switch *activates* the solenoid, which prevents the transmission from shifting into overdrive. Therefore, when testing the switch, there is no continuity when the switch is on, but there is continuity when the switch is off—a good example of the importance of having the right technical information when troubleshooting!

The E4N71B provides electronically controlled lock-up in all forward speeds—again activated by the ECU when preprogrammed conditions are present. The ECU also selects "standard" or "power" shift pattern depending on the rate at which the accelerator pedal is depressed. The "power" pattern activates the overdrive solenoid, unlocking the converter so that torque multiplication can take effect.

The JATCO transmissions also use a downshift solenoid. Note also that the vacuum modulator is called the vacuum diaphragm. It and both the overdrive band and second gear band are adjustable.

Clutch and band applications are summarized in Figure 14-3 for the three-speed models and Figure 14-4 for the four-speed models.

TOYOTA AUTOMATIC TRANSMISSIONS

Model A4OD is one of several similar four-speed, overdrive transmissions produced for various RWD

Toyota models; it is found in the Celica. The Corolla uses A-42DC; the pickup uses A-43D; the Cressida and Supra use A-43DE (an electronically controlled hydraulic shift—see the Toyota Automatic Transaxle section later in this chapter); the van uses A-44DC. All except the A-4OD and A-43D use lock-up torque converters. A Simpson compound planetary is used for three forward speeds and reverse. Overdrive is provided through a simple planetary gearset (Figure 14-5). Note that Toyota uses radial roller bearings rather than thrust washers. The IX gear pump is driven by the torque converter hub.

The planetaries are controlled by three multiple-disc clutches, two **multiple-disc brakes** (instead of bands), and three one-way clutches. Multiple-disc brakes are simply multiple-disc clutches that have one element anchored rather than both elements rotating.

Toyota also makes a front-wheel-drive transmission, the Model A-55, shown in Figure 14-6. Sometimes referred to as a transaxle, this unit sits in-line with a longitudinally mounted engine and has a beveled hypoid ring-and-pinion final drive. Its general configuration is similar to the General Motors THM-325, 325-L and the older THM-425 transmissions.

AISIN-WARNER/BORG-WARNER AUTOMATIC TRANSMISSIONS

These transmissions may be supplied by either of the two manufacturers. The AW-55 or BW-55 is a three-speed unit, and the AW-70 and AW-71 are four-speed. Manufacturers, model number, and serial number appear on a plate on the left side of the transmission. Vehicles that use these transmissions include Isuzu I-Mark, Impulse, P'UP, and Volvo. Beginning in 1987, certain Chrysler models use an adaptation of the four-speed.

A Simpson compound planetary gearset is used for both three- and four-speed, with a simple planetary added to the latter for overdrive (Figure 14-7).

The three-speed is controlled by two multiple-disc clutches three multiple-disc brakes (anchor clutches), and two one-way clutches. Clutch and band applications for both the three- and four-speed units are summarized in Figure 14-8.

TABLE 14-1

JATCO transmissions

Jatco Model No.[a]	Speeds	Gearsets	Multiple-Disc Clutches[b]	Multiple Disc Brake[c]	Brake Band	One-way Clutch	Lock-Up Converter	Other
3N17B	3	1 Simpson	2	1	1	1	No	—
L3N71B	3	1 Simpson	2	1	1	1	Yes	—
L4N71B	4	1 Simpson 1 Simple (O.D.)	3	1	2	1	Yes	Electronic control of lock-up and third/overdrive
E4N71B	4	1 Simpson 1 Simple (O.D.)	3	1	2	1	Yes	Electronic control of lock-up in all forward speeds; "Std" or "pwr" shift patterns

[a]The Chrysler JATCO is a four-speed designated JM 600.
[b]Quantity of plates varies depending on application.
[c]Multiple-disc clutch anchored to case.

236

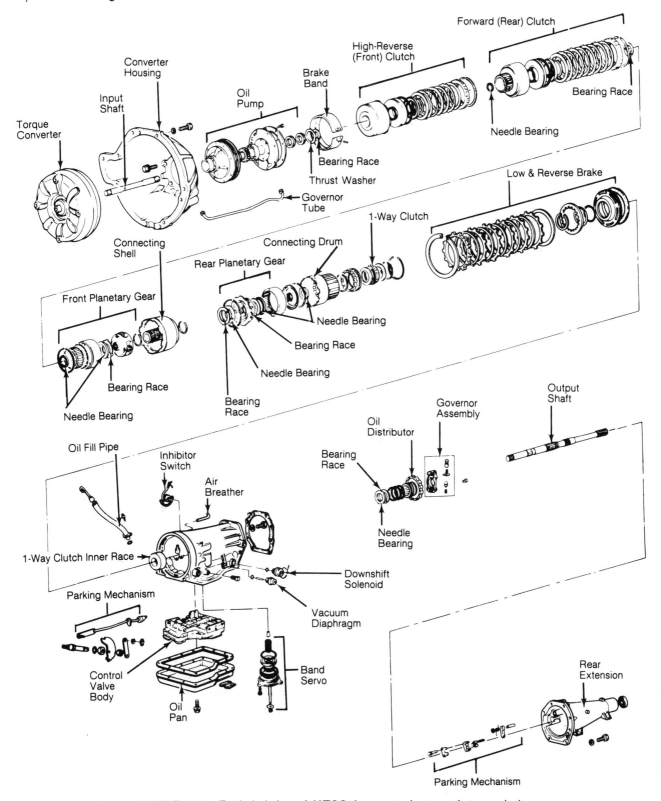

FIGURE 14-1   Exploded view of JATCO three-speed automatic transmission.

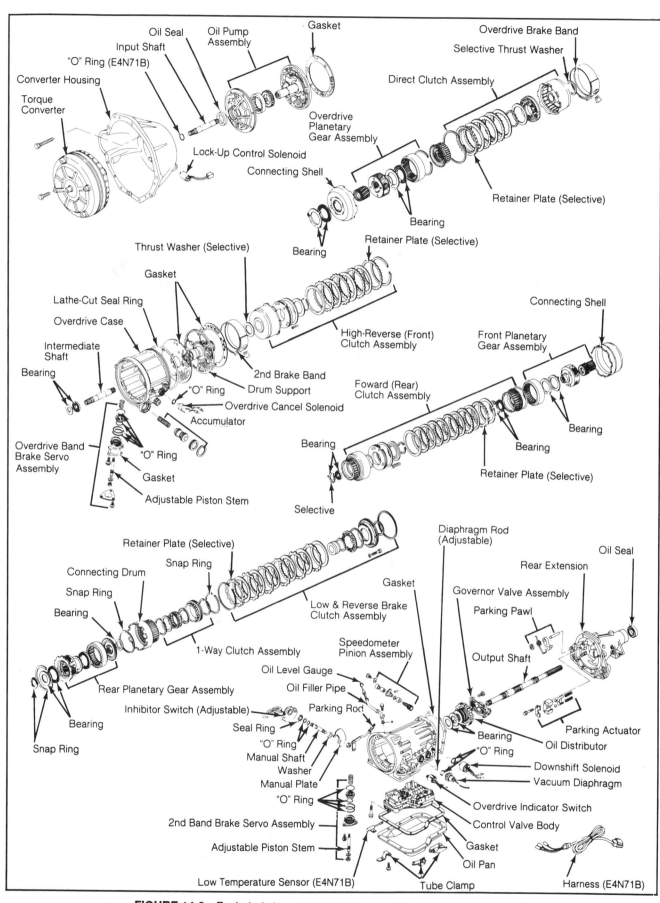

FIGURE 14-2 Exploded view of JATCO four-speed automatic transmission.

Selector Lever Position	High-Reverse (Front) Clutch	Forward (Rear) Clutch	Low-Reverse Brake	Brake Band	One-Way Clutch
P – PARK			X		
R – REVERSE	X		X		
N – NEUTRAL [1]					
D – DRIVE					
First		X			X
Second		X		X	
Direct	X	X			
2 – SECOND		X		X	
1 – LOW					
First		X	X		
Second		X		X	

[1] – NEUTRAL or PARK – All clutches and bands released and/or ineffective.

FIGURE 14-3   Clutch and band application summary for JATCO three-speed automatic transmissions.

HONDA AUTOMATIC TRANSAXLES

The Honda three-speed (Civic) and four-speed (Accord and Prelude) automatic transaxles are unconventional. Instead of using planetary gearsets, they use **constant-mesh** helical- and square-cut gears that are controlled by multiple-disc clutches, a sprag (one-way clutch), and a shift fork for sliding gear engagement of reverse. They are something like a manual transmission, having a mainshaft and countershaft, except that more gears turn independently on the shafts, the gears can be locked to the shafts by application of the clutches. Hydraulic clutch application is controlled by valves and servos under throttle and governor pressure. Design of the oil pump incorporates two external spur gears, one of which is driven by the torque converter hub. Final drive consists of a helical cut ring gear bolted to the differential carrier and in constant mesh with a pinion that is integral with the countershaft.

Figure 14-9 shows a cutaway view of the three-speed unit, and a summary of clutch applications appears in Figure 14-10.

MITSUBISHI AUTOMATIC TRANSAXLES

Variations designated KM170, KM171, and KM172 identify these three-speed transaxles. They are used in the Dodge Colt, Vista, Mitsubishi Cordia, and Tredia vehicles—the last three with a lock-up torque converter. What makes these transaxles unique is that they mount on the passenger side with the engine on the driver's side. This requires a CCW output that is accomplished by placing an idler gear between the transfer drive gear and driven gear. (There is a cross-section illustration that appears in many manuals—both manufacturers' and independents'—that shows the idler gear running off the driven gear only, instead of between the two trans-

MERCEDES AND HONDA PUMPS

Honda is not the only one with a unique hydraulic pump system. Mercedes uses two pumps in its transmission, just like some early domestic transmissions did. The primary pump is an IX gear type located at the front of the transmission, and the secondary pump located at the rear uses two external gears, just like the Honda does.

Selector Lever Position	Direct Clutch	Overdrive Band	High-Reverse (Ft.) Clutch	Forward (Rear) Clutch	Low & Reverse Brake	Brake Band	One-Way Clutch
P – PARK	X	X			X		
R – REVERSE	X	X	X		X		
N – NEUTRAL [1]	X	X					
D – DRIVE							
First	X	X		X			X
Second	X	X		X		X	
Direct	X	X	X	X		X	
Overdrive		X	X	X		X	
2 – SECOND	X	X		X		X	
1 – LOW							
Second	X	X		X		X	
First	X	X		X	X		X

[1] – NEUTRAL or PARK – All clutches and bands released and/or ineffective.

FIGURE 14-4 Clutch and band application summary for JATCO four-speed automatic transmissions.

◄ FRONT

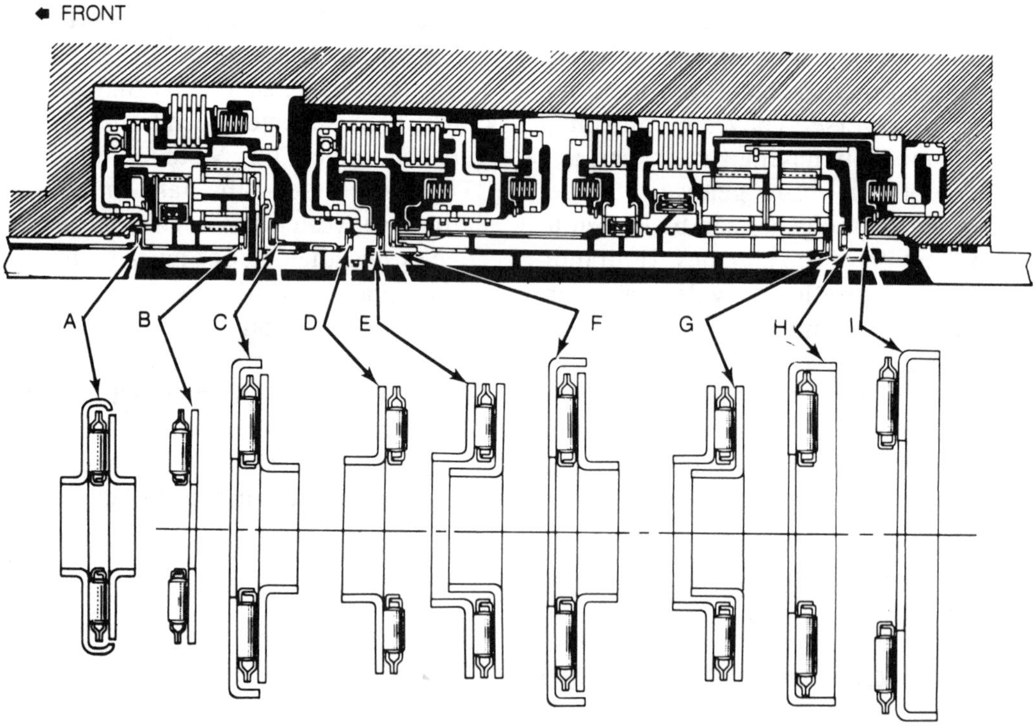

FIGURE 14-5 Toyota A-40 series automatic transmission section showing thrust bearing location.

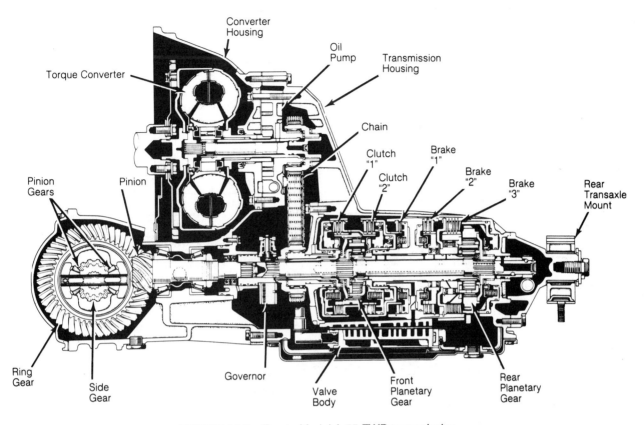

FIGURE 14-6 Toyota Model A-55 FWD transmission.

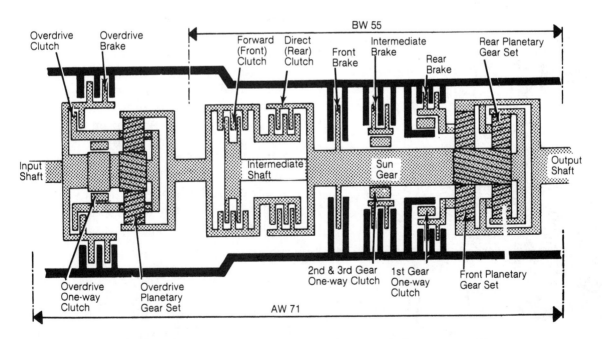

FIGURE 14-7 AW-71/BW-55 automatic transmission power train schematic.

Selector Lever Position	Forward (Front) Clutch	Direct (Rear) Clutch	Overdrive (OD) Clutch (70 & 71 Only)	Planetary Gear	Brake	One-Way Clutch	Overdrive Brake (70 & 71 Only)
D – DRIVE							
First	Applied		Applied	Both		Rear/OD	
Second	Applied		Applied	Rear	No. 2	Front/OD	
Third	Applied	Applied	Applied	Direct ¹	No. 2	OD	
Overdrive (70 & 71 Only)	Applied	Applied		Direct/OD	No. 2		Applied
2 – SECOND							
First	Applied		Applied	Both		Rear/OD	
Second	Applied		Applied	Rear	No. 1 & No. 2	Front/OD	
1 – LOW	Applied		Applied	Both	No. 3	Rear/OD	
R – REVERSE		Applied	Applied	Front	No. 3	OD	
P – PARK			Applied ²		No. 3 ²		
N – NEUTRAL			Applied				

¹ – Direct means planetary gear set is locked up with 1:1 ratio.
² – With engine running.

FIGURE 14-8 Clutch and band application summary for Aisin-Warner/Borg-Warner three- and four-speed automatic transmissions.

fer gears; this is an error.) Figure 14-11 showing pressure test and other connections, also labels the locations of drive, idler, and driven gears.

An IX gear pump is driven by the torque converter hub, and the transaxle uses a Ravigneaux compound planetary gearset controlled by three multiple-disk clutches (one of which is grounded to act as a brake), a band, and a one-way clutch (Figure 14-12). Clutch and band application is summarized in Figure 14-13.

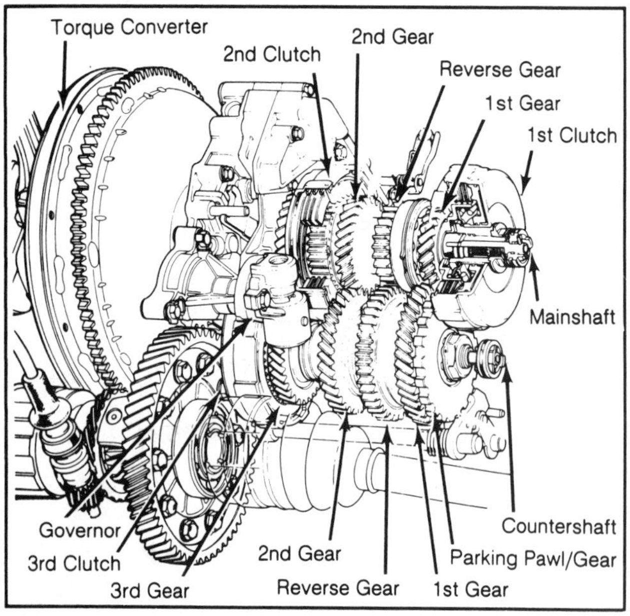

NISSAN/DATSUN AUTOMATIC TRANSAXLE

This is a three-speed unit that uses a lock-up converter for gasoline engine applications (RS3F01A). When used with diesel engines, a standard three-element converter is used, and the transaxle is designed RN3F01A. A Simpson compound planetary gearset is controlled by three multiple-disc clutches (one of which is a brake), a band, and a one-way clutch. An IX gear pump is driven by the torque converter hub. A sectional view is shown in Figure 14-14. Clutch and band application is summarized in Figure 14-15.

RENAULT AUTOMATIC TRANSAXLES

Renault makes two entirely different transaxles: Model MB1/MB3 for the Renault Alliance and MJ1/MJ3 used in the Renault Fuego and Renault 18 and 18i. The configuration of the latter makes it readily identifiable; its two-piece case locates the

FIGURE 14-9 Honda three-speed automatic transaxle.

Selector Lever Position	Low Clutch	Second Clutch	Third Clutch	Sprag Clutch
D — DRIVE				
First	X			X
Second	X	X		
Third	X		X	
2 — MANUAL		X		
REVERSE		X		

NEUTRAL OR PARK — All clutch and sprag clutch released and/or ineffective.

FIGURE 14-10 Clutch application summary for Honda three-speed automatic transaxle.

final drive between the torque converter and gearbox, and it is designed for longitudinally mounted engines (Figure 14-16). Note that the change of rotation is achieved by gears labeled "**step-down gears**" on the end of the pinion gear shaft and output shaft—what domestic manufacturers call transfer gears (Figure 14-17). This transmission, Model MJ, uses a Ravigneaux compound planetary gearset controlled by four multiple-disc clutches (two acting as brakes) and a one-way roller clutch.

Model MB is designed for the transverse-mounted engine configuration and is a true transaxle. It, like the MJ, has a stepdown gearset; but it provides CW wheel rotation in forward speeds for the right-hand-mounted engine. It uses a Simpson compound planetary gearset controlled by four multiple-disc clutches (two acting as brakes) and a one-way roller clutch (Figure 14-18).

Both the MB and MJ models are three-speed units, and shifting is accomplished with hydraulic pressure controlled by solenoid valves. The governor is electronic and feeds to a computer, which interprets road speed and throttle opening (through a potentiometer) to open or close the solenoid valves at programmed shift points. IX gear pumps are located opposite the torque converter and are driven by their own shafts.

TOYOTA AUTOMATIC TRANSAXLE

Toyota has both a transmission (A43DE used in Cressida and Supra) and a transaxle that incorporates electronically controlled shifting. They are often referred to as **ECT** for Electronically Controlled Transmission/Transaxle.

The transaxle, designated A140E, was introduced in the Camry. Figure 14-19 presents a cross section of the A140E showing a Simpson compound planetary gearset which produces all speeds but overdrive; the latter is furnished by a simple planetary gearset located on the intermediate shaft beyond the counter gear. Power transfer is achieved through the **counter gears**—one on the main shaft and one on the pinion shaft—to produce CW wheel rotation in forward speeds for the right-hand-mounted engine. These gearsets are controlled by six multiple-disc clutches (three of which act as brakes), a band, and three one-way clutches. The lock-up torque converter is also electronically controlled for lock-up in second, third, or fourth gears. A detailed description of the electronic control shifting appears in Chapter 7.

Toyota also makes a three-speed conventionally shifted automatic transaxle designated the A-130L or A-131L. The primary difference between the two is in final drive gear ratio, valve body springs, and line and governor pressures. This results in different shifting patterns for the two, as shown in Figure 14-20.

VOLKSWAGEN

The transaxle used in transverse-engine FWD vehicles made by Volkswagen is called Type 010. It is one of two configurations: one for transverse-mounted engines and one for longitudinally

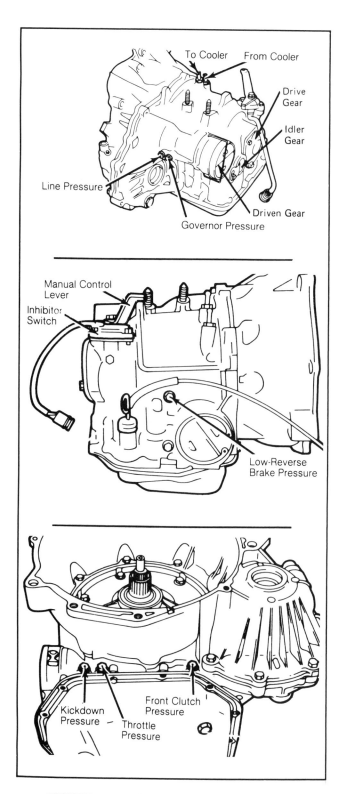

FIGURE 14-11 Mitsubishi automatic transaxle external connections and pressure test locations.

mounted engines. The latter includes Type 090, used in the Vanagon and Types 087 and 089. Type 089 is used in certain models of the Audi and Volkswagen Quantum, and Type 087 is used in other models of both those makes as well as in the Porsche 944. The main difference between Type 087 and Type 089 is the length of the turbine shaft: 16.71 in. (424.5 mm) and 15.82 in. (401.7 mm), respectively.

Both Type 010 and Types 087/089 are equipped with **"E" mode**: when the selector lever is in "E" position and the accelerator is released, freewheeling takes place. This is achieved by manufacturing changes in the valve body and forward clutch. "E" mode transaxles are used in diesel models to improve fuel economy.

All four types are three-speed units incorporating a Simpson compound planetary gearset controlled by three multiple-disc clutches (one of which—First/Reverse—acts as a brake), a band for second gear, and one-way clutch. An IX gear pump is driven by its own shaft off the torque converter, and the turbine shaft runs through the center of the final drive pinion and transmission shaft.

Figures 14-21 and 14-22 show the transmission and final drive, respectively, for Types 087/089/090. Look at the final drive exploded view (Figure 14-22). The differential assembly and final drive unit just visible at the left, or front, of the case is installed through the torque converter end over to where it aligns with the differential side bearing outer races and the drive flanges: The left end of the pinion shaft passes over the differential to the front cover, and the right end of the pinion shaft rides in the rear cover, which bolts to the right, or rear, end of the case. This leaves part of the pinion shaft projecting, and when the transmission is bolted on, that part of the pinion shaft becomes the output shaft. Figure 14-23 shows a more complete external view typical of Types 087/089/090. Note the tip of the oil pump shaft at the left of the final drive housing. Protruding from the right side is the turbine (input) shaft spline; and the spline just to the left of that is the output shaft spline (integral with the pinion shaft and gear, as can be seen in Figure 14-22).

Type 010 deviates from the customary case design for transverse-engine FWD units. The housing for its torque converter and final drive is one

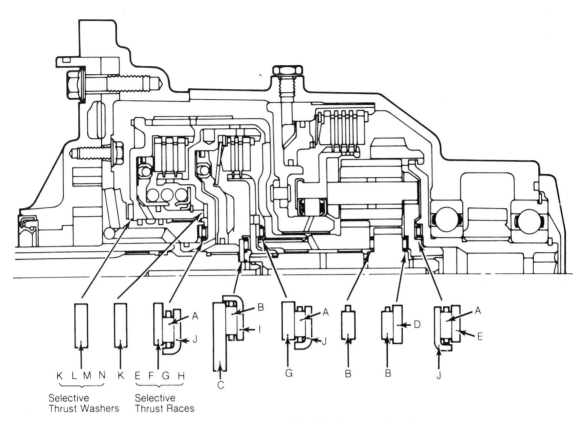

FIGURE 14-12 Half section of Mitsubishi transaxle showing thrust washer and selective thrust race locations.

Selector Lever Position	Forward Clutch	Direct-Reverse Clutch	First-Reverse Brake	Second Gear Band	One-Way Clutch
D – DRIVE First Gear Second Gear Third Gear	 X	 X X X		 X	 X X
2 – INTERMEDIATE First Gear Second Gear		 X X		 X	 X
1 – LOW (First)		X	X		
R – REVERSE	X		X		

NEUTRAL OR PARK – All clutches, brakes, and bands released or ineffective.

FIGURE 14-13 Clutch and band application summary for Mitsubishi automatic transaxle.

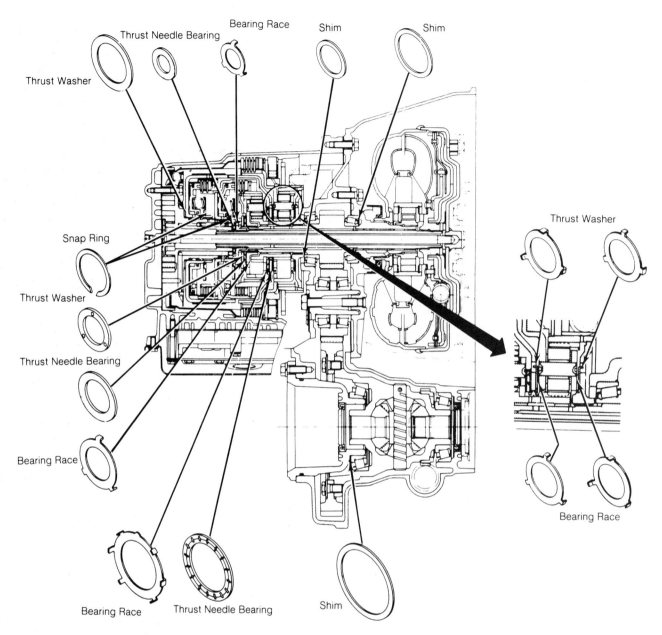

FIGURE 14-14   Nissan/Datsun automatic transaxle sectional view showing thrust washer location.

unit (Figure 14-24.) So, as with the other Volkswagen transaxles, the transmission case bolts to one end and the engine to the other. But unlike the others, its final drive consists of two helical cut gears. Figure 14-25 shows the complete final drive unit at a later stage of assembly. Studied together, these two illustrations present a pretty thorough picture of the entire assembly.

Clutch and band application for all four transaxles is identical and is summarized in Figure 14-26.

(Trade Terms for this chapter follow on p. 249)

| Selector
Lever Position | Clutch | | Low-Reverse
Brake | 1-Way
Clutch | Band Servo | |
	High-Reverse (Front)	Forward (Rear)			Operation	Release

D – DRIVE
  Low
  Second
  Third [2]
	
	X
		
		X
		X
		X
			
			1
			
				X
				
					X
					X
						
						X

2 – Second Gear
  Low
  Second
		
		X
		X
				
				X
				
					X	

1 – First Gear
  Low
  Second
		
		X
		X
			
			X
			
				X
				
					X	

R – Reverse	X		X			

NEUTRAL OR PARK – All clutches and brakes released and/or ineffective.

1 – Low & reverse brake applied to prevent free wheeling when coasting and to provide engine braking.
2 – Lock-up converter engaged on all models except Sentra Diesel.

FIGURE 14-15   Clutch and band application summary for Nissan/Datsun three-speed transaxle.

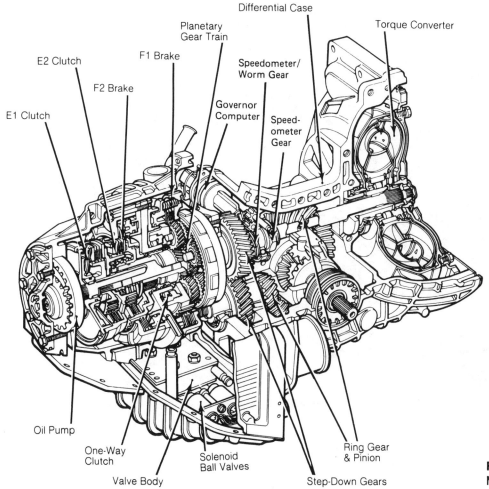

FIGURE 14-16   Renault Model MJ automatic transaxle.

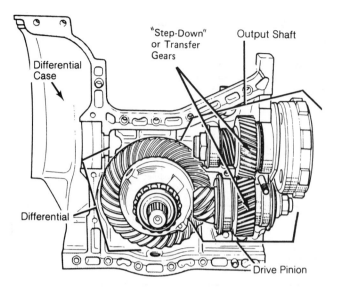

FIGURE 14-17 "Step-down" or transfer gears shown with ring and pinion final drive for Renault Model MJ transaxle.

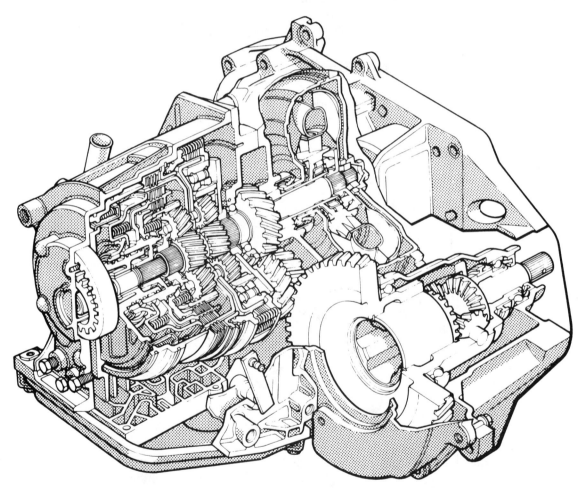

FIGURE 14-18 Renault Model MB automatic transaxle. (Courtesy of American Motors Corporation.)

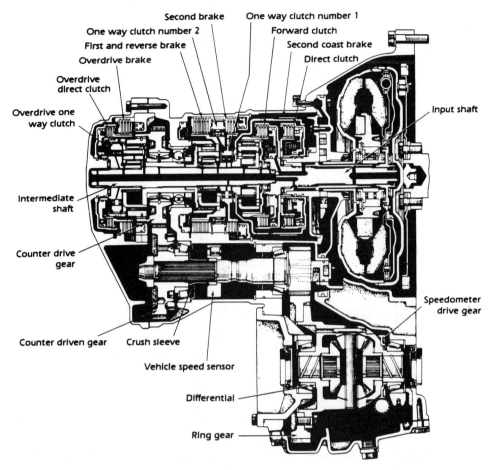

FIGURE 14-19   Toyota Model A140E automatic transaxle. (Courtesy of Toyota Motor Sales, USA.)

TRADE TERMS

Constant mesh	JATCO	Step-down gears
Counter gears	Multiple-disc	
ECT	brake	
"E" mode	Nomenclature	

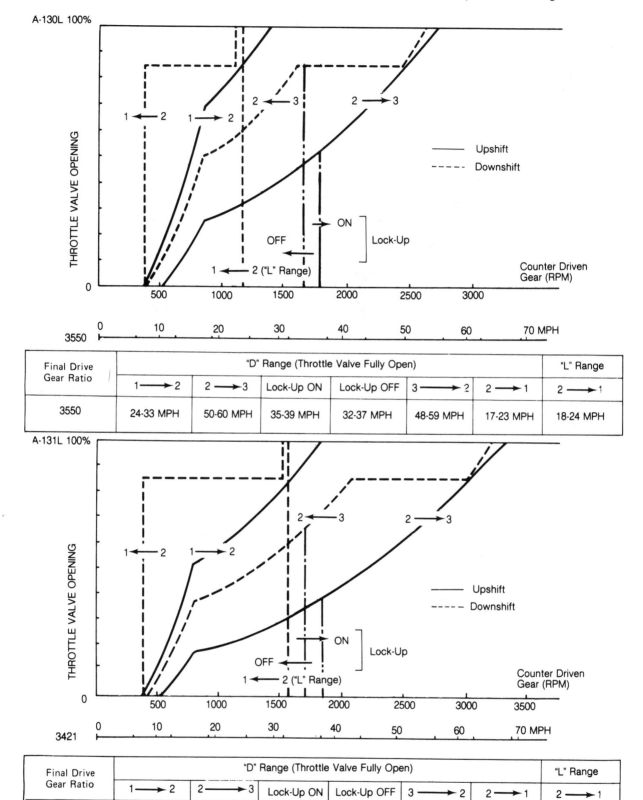

Final Drive Gear Ratio	"D" Range (Throttle Valve Fully Open)						"L" Range
	1 ⟶ 2	2 ⟶ 3	Lock-Up ON	Lock-Up OFF	3 ⟶ 2	2 ⟶ 1	2 ⟶ 1
3550	24-33 MPH	50-60 MPH	35-39 MPH	32-37 MPH	48-59 MPH	17-23 MPH	18-24 MPH

Final Drive Gear Ratio	"D" Range (Throttle Valve Fully Open)						"L" Range
	1 ⟶ 2	2 ⟶ 3	Lock-Up ON	Lock-Up OFF	3 ⟶ 2	2 ⟶ 1	2 ⟶ 1
3421	32-42 MPH	63-72 MPH	35-40 MPH	32-37 MPH	59-71 MPH	25-31 MPH	25-32 MPH

FIGURE 14-20 Shift patterns for the Toyota A-130 L and A-131 L three-speed automatic transaxles.

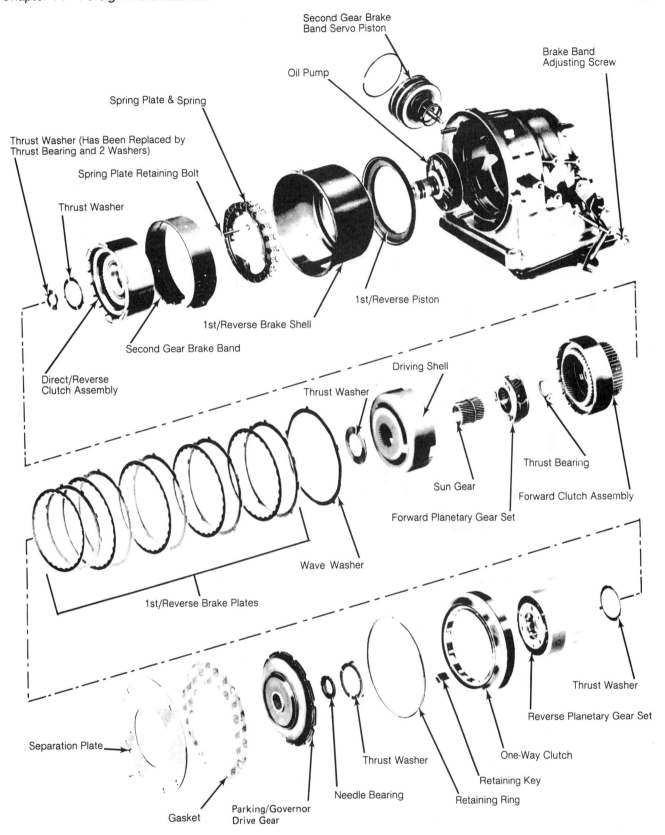

FIGURE 14-21   Volkswagen types 087/089/090 transmission assembly.

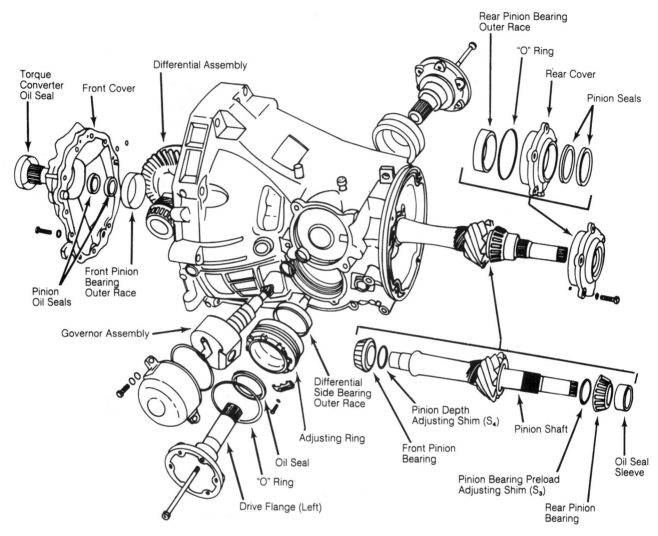

FIGURE 14-22 Volkswagen types 087/089/090 final drive assembly.

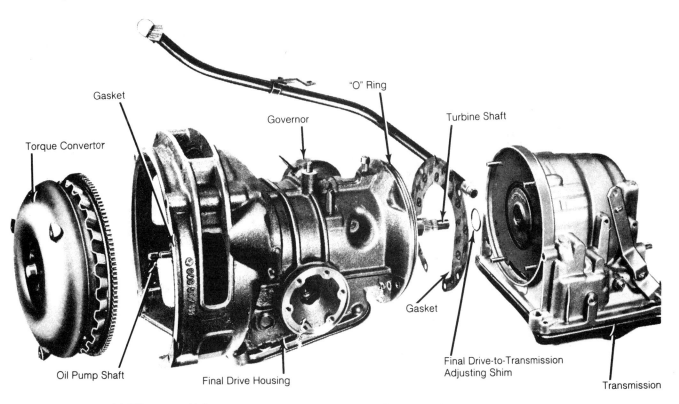

FIGURE 14-23 Volkswagen types 087/089/090 complete transmission/final drive assembly.

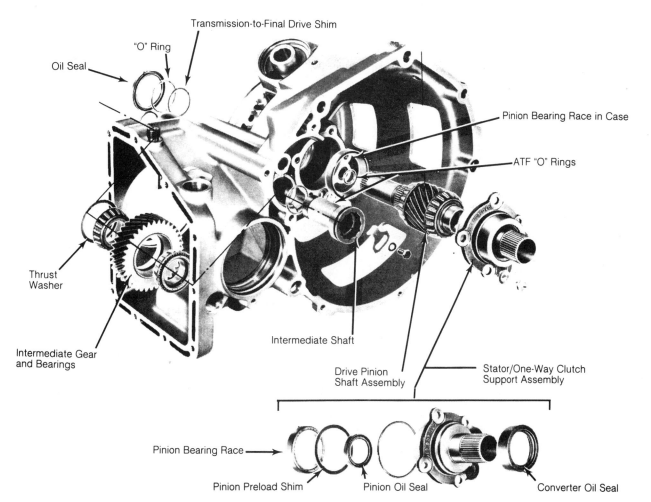

FIGURE 14-24 Volkswagen type 010 final drive/torque converter housing showing drive pinion and intermediate (transfer) gear.

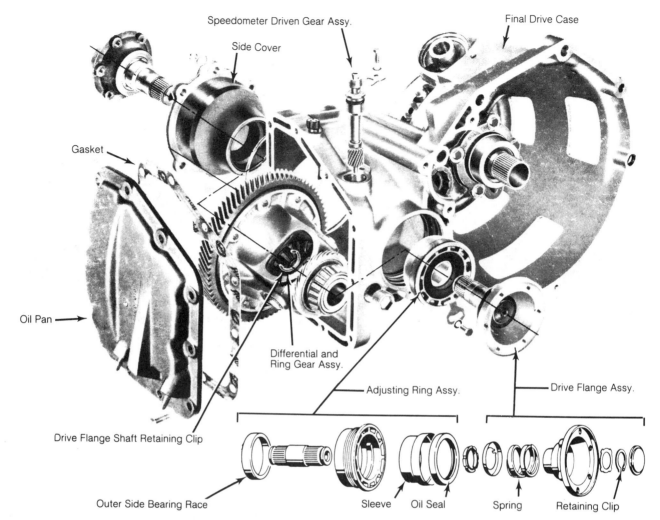

FIGURE 14-25 Volkswagen types 010 final drive/torque converter housing showing final drive ring gear/differential unit.

Selector Lever Position	Forward Clutch	Direct-Reverse Clutch	First-Reverse Brake	Second Gear Band	One-Way Clutch
D – DRIVE					
First Gear	X				X
Second Gear	X			X	
Third Gear	X	X			
2 – INTERMEDIATE					
First Gear	X				X
Second Gear	X			X	
1 – LOW (First)	X		X		
R – REVERSE		X	X		

NEUTRAL OR PARK – All clutches, brakes, and bands released and/or ineffective.

FIGURE 14-26 Clutch and band application summary for Vanagon automatic transaxle.

REVIEW QUESTIONS

14-1. The manufacturers of three foreign-made transmissions are _____, _____ and _____.

14-2. The manufacturers of four foreign-made transaxles are _____, _____, _____, and _____.

14-3. A significant difference between Honda automatic transaxles and others is that they do not use _____ gearsets.

14-4. Both Renault and Toyota have transaxles that incorporate _____ controlled shifting.

14-5. One of the JATCO models uses electronic controls, but only for lock-up of the torque converter.   T   F

14-6. What transmission make uses radial roller bearings in place of many thrust washers? _____

14-7. The Mitsubishi automatic transaxle mounts on the _____ side and has a _____ rotating output.

14-8. Renault makes two transaxles: one is for _____-mounted engines and the other is for _____-mounted ones.

14-9. What many manufacturers call transfer gears are labeled _____ gears by Renault and _____ gears by Toyota.

14-10. Instead of a centrifugally operated hydraulic governor valve used in most transaxles, the Renault and Toyota transaxles use an _____ operated governor that signals an electronic control unit, or computer, for shift timing.

14-11. The JATCO L4N71B shifts from third to overdrive electronically.   T   F

14-12. Instead of a modulator or direct-mechanical linkage, electronically controlled transmissions and transaxles such as those built by Toyota and Renault use a throttle position sensor, or _____.

14-13. The significant difference between the Toyota A-130L and A-131L transaxles is their _____ _____.

14-14. Which of the following Volkswagen transaxles is significantly different from the other three?
 (a) Type 010.
 (b) Type 087.
 (c) Type 089.
 (d) Type 090.

14-15. All four Volkswagen transmission models have identical clutch and band application.
 T   F

ESSAY QUESTIONS

14-1. Describe the most significant design characteristics of the Honda transaxles compared to any others.

14-2. Compare the major design characteristics of Volkswagen's Type 010 with those of the other Volkswagen types.

CHAPTER ACTIVITIES

14-1. Select four or five foreign cars or light trucks owned by people you know. Can you make an educated guess as to what transmission model is in each?

14-2. Identify as many of the foreign car transmissions in your shop as you can.

15

Modification for Heavy-Duty Operation

OBJECTIVES

When you have completed this chapter, you should be able to:

- Recognize system modifications if you encounter them during disassembly and repair of automatic transmissions.
- Name the modified parts likely to be found in most shift recalibration kits.
- Discuss, in general terms, the trade-off among such requirements as economy, comfort, reliability, and performance with respect to automatic transmission design.

Automatic transmissions, like anything else, are designed to meet particular requirements. Automotive design engineers have based these requirements on the needs of the majority of the users. In very general terms, these include economy, comfort, reliability, and performance. But there are trade-offs among these needs. For example, if greater emphasis is placed on economy, there may be some sacrifice in comfort or performance.

The manufacturer considers all the needs for a particular transmission application and then prepares design requirements based on what it considers the best trade-off balance. So the initial transmission design suits the biggest part of the market. The remainder of the market is reconsidered for variations of the initial design.

But there is a practical limit to the number of design variations. And the best balance, by definition, never completely satisfies all the needs. Consequently, a relatively small percentage of the original market is sufficiently dissatisfied to be willing to pay for further design variations that will produce a transmission that better meets its needs. But this part of the market is too small for the giant OEMs to serve. So this creates what has come to be referred to as the "**aftermarket**." It includes parts manufacturing and associated services for repair and for modification.

It is important for automotive technicians to be familiar with manufacturers' original equipment specifications and procedures. It is also very helpful to become familiar with aftermarket equipment, specifications, and procedures to help enrich one's technical knowledge and practice.

MODIFICATION APPLICATIONS

When we think of modifying automotive systems and subassemblies, racing, tractor pulls, and other such forms of sports competition come to mind. Yet there is another, less dramatic, but equally challenging and rewarding application—heavy-duty operation. Anything other than the ideal operating conditions can fall under extreme operating conditions, as we discussed in Chapter 10. And extreme operating conditions and heavy-duty operation are the same thing. It can apply to passenger cars as well as delivery vehicles and off-road vehicles; to motor homes as well as other special-duty truck applications.

Most aftermarket suppliers and services focus on domestic makes and models with regard to heavy-duty operation. This follows, since the domestic emphasis has been on power and the foreign more on economy. So aftermarket parts and modification kits for heavy-duty operation are made available mostly for selected models of Chrysler, Ford, and General Motors.

Of course, there are a number of inventors in the field who do their own modification design and fabrication. Some have studied engineering; others are simply competent, creative journeymen. Most are involved in racing competition and heavy-equipment rebuilding and repair.

But the aftermarket has brought ready-modification within anyone's reach. So even of you are working for a new car dealer where the emphasis is on the OEM parts and assemblies, you are quite possibly going to run into transmissions that customers have had modified elsewhere.

Generally speaking, modifications fall into three categories:

- System modification
- Structural modification
- Supplemental modification

System modification involves one or more functional changes which consider the entire assembly as well as other assemblies related to its performance. **Structural modification** consists of substituting improved parts and assemblies that have been strengthened to correct some inherent structural weakness, or changed to improve durability, operation, or lubrication. Occasionally, these are OEM parts for other applications. **Supplemental modifications** add parts and assemblies to the original design.

SYSTEM MODIFICATION

Shift timing and quality is one of the most popular modifications. It is called **shift modification** or shift recalibration.

Shift timing is set by the manufacturer to make best use of engine peak horsepower for a specific vehicle under set driving conditions. If any of the vehicle specifications or driving conditions change, the shifts may then take place before peak horsepower has been reached.

Shift quality is set by the manufacturer to provide the best trade-off between comfort and economy—a relatively soft shift, but not one of excessive duration. If comfort is not as important, modifications to provide firmer shifts of shorter duration will improve power, efficiency, and economy.

Shift recalibrating is a system modification. It can include modifications to the valve body assembly, governor, modulator, and accumulator.

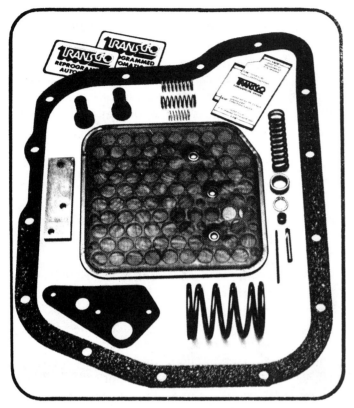

FIGURE 15-1 Shift recalibration kits improve performance and durability.

Most good aftermarket manufacturers consider the entire power train—the whole system—when designing modifications. The modified parts are then sold as kits (Figure 15-1).

A shift recalibrating kit usually includes one or more spool valves whose land size and location may be modified, a number of valve springs of modified tension and stiffness, and of course, gaskets and occasionally filters. Many include a new separator plate with orifices that have been closed (e.g., to eliminate an accumulator circuit) or modified to increase pressure. Some include a new adjustable vacuum modulator and/or new accumulator pistons. Each part in the kit has been designed to work best with other parts in the kit and the remaining parts and assemblies in the transmission itself.

Governor kits are also available for further adjustment in shift timing. Governor modification kits include a number of different-size flyweights and springs. These are designed to delay wide-open throttle shifts, however, so they are used more for competition modification than for heavy-duty

operation. The OEM governor is usually set for peak horsepower rpm, so there is little need to change it unless the engine has been modified to peak at higher rpm.

Another system modification is the **high-stall torque converter**. Its purpose is to extend the duration of torque multiplication so that the coupling phase is reached at higher rpm, where competition engines reach their peak of horsepower. Higher stall speed can be achieved by using a smaller-diameter torque converter (Figure 15-2). There are other means of changing stall speeds that involve modifications of the torque converter itself, but these are more expensive.

So stall speed for any particular torque converter will be somewhere in a *range* of stall speed, depending on the power curve for the engine that is running it. In other words, the same torque converter will stall at a higher rpm when driven by a larger engine than it will when driven by a small one. In fact, stall speed will also depend on engine condition. The same converter run by a poorly tuned engine will stall at a lower speed than it will when the engine is tuned up. Consequently, torque converter stall speeds are specified as a range.

In contrast to high-stall converters, low-stall converters, slip less and run cooler. So heavy-duty applications, such as motor homes, do better with lower-stall-speed (larger-diameter) converters. They reach the coupling phase earlier, which minimizes slipping and heat buildup for greater operating economy.

But, here too, the stall speed and engine power curve must be considered together, or there will be

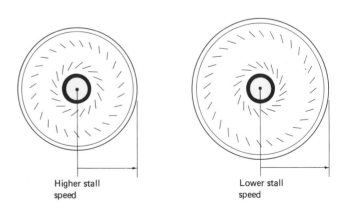

Higher stall speed　　　　　　　Lower stall speed

FIGURE 15-2 On the same engine, the larger torque converter stalls at a lower speed than the smaller.

an engine/torque converter mismatch. Rarely would any advantage be gained by changing to a larger torque converter in a vehicle made for heavy-duty operation (even if there were room in the bell housing to do it), because the manufacturer has already made the best stall speed/power curve match.

Still another system modification—one you are not likely to run into unless you are working on competition vehicles—is manual control of the torque converter clutch. For vehicles using a solenoid valve (GM and others) it is simply a matter of locking out a couple of electrical circuits and installing a toggle switch on the dash. Some production vehicles now have a driver-controlled switch that prevents a shift from direct to overdrive. Some also prevent clutch lock-up through computer controls when torque multiplication for hard pulls or acceleration is sensed.

Valve body modification kits are also available that permit a shift to low gear at any speed, and others are available that convert totally to manual shift operation. These are used exclusively for competition, however.

STRUCTURAL MODIFICATION

Occasionally, a production assembly appears with some inherent structural weakness. More often than not, it lies with one part. There can be one or more reasons for this: Perhaps the part did not receive full design attention or testing; or perhaps the problem can be attributed to slight modifications made in material or fabrication techniques in order to suit production processes. Whatever the reason, if its failure is sufficiently widespread, the aftermarket will soon offer an improved replacement part.

OEMs do this, too, but they are not always as fast to respond.

Examples of structurally modified parts include those made from stronger materials (e.g., metal rather than some weaker material) and those made with more material or reinforcement at critical stress areas (such as fillets and webs). OEMs, in striving to hold down costs, can inadvertently compromise material or fabrication quality. Another example occurs among standard parts such as bearings, bushings, and one-way clutches. These parts are selected from manufacturers of parts and subassemblies by the assembly designer on the basis of furnished specifications. Sometimes they do not stand up as expected and a new selection can be made from standard parts catalogs that will better fit the application.

Also on the market are modified parts of questionable real improvement but which offer an alternative in cases where technical opinion differs. Clutch disk composition and groove patterns are one example. There are some fairly well-established criteria for when to use paper and when to use molded semimetallic material for normal operation, but within these two categories there are as many variations of opinion of what is best as there are different compositions; the same is true of groove patterns.

SUPPLEMENTAL MODIFICATIONS

Auxiliary coolers and additions to clutch packs are two examples of supplemental modifications. In fact, one of the significant differences among OEM transmission model variations is the number of clutch discs and plates used. Some aftermarket

SERIES VERSUS PARALLEL

Just what is the difference between transmitting energy to several points in *series* and transmitting it in *parallel*? Whether it is electricity, fluid, or any other medium, points that are connected in parallel will remain connected even if one of them is disconnected. On the other hand, a disconnection in series disconnects all points further along the series.

Another way of remembering it is that in series, energy must go through one point to reach another, and so on. In parallel, energy reaches all points simultaneously. Series is sequential; parallel is simultaneous.

SUPPLEMENTAL FILTER

The aftermarket offers a cartridge-type oil filter unit than can be installed in the transmission cooling circuit for additional filtering. It is the same "spin-on" design that is used on most engines. In fact, the cartridge can be replaced with any of several popular brands of engine oil filter.

ATF TEMPERATURE GAUGE

There are a number of makes and styles of temperature gauge sold in the aftermarket. Some are digital, others analog. Many have probe-type sending units; some use a sensor that can be bonded to a surface. A temperature gauge with the right sending unit can be used to measure the temperature of anything, as long as its range of scale includes that anticipated range of temperature you want to measure. The types with probe sensors respond faster than those with surface sensors that bond to the case, but the latter are easier to install if there is no existing probe fitting. Transmission temperature gauges are standard instrumentation in most heavy equipment, and they are often added to the larger recreational vehicles and others used for a lot of towing.

manufacturers offer instructions for machining clutch pistons for more clearance to accept additional discs and plates.

Of all modifications, cooling is perhaps the most popular and easiest to achieve. Auxiliary coolers are the most effective (Chapter 6) and are readily available from a number of aftermarket suppliers. With few exceptions they are hooked up in series; that is, hot ATF circulates first through the existing cooler (usually through coils within the engine cooling system radiator) then through the auxiliary cooler, which is an air-cooled radiator mounted in front of the engine radiator—and air conditioning condenser (also a radiator) if so equipped (Figure 15-3). The exceptions to installing auxiliary coolers in series occur when there is a damaged or leaking internal OEM radiator cooler; also, some vehicles have insufficient room in front of the radiator, requiring the cooler to be mounted elsewhere. Obviously, it should be mounted where it is exposed to the coolest circulating air. But where it is to be used together with the OEM cooler, it must be connected in series. If connected in parallel, the inherent differences in flow rate for each cooler can render one of them less effective than it would be if connected in series.

Other types of cooling modifications include finned sump pans and oversized pans—the latter

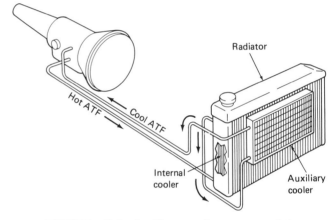

FIGURE 15-3 Auxiliary cooler connected in series with internal radiator cooler.

helpful primarily when adding an auxiliary cooler, which increases the transmission capacity for ATF.

Another popular supplemental modification is the sump pan drain plug (Figure 15-4). Although this is not necessarily just a heavy-duty modification, it might be installed in vehicles that operate in conditions where fluid contamination is more likely, or any vehicle in which ATF is changed frequently. But the value of this modification is questionable: on one hand, the last time you pulled a transmission pan, you probably once again cursed the manufacturer for not putting a drain plug in it

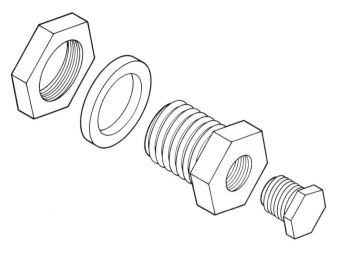

FIGURE 15-4   Aftermarket sump pan drain plug.

after the inevitable splash of ATF; but on the other, a drain plug offers the lazier ones among us the option for changing fluid without pulling the pan and checking for excess metal flakes or carbon bits from burnt clutches and bands. And anyway, practice under relatively normal use would have you changing ATF only three or four times during the life of the transmission, so the OEMs figure that no drain plug forces the pan to be pulled and inspected. Makes sense. The same is true for the torque converter drain plug.

In summary, heavy-duty rather than competition modifications of factory parts and assemblies are more likely to be encountered by automotive technicians working in dealerships and independent repair shops. But some modifications apply to both. Thus, it is well worthwhile keeping abreast of aftermarket developments. These include system, structural, and supplemental modifications. OEMs conduct ongoing activities of testing and field (dealer) feedback (e.g., warranty programs) and produce modified (improved) parts through engineering changes. Relatively little is made of this, except for the common plea among OEMs to use "original" or "genuine" replacement parts.

TRADE TERMS

Aftermarket	Shift	Supplemental
High-stall	recalibration	modification
torque	Structural	System
converter	modification	modification

REVIEW QUESTIONS

15-1. Of two different-diameter torque converters driven by the same engine, the (smaller, larger) _____ will be the high-stall converter.

15-2. Low-stall torque converters create more heat then high-stall converters do.   T   F

15-3. Manual control of torque converter clutches and automatic transmission shifting are usually applied to vehicles used for _____.

15-4. Extreme operating conditions and heavy-duty operations are similar.   T   F

15-5. Shift recalibration kits are sold only for vehicles that have computer-controlled engines or electronic shift control.   T   F

15-6. Aftermarket automatic transmission performance improvement kits are limited primarily to_____ vehicles because most foreign vehicles are designed for _____.

15-7. Parts of other transmission models are sometimes found to be suitable for improved structural modifications.   T   F

15-8. Sometimes alternate selections from catalogs of standard parts provide suitable modifications.   T   F

15-9. Of all modifications, one of the easiest and most effective is _____.

15-10. Give one example of supplemental modification. _____

ESSAY QUESTIONS

15-1. Discuss, in general terms, the trade-off between economy and performance with respect to automatic transmission design.

15-2. What might be some modifications you would like to make? In what vehicles would you make them, and why?

FOR DISCUSSION

15-1. Aftermarket modifications usually void manufacturers' warranties. Do you think this is justified? Why?

15-2. In your opinion, why don't the OEMs market their modified (improved) parts in the same energetic manner that the aftermarket does?

16

Technical Manuals and Information

OBJECTIVES

When you have completed this chapter, you should be able to:

- Select from among available forms of technical publications the ones that will best suit your needs for a particular job.

- Make use of technical manuals with the same level of skill needed to use other forms of automotive tools and equipment.

- Keep up-to-date on areas of automotive technology that you are most heavily involved in by selecting appropriate magazines, bulletins, and video programs.

- Examine the content and organization of a technical manual, bulletin, or magazine article to determine your interest by surveying its key elements, such as table of contents, chapter titles, index, section heads and paragraphs.

Books are no substitute for experience, and as such, even the best of technical manuals only complement the efforts of a well-trained and experienced automotive technician. But successful journeymen clearly recognize the value of good technical reference materials—selecting them with the same care, and valuing them to the same degree that they do their personal tools and equipment.

In contrast to many books, technical manuals, or shop manuals, like any professional reference books, are expensive; but their reference value very quickly offsets their cost by providing up-to-date information that improves work efficiency, accuracy, and quality. The mark of any successful professional is underscored by how well that person stays abreast of new methods and developments in the field—it is as true for the automotive field as it is for medicine, law, education, and construction, to name a few.

FORMS OF TECHNICAL INFORMATION

Manuals of automotive technology fall into one of the following general categories:

- Manufacturer-published technical manuals
- Independently published technical manuals
- How-to-do-it books

Most manufacturers' technical manuals cover one vehicle model per volume and are topically organized by subassembly. Occasionally, manufacturers will publish a volume that deals with only one subassembly, but these are used primarily for training. The manufacturers' technical manuals are the primary source for the most complete information, since the manufacturing documents (drawings, blueprints, analysis, and test data) and the product itself are created there. And, of course, it is in the manufacturer's interest to publish this information and make it available to its dealers to ensure good maintenance and repair services for its products.

But if you run a general repair facility and regularly handle competing vehicle makes (as many dealers also do) you would spend a tremendous amount of money on manuals for each of the different domestic and foreign makes and models that you work on if you relied solely on the manufac-

turer. This is where the independent technical manual publishers come in; they can save you time and money. They are staffed with experienced technical writers and editors who compile, select, and organize manufacturers' information to best meet the needs of automotive technicians. Because the independent publishers have no vested interest in one make over another, they are able to select only that information most often needed and publish it in its most efficient form. Thus in a volume of length equal to what a manufacturer publishes for one make and model, independent publishers can include most domestic and foreign makes, or eight-to-ten years' models of a specific make. Some of the independents also publish major system and subassembly volumes; for example: air conditioning, fuel injection, automatic transmissions, and so on.

The remaining category—the how-to-do-it books—are also produced by independent publishers. The majority are single-topic books covering one vehicle model and are very selective in content. This holds down the book's price and usually targets the individual owner who does some of his or her own service and repair. Many of these books contain good, helpful information, and they are used by practicing automotive technicians on occasion. Some independents publish books that go beyond the manufacturers' information resources. There are books on modifications for increased performance, extended durability, and greater reliability. They have been published as a result of independent research and development carried out by individuals, institutions, and businesses involved in racing, recreation, and other special-use activities.

There is one other kind of technical information. It consists of articles published in consumer magazines, trade journals, and **technical bulletins**—

VIDEO

This form of technical information is becoming more and more popular, especially as a training device. Its greatest advantage is in showing action—either live or animated—explaining repair or operating sequences. Its disad-

vantage is its limited access: it requires video equipment, and it is very expensive for the amount of information it presents in contrast with a technical manual of equal cost.

It will probably find its greatest use in training, but may become more widely available through public libraries and perhaps through video rental and auto parts stores.

the latter often published and circulated by the manufacturers. The articles cover some aspect in the operation, repair, or servicing of a specific automotive part or assembly and often are based on information gleaned from practicing automotive technicians as they experience new problems and create new solutions. Others result from ongoing research and development efforts by the manufacturer.

ORGANIZATION AND PRESENTATION OF TECHNICAL INFORMATION

Just as a transmission is an assembly of parts encased in a housing, a book can be thought of as information encased in a cover. When we look at either from the outside, there is no way of telling what is inside until we open them up. And if its our first book or first transmission, we can be equally confused by the number of pages and parts, chapters and assemblies, and how to find what we are looking for. If we persist, we can learn about how best to use a book as we have learned how best to use and work on a transmission. We need to become familiar with its parts and how they work with respect to the whole.

Just as most people know there are gears and nuts and bolts in a transmission, so do they know there are pages, chapters, and words in a book. Some, even though they know how to operate a transmission, never go further and consequently never fully understand the use and proper care of the transmission. The same is true with books. So we are going to look at some of the parts—or elements—that make up books and learn how to make best use of them.

Paragraphs

We all are familiar with words and sentences and can do pretty well stringing them together. But those who know that a correctly written **paragraph** is *limited to one main idea* can read much more efficiently and find information quicker. A paragraph is somewhat like one of the many major parts in a transmission.

Sections and Chapters

Several paragraphs can make up a **section**, just as several parts make up a subassembly. Sometimes the section is identified by a **heading** that briefly describes the section's focus. The heading of this section, *"Organization and Presentation of Technical Information,"* tells in brief, general terms what is covered in this section. Sections can also be identified by numbered headings, or by numerals only. A number of sections are grouped under a larger section, often called a *chapter*, which also has a descriptive head called a *title*, or it can just be numbered.

Organization or Structure

To understand how a book is organized is to know how it is put together. It is easier to find a problem in a transmission when we know how it is put together—what its **structure** is. Transmission parts and assemblies are organized with respect to their function and how they relate to each other. No point in putting the torque converter on the output shaft! Book chapters are also structured or organized relative to each other. Some books are organized by **topic**; some by **sequence**. Many technical manuals use both. Their chapters are organized by vehicle make and model (topics) or by assemblies, such as *Transmission*, *Engine*, or *Suspension* (also topics) and then sequentially under subheads such as *Disassembly* (1)...(2)...(3)...*Cleaning and Inspection* (1)...(2)...(3)..., and so on.

The Book's Major Elements—Like Major Assemblies

The paragraphs and sections in a chapter are referred to as the **text**. This form of information, the text, is supplemented by data in **tabular** form and by **illustrations**. The illustrated information may be photographs or drawings. The drawings may be of real objects or they may be graphs or diagrams (e.g., electrical, hydraulic). The tabular data just provide a means of presenting information in a highly organized and efficient form. Tables are also one of the best means of comparing information about one thing with that about another. So the text is the main line of information and the tables and illustrations help support what is being said in the text.

The Extras

There are at least three other elements that a book can have: a table of contents, an index, and a glossary. The last two are usually at the end of the book, and the contents are listed at the front. Also located in the front of most books is a brief description of the book itself. In many books, its called a **Preface** or **Foreword** and tells something about the book's concept or how it happened to be written or maybe something about the author. In other books, it may be more descriptively titled—for example, "How to Use This Book." And in still others, it might have no title at all, but appear as brief notes to the reader. Whatever its form, it is well worth reading. If you tend to skip over it—don't; it helps you to use the book more efficiently and to use it to its fullest potential. If the book's first chapter is titled "Introduction," don't skip it either; it is also important to read. It usually gives you a bird's-eye view of the book's content and may even include some of the information mentioned above.

Contents.   The **table of contents** can be very helpful, especially if it is the first time you have opened the book. Most tables of contents list the major section heads along with the chapter title, and by reading through this list, you can quickly get an idea of what kind of information the book has and how it is presented. Of course, this table also includes the page numbers on which each large category of information (chapter) starts.

Index.   But suppose you want information about something very specific. Turn to the **index**. It lists selected topics, and names of things, and on what pages each is handled in the book. The entries in most indexes are listed alphabetically. Some books contain more than one index: an index of automatic transmissions and another of automatic transaxles, for example; or one of authors and another of titles, as another.

Some technical manuals choose to replace the table of contents with one or more indexes at the *front* of the book.

Glossary.   The **glossary** is like a dictionary. It lists single words and short phrases used in the book and briefly defines their use and meaning. Sometimes the glossary is incorporated in the index merely by slipping the entries into place alphabetically with their definitions.

HOW TO MAKE BEST USE OF YOUR SHOP MANUALS

First, know what you need; it is very frustrating when you are ready to button up a job and nobody knows the final torque specs. If you work in a large shop, make yourself familiar with the technical information resources that are there. Suggest adding any that you notice are missing.

Before you start a job, quickly **survey** that section of the shop manual that covers it. Suppose that you have an '86 Buick Century with no "Drive." The shop manual will tell you how to identify whether it is a THM 125C or THM 440-T4 by checking pan shape (Figure 16-1) and what model identification code to look for and where to find it (Figure 16-2).

Look first at the major headings in the section covering your transmission. Is there information on diagnosis and testing there or in some other part of the manual (Figure 16-3)? How about transmission removal information? Sometimes it is located in another part of the book, too. (Figure 16-4). Are there separate headings for transmission disassembly and disassembly of major subassemblies, or components (Figure 16-5)? Are there summary charts of hydraulic pressures and clutch and band applications (Figure 16-6)? Exploded and sectional views (Figure 16-7)? Applications of special tools (Figure 16-8)? Selective parts tables for such items as pins and thrust washers and notes or other helpful information emphasized in boxes or by heavy type (Figure 16-9)? Electrical and hydraulic circuit diagrams? Torque specifications? Note these and read in more detail any that you wish to help you go about performing the task more efficiently.

Now as you begin the job you have an idea of when to refer to the manual and where in the manual to find what you are looking for. A good manual will tell you if there are any special tools required for disassembly. It will give a disassembly sequence that will save you a lot of time and frustration. It will tell you what wear measurements to make during disassembly that will save you much time during reassembly (Figure 16-9). Many show pictorial views of thrust washers, bearings, and bushings and their locations (Figure 16-7). Even though you will be grouping parts during disassembly and rebuilding subassemblies one-by-one, the exploded

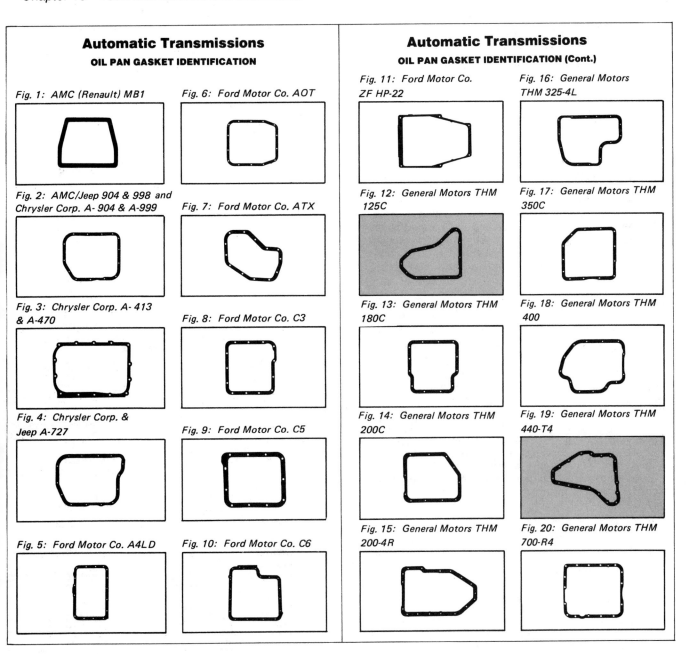

FIGURE 16-1 Oil pan gaskets provide a means of initial transmission model identification.

views and special assembly illustrations showing assembly sequence can help expedite the process.

A good manual will also identify the kinds of cleaning solvents to use to avoid damaging bonded surfaces or swelling composition parts. It gives reassembly sequence, clearances, and torque values (Figure 16-10). And it provides upper limits for air pressure testing to avoid blowing seals. It may also have a separate section or supplement on engineer-ing changes—latest modifications, changes in specifications, or changes in torque values (Figure 16-11).

In addition to the extensive line of *Mitchell Manuals*, which have been the mainstay of inde-pendently published reference materials in automo-tive technology for over 60 years, there are a

IDENTIFICATION

MODEL IDENTIFICATION

Models	Body Code
Celebrity, Century Cutlass Ciera, 6000	A
Cavalier, Cimarron Firenza, Skyhawk, Sunbird	J
Calais, Grand Am, Somerset Regal	N
Citation II, Skylark	X
Fiero	P

The transaxle Vehicle Identification Number (VIN) code is stamped on a machined pad located to the rear of the valve body cover and to the right of the dipstick tube. The transaxle model code is stamped on a machined pad located on the top center of the transaxle case.

TRANSAXLE CODES

Application	Code Letters
Buick	BF, BL, BP, CA, CB, CE CL, CT, CX, HS, OP, PD PE, PG, PJ, PN, PW,
Cadillac	CA, CB, CC, CI, CJ
Chevrolet	CA, CB, CC, CE, CI, CJ, CK CL, CT, CX, HS, HV, OP, PD PW, HW, H6, OP, PL, PW
Oldsmobile	BL, BF, BP, CA, CB, CJ, HS OP, PD, PE, PG, PN, PW, 5HJ
Pontiac	BP, CA, CB, CD, CL, CT, CU, HS OP, PD, PE, PF, PJ, PN, PW, 5PS

Automatic Transmissions
GENERAL MOTORS TURBO HYDRA-MATIC 125C TRANSAXLE

Buick
Century, Skyhawk, Skylark
Somerset Regal
Cadillac
Cimarron
Chevrolet
Cavalier, Celebrity, Citation II
Oldsmobile
Calais, Cutlass Ciera, Firenza
Pontiac
Fiero, Grand Am, Sunbird, 6000

hydraulic system is pressurized by a vane-type pump which provides the working pressure required to operate the friction elements and automatic controls.

The differential is integral with the transmission. Power transfer to the differential is by direct mesh of final drive sun gear to final drive sun gear pinions, located in the differential housing. An internal gear, held stationary by the case, provides the pinion track that forces rotation of final drive assembly.

LUBRICATION & ADJUSTMENT
See appropriate AUTOMATIC TRANSMISSION SERVICING article in DOMESTIC GENERAL SERVICING section.

TROUBLE SHOOTING
See appropriate AUTOMATIC TRANSMISSION TROUBLE SHOOTING article in DOMESTIC GENERAL SERVICING section.

TESTING
ROAD TEST
"D" Range
1) With selector lever in "D" range, accelerate from a standstill. A 1-2 and 2-3 shift should occur at all throttle openings (shift points will vary depending upon throttle opening).
2) Check part throttle 3-2 downshift at 30 MPH by quickly opening throttle approximately 3/4. At 50 MPH, transmission should downshift 3-2 by depressing accelerator fully.

"2" Range
1) With selector lever in "2", accelerate vehicle from a standstill. A 1-2 shift should occur at all throttle openings (no 2-3 shift can be obtained in this range). The 1-2 shift point will vary with throttle opening.
2) At approximately 20 MPH move selector from "2" to "1", a 2-1 downshift should occur. The 1-2 shift in "2" range is normally somewhat firmer than in "D" range.
3) With selector lever in "D" range and vehicle speed at approximately 50 MPH, release accelerator and move selector lever to "2" range. A 3-2 downshift should occur accompanied by an increase in engine speed and an engine braking effect.

"1" Range
1) With selector lever in "1" range, accelerate vehicle from a standstill. No upshift should occur in this range. At 40 MPH in "2" range, with throttle closed, move selector lever to "1".
2) A 2-1 downshift should occur between approximately 25 to 45 MPH, depending on valve body calibration. A 2-1 downshift at closed throttle should be accompanied by increased engine speed and an engine braking effect.

Converter Clutch
Install a tachometer and bring engine to normal operating temperature. With vehicle speed between 40-45 MPH, in 3rd gear, converter clutch should apply. Observing tachometer, a drop of 200 RPM's will occur when clutch is applied.

IDENTIFICATION

MODEL IDENTIFICATION

Models	Body Code
Celebrity, Century Cutlass Ciera, 6000	A
Cavalier, Cimarron Firenza, Skyhawk, Sunbird	J
Calais, Grand Am, Somerset Regal	N
Citation II, Skylark	X
Fiero	P

The transaxle Vehicle Identification Number (VIN) code is stamped on a machined pad located to the rear of the valve body cover and to the right of the dipstick tube. The transaxle model code is stamped on a machined pad located on the top center of the transaxle case.

TRANSAXLE CODES

Application	Code Letters
Buick	BF, BL, BP, CA, CB, CE CL, CT, CX, HS, OP, PD PE, PG, PJ, PN, PW,
Cadillac	CA, CB, CC, CI, CJ
Chevrolet	CA, CB, CC, CE, CI, CJ, CK CL, CT, CX, HS, HV, OP, PD PW, HW, H6, OP, PL, PW
Oldsmobile	BL, BF, BP, CA, CB, CJ, HS OP, PD, PE, PG, PN, PW, 5HJ
Pontiac	BP, CA, CB, CD, CL, CT, CU, HS OP, PD, PE, PF, PJ, PN, PW, 5PS

DESCRIPTION
The THM-125C transaxle combines a torque converter, fully automatic 3-speed transmission, final drive gearing and differential into a front wheel drive system (except RWD Fiero). The 4-element torque converter couples the engine crankshaft to the planetary gear set through a dual sprocket and drive link assembly.

The 4-element torque converter consists of a pump, a turbine, a pressure plate splined to the turbine and a stator assembly. The pressure plate, when applied, provides a mechanical direct drive coupling between the engine and the planetary gear set.

Three multi-disc clutches, a roller clutch and a single band provide the friction elements required to obtain the desired function of the planetary gear sets. The

FIGURE 16-2   Transmission model code letters are critical for proper identification.

Automatic Transmissions
GENERAL MOTORS TURBO HYDRA-MATIC 125C TRANSAXLE

Buick
  Century, Skyhawk, Skylark
    Somerset Regal
Cadillac
  Cimmaron
Chevrolet
  Cavalier, Celebrity, Citation II
Oldsmobile
  Calais, Cutlass Ciera, Firenza
Pontiac
  Fiero, Grand Am, Sunbird, 6000

IDENTIFICATION

MODEL IDENTIFICATION

Models	Body Code
Celebrity, Century	
Cutlass Ciera, 6000	A
Cavalier, Cimmaron	
Firenza, Skyhawk, Sunbird	J
Calais, Grand Am, Somerset Regal	N
Citation II, Skylark	X
Fiero	P

The transaxle Vehicle Identification Number (VIN) code is stamped on a machined pad located to the rear of the valve body cover and to the right of the dipstick tube. The transaxle model code is stamped on a machined pad located on the top center of the transaxle case.

TRANSAXLE CODES

Application	Code Letters
Buick	BF, BL, BP, CA, CB, CE CL, CT, CX, HS, OP, PD PE, PG, PJ, PN, PW,
Cadillac	CA, CB, CC, CI, CJ
Chevrolet	CA, CB, CC, CE, CI, CJ, CK CL, CT, CX, HS, HV, OP, PD PW, HW, H6, OP, PL, PW
Oldsmobile	BL, BF, BP, CA, CB, CJ, HS OP, PD, PE, PG, PN, PW, 5HJ
Pontiac	BP, CA, CB, CD, CL, CT, CU, HS OP, PD, PE, PF, PJ, PN, PW, 5PS

DESCRIPTION

The THM-125C transaxle combines a torque converter, fully automatic 3-speed transmission, final drive gearing and differential into a front wheel drive system (except RWD Fiero). The 4-element torque converter couples the engine crankshaft to the planetary gear set through a dual sprocket and drive link assembly.

The 4-element torque converter consists of a pump, a turbine, a pressure plate splined to the turbine and a stator assembly. The pressure plate, when applied, provides a mechanical direct drive coupling between the engine and the planetary gear set.

Three multi-disc clutches, a roller clutch and a single band provide the friction elements required to obtain the desired function of the planetary gear sets. The

hydraulic system is pressurized by a vane-type pump which provides the working pressure required to operate the friction elements and automatic controls.

The differential is integral with the transmission. Power transfer to the differential is by direct mesh of final drive sun gear to final drive sun gear pinions, located in the differential housing. An internal gear, held stationary by the case, provides the pinion track that forces rotation of final drive assembly.

LUBRICATION & ADJUSTMENT

See appropriate AUTOMATIC TRANSMISSION SERVICING article in DOMESTIC GENERAL SERVICING section.

TROUBLE SHOOTING

See appropriate AUTOMATIC TRANSMISSION TROUBLE SHOOTING article in DOMESTIC GENERAL SERVICING section.

TESTING

ROAD TEST
"D" Range
1) With selector lever in "D" range, accelerate from a standstill. A 1-2 and 2-3 shift should occur at all throttle openings (shift points will vary depending upon throttle opening).
2) Check part throttle 3-2 downshift at 30 MPH by quickly opening throttle approximately 3/4. At 50 MPH, transmission should downshift 3-2 by depressing accelerator fully.

"2" Range
1) With selector lever in "2", accelerate vehicle from a standstill. A 1-2 shift should occur at all throttle openings (no 2-3 shift can be obtained in this range). The 1-2 shift point will vary with throttle opening.
2) At approximately 20 MPH move selector from "2" to "1", a 2-1 downshift should occur. The 1-2 shift in "2" range is normally somewhat firmer than in "D" range.
3) With selector lever in "D" range and vehicle speed at approximately 50 MPH, release accelerator and move selector lever to "2" range. A 3-2 downshift should occur accompanied by an increase in engine speed and an engine braking effect.

"1" Range
1) With selector lever in "1" range, accelerate vehicle from a standstill. No upshift should occur in this range. At 40 MPH in "2" range, with throttle closed, move selector lever to "1".
2) A 2-1 downshift should occur between approximately 25 to 45 MPH, depending on valve body calibration. A 2-1 downshift at closed throttle should be accompanied by increased engine speed and an engine braking effect.

Converter Clutch
Install a tachometer and bring engine to normal operating temperature. With vehicle speed between 40-45 MPH, in 3rd gear, converter clutch should apply. Observing tachometer, a drop of 200 RPM's will occur when clutch is applied.

FIGURE 16-3 Diagnosis information is often located in a special troubleshooting section.

number of other independent publishers, some of which are listed below.

Mitchell sales representatives regularly call on the leading dealers and independent shops throughout the country, and complete information on their products can be made available to you by writing or calling:

Mitchell International, Inc.
P.O. Box 26260
San Diego, CA 92126
Toll free, call:
800-854-7030
(From California, call 800-421-0159)

INDEPENDENT PUBLISHERS OF SINGLE TOPIC, HOW-TO, AND SPECIALTY BOOKS AND MANUALS

• Automatic Transmission
  Rebuilders Association
  6663 Ventura Blvd., Suite B
  Ventura, CA 93003

• Hayden Trans-Tool
  110 Connelly
  San Antonio, TX 78203

• Haynes Publications Inc.
  861 Lawrence Drive
  Newberry Park, CA 91320

Automatic Transmissions
GENERAL MOTORS TURBO HYDRA-MATIC 125C
TRANSAXLE (Cont.)

4) Disengage snap ring retaining drive axle at transaxle. Using slide hammer and Adapter (J-33008), remove drive axle from transaxle assembly. DO NOT hold drive axle assembly vertically or joints will separate.

Disassembly (Fiero & All Tripod Joint Models)

1) Remove and disassemble outer CV joint as previously described. To remove inner Tripod joint, first detach seal retainer clamp by cutting it off of boot.

2) Using brass drift, tap lightly and evenly around seal retainer until loose. Remove retainer. Detach drive shaft retaining snap ring and slide spider assembly off drive axle. Remove spacer ring.

Inspection (Fiero & All Tripod Joint Models)

Inspect drive axle boot for tears or excessive wear. Check spider assembly for worn or damaged needle bearings. Inspect snap rings, spacer ring and drive shaft grooves for excessive wear. Replace components as necessary. If drive axle is replaced, install new knuckle seal.

Reassembly (Fiero & All Tripod Joint Models)

1) Flush grease from housing and repack with half of grease furnished with new seal. Apply remainder of grease to seal. Slide spacer ring on end of drive shaft. Ensure ring is seated in groove.

2) Slide spider gear onto axle with counter bore facing inner (transaxle) end of shaft. Install shaft retaining ring. Install inner and outer boot seal protectors.

Installation (Fiero)

1) Drive axle assembly into transaxle. Seat axle using screwdriver and groove provided on inner retainer. Install axle through hub at knuckle. Install seal boot clamps and tighten using Keystone Clamp Pliers (J-22610).

2) Remove boot protectors. Install and tighten lower control arm ball stud bolt to 33 ft. lbs. (45 N.m). Install toe link rod-to-knuckle assembly and tighten mount bolt to 35 ft. lbs. (47 N.m).

3) Install remaining components in reverse of disassembly procedure. Install and tighten new hub nut to 70 ft. lbs. (100 N.m). Install wheels and tires. Lower vehicle. Retighten hub nut to 185-225 ft. lbs. (250-305 N.m).

REMOVAL & INSTALLATION

TRANSAXLE

See appropriate AUTOMATIC TRANSMISSION REMOVAL article in DOMESTIC GENERAL SERVICING section.

TORQUE CONVERTER

NOTE: Torque converter is a sealed unit and cannot be disassembled for service or repair.

LEAKAGE CHECK

1) Install Pressure Tester (J-21369-B) into converter hub. Tighten hex nut on tool to expand it. Ensure safety strap is installed to prevent tool from blowing out when air pressure is applied. *See Fig. 9.* Apply 80 psi (5.6 kg/cm²) air pressure to air valve in tool. Submerge converter in water and check for air bubbles in water indicating leaks.

***Fig. 9:** Installing Torque Converter Leakage Tester*

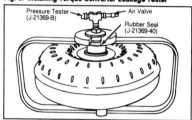

Apply 80 psi (5.6 kg/cm²) air pressure to air valve.

CAUTION: After leak checking converter, bleed air pressure from test tool before removing tool from converter hub.

2) With leakage tester removed, inspect converter hub surfaces for signs of scoring or wear. Check converter bushing for damage, cracks or scoring. If any components are excessively worn or damaged, replace torque converter assembly.

END CLEARANCE CHECK

1) Install collet end of End Clearance Checker (J-28538) into converter hub and hand tighten counterclockwise. Mount dial indicator onto hub of tool collet so dial indicator plunger rests on converter.

2) Zero dial indicator. Lift up on tool and read clearance at dial indicator. Converter end clearance should be 0-.050" (0-1.27 mm). If clearance is greater than .050" (1.27 mm), replace torque converter assembly.

***Fig. 10:** Measuring Torque Converter End Play*

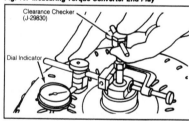

The converter end play must not exceed .050" (1.27 mm).

3) When replacing torque converter, ensure converter is installed fully toward rear of transaxle. Ensure converter is installed so that there is at least .50" (13 mm) between engine mounting face of case and front face of converter cover lugs.

FIGURE 16-4   Instructions common to many models may appear in a separate section.

INDEPENDENT PUBLISHERS OF MULTIPLE VEHICLE/MULTIPLE YEAR TECHNICAL MANUALS

- Mitchell Manuals
  (see ordering information above)
- Chilton Book Company
  Chilton Way
  Radnor, PA 19089

- Helm Inc.
  Publications Division
  P.O. Box 07130
  Detroit, MI 48207
- Motor
  The Hearst Corporation
  555 West 57th Street
  New York, NY 10019

Automatic Transmissions

GENERAL MOTORS TURBO HYDRA-MATIC 125C TRANSAXLE (Cont.)

NOTE: After end play and leakage tests, check torque converter stator assembly for freewheeling in both directions or assembly remains locked up at all times. Replace converter assembly if either condition exists.

TRANSAXLE DISASSEMBLY

Before disassembling unit, throughly clean exterior of transaxle case to prevent dirt from entering transaxle internal mechanism. During inspection and reassembly, all parts should be washed with cleaning solvent and air dried. DO NOT use rags to dry components. Remove torque converter by pulling it straight out. Place transaxle in Holding Fixtures (J-28664 and J-3289-20). Position so right side axle end is down to drain fluid.

SPEEDOMETER DRIVE GEAR & GOVERNOR ASSEMBLY

Reposition transaxle to normal position. Remove speedometer driven gear mount bolt with retainer. Withdraw driven gear assembly from governor cover. Remove governor cover bolts and lift off cover with "O" ring. Lift out governor and speedometer drive gear as an assembly.

INTERMEDIATE SERVO ASSEMBLY

1) Position transaxle so oil pan is up. Remove oil pan, gasket and oil strainer assembly from lower case assembly. Remove and discard oil strainer "O" ring.

2) Remove bolt holding reverse oil pipe retaining bracket to servo cover. Remove remaining servo cover bolts. Lift off servo cover and gasket. Withdraw intermediate servo assembly. See Fig. 11.

Fig. 11: Removing Intermediate Servo Assembly

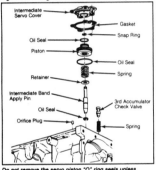

Do not remove the servo piston "O" ring seals unless replacement is necessary.

3) If necessary, detach "E" clip and remove intermediate band apply pin from intermediate servo piston. Discard "O" ring seals. Remove 3rd accumulator check valve and spring. See Fig. 12.

Fig. 12: Removing 3rd Accumulator Check Valve & Spring

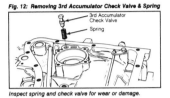

Inspect spring and check valve for wear or damage.

NOTE: Make intermediate band apply pin selection check at this time to determine correct pin to use during reassembly.

Band Apply Pin Selection Check

1) Install Intermediate Band Apply Pin Gauge (J-28535) over intermediate servo bore. Retain with 2 servo cover bolts. Remove band apply pin from intermediate servo assembly.

2) Install Band Apply Ain Gauge Extension (J-28535-4) onto servo piston end of band apply pin. Install band apply pin and gauge extension into gauge on servo bore. See Fig. 13.

Fig. 13: Checking for Proper Band Apply Pin

Ensure the White line on gauge extension appears in the window of gauge or different length pin will be needed.

3) Apply 100 INCH lbs. (11.2 N.m) of torque to hex nut on selection gauge to compress band. White line, on gauge extension, should appear in window on selection gauge to indicate proper pin installed.

4) If White line cannot be seen, change band apply pin (longer or shorter as necessary) and recheck. See INTERMEDIATE BAND APPLY PIN table. With proper apply pin selected, remove gauge. Install new seals, assemble and install components in reverse of removal procedure.

Automatic Transmissions

GENERAL MOTORS TURBO HYDRA-MATIC 125C TRANSAXLE (Cont.)

Fig. 21: Removing Low-Reverse Clutch Housing

Use lifter to lift out Low-Reverse Clutch housing.

reaction carrier-to-reaction internal gear thrust washers off end of reaction carrier (or inside reaction internal gear).

8) Remove Low-Reverse clutch plates off final drive sun gear shaft. Remove reaction internal gear-to-reaction sun gear thrust bearing assembly off reaction gear. Remove reaction internal gear off final drive sun gear shaft.

FINAL DRIVE UNIT

NOTE: Before proceeding with transaxle disassembly, final drive-to-case end play should be checked to determine proper final drive differential-to-case selective thrust washer for install during reassembly. Also, case bushing should be inspected for wear and replaced if necessary.

Final Drive-to-Case End Play

1) Rotate transaxle so right hand axle end is up. With Output Shaft Aligner/Loader Adapter Plug (J-26958-10) in place, press down on adapter to fully seat final drive onto final drive internal gear-to-case snap ring.

2) Install dial indicator onto post and install post into one of the motor mount bolt holes. Ensure indicator plunger rests on top of adapter. Zero dial indicator while pressing down on adapter.

3) Insert large screwdriver into transaxle governor bore. Lift final drive by prying up on governor drive gear. Read end play at dial indicator. End play should be .005-.032" (.12-.82 mm).

4) Selective washer controlling end play is located between differential carrier and differential carrier case thrust bearing assembly. Select correct thrust washer. See FINAL DRIVE-TO-CASE END PLAY table.

5) Remove dial indicator, indicator post and loader/aligner adapter. Remove final drive internal gear spacer-to-case snap ring. The snap ring is .092" (2.36 mm) thick. Remove final drive internal gear spacer. DO NOT deform or bend spacer when removing.

6) Using Final Drive Unit Remover/Installer (J-28545), lift final drive unit from case. Remove final drive differential-to-case selective thrust washer. Remove differential carrier-to-case thrust roller bearing assembly from final drive assembly. The thrust washer and thrust bearing may be located in case.

FINAL DRIVE-TO-CASE END PLAY

Thickness In. (mm)	Identification Code
.055-.059 (1.40-1.50)	0
.059-.062 (1.50-1.60)	1
.062-.066 (1.60-1.70)	2
.066-.070 (1.70-1.80)	3
.070-.074 (1.80-1.90)	4
.074-.078 (1.90-2.00)	5
.078-.082 (2.00-2.10)	6
.082-.086 (2.10-2.20)	7
.086-.091 (2.20-2.30)	8
.091-.095 (2.30-2.40)	9

COMPONENT DISASSEMBLY & REASSEMBLY

NOTE: During disassembly, note component locations for reassembly reference. When reassembling transaxle unit, lubricate all bushings, seals, thrust bearings and internal mating surfaces with transmission fluid. Use petroleum jelly to lubricate and retain all thrust washers.

TRANSAXLE CASE

NOTE: Disassembly procedures include drive sprocket support, drive sprocket roller bearing, third oil cup plug, parking pawl and governor oil cup plug removal. It is not necessary to remove and service these components unless they are damaged or worn.

Disassembly

1) Rotate transaxle case until case cover side is up. Using slide hammer and Adapter (J-26941), remove drive sprocket support roller bearing assembly. Inspect bearing bore and roller bearing race on drive sprocket for wear or damage. Replace components as needed.

2) Inspect drive sprocket support for damaged journals or splines. If removal is needed, turn transaxle case so right axle side is up. Remove converter oil seal. From inside torque converter housing, unbolt and remove drive sprocket support.

3) Inspect parking pawl shaft cup plug for damage. If replacement is needed, turn transaxle case so oil pan side is up. Using a 3/8" drift, remove parking pawl shaft cup plug from oil pan side of case. Inspect parking pawl for damage.

4) If replacement is needed, remove parking pawl shaft retainer, parking pawl shaft, parking pawl and return spring from case. Check governor pipe for damage, cracks or possible leak points. If replacement is necessary, remove governor oil pipe clamp screw and clamp.

CAUTION: If governor pipe needs replacement, remove right hand axle end first. The pipe is sealed strongly in place and may require a high effort to break loose. DO NOT damage machined case surface if pipe must be pryed out.

FIGURE 16-5 Separate instructions for both major assemblies and sub-assemblies, or components.

PUBLISHERS OF BOOKS AND MANUALS FOR SELECTED VEHICLE TYPES

- Theodore Audel & Company
  70 Lincoln Street
  Boston, MA 0211

- Clymer Publications, Div. of Intertec

- Intertec Publishing Corporation
  Technical Publications Division
  P.O. Box 12901
  Overland Park, KS 66212

CONSUMER MAGAZINES, TRADE JOURNALS, AND TECHNICAL BULLETINS

- Automotive Engineering
  Society of Automotive Engineers Inc.
  400 Commonwealth Drive
  Warrendale, PA 15096

- Transmission Digest
  MD Publications Inc.
  304 East Pershing Road
  Box 1067 S.S.S.,
  Springfield, MO 65805

Automatic Transmissions
GENERAL MOTORS TURBO HYDRA-MATIC 125C TRANSAXLE (Cont.)

THROTTLE VALVE LINE PRESSURE CHECK

Model	Range	MINIMUM T.V.		MAXIMUM T.V.	
		psi	kg/cm²	psi	kg/cm²
EB, EF, EI, EJ, EK, EM, EN, EQ, EW	"P" @ 1000	58-62	4.08-4.36		
CA, CB, CF, EL, HC, HN, HY, PD					
PE, PF, PG, PI, PW	"P" @ 1000	67-75	4.71-5.27	No T.V. pressure in Park.	
BF, BL, CC, CE, CK, CL, HD, HM				Line Pressure is the same	
HP, HS, HV, PJ, OP	"P" @ 1000	75-85	5.27-5.98	as Park at Minimum T.V.	
EP	"P" @ 1000	75-85	5.27-5.98		
EM, EN, EW	"R" @ 1000	100-107	7.03-7.52	200-220	14.06-15.47
EF, EK	"R" @ 1000	100-107	7.03-7.52	235-255	16.52-17.93
EB, EI, EJ, EQ	"R" @ 1000	110-117	7.73-8.23	240-280	16.87-19.69
CA, CB, CF, EL, HC, HY, PE, PG, PW	"R" @ 1000	118-130	8.30-9.14	217-240	15.26-16.87
HN, PD, PF, PI	"R" @ 1000	118-130	8.30-9.14	217-280	15.26-19.69
CC, CK, CL, HD, HM, HP, HS, HV, OP	"R" @ 1000	130-150	9.14-10.55	240-295	16.87-20.74
PJ	"R" @ 1000	130-150	9.14-10.55	240-320	16.87-22.50
BF, BL	"R" @ 1000	140-160	9.84-11.25	240-285	16.87-20.04
CE, EP	"R" @ 1000	130-150	9.14-10.55	225-260	15.82-18.28
EM, EN, EW	"D/N" @ 1000	58-62	4.08-4.36	115-125	8.09-8.79
EI	"D/N" @ 1000	58-62	4.08-4.36	125-135	8.79-9.49
EB, EF, EJ, EK, EQ	"D/N" @ 1000	58-62	4.08-4.36	135-145	9.49-10.19
CA, CB, CF, EL, HC, HY, PE, PG, PW	"D/N" @ 1000	67-75	4.71-5.27	123-140	8.65-9.84
HN, PD, PF, PI	"D/N" @ 1000	67-75	4.71-5.27	140-160	9.84-11.25
CC, CK, CL, HD, HM, HP, HS, HV, OP	"D/N" @ 1000	75-85	5.27-5.98	150-170	10.55-11.95
BF, CL, CE, EP	"D/N" @ 1000	75-85	5.27-5.98	130-150	9.14-10.55
PJ	"D/N" @ 1000	75-85	5.27-5.98	165-185	11.60-13.01
EF, EK, EM, EN, EW	2/Low @ 1000	105-110	7.38-7.73		
EB, EI, EJ, EQ	2/Low @ 1000	125-130	8.79-9.14		
CA, CB, CF, EL, HC, HN, HY				No T.V. in intermediate or	
PE, PF, PG, PI, PW	2/Low @ 1000	115-132	8.09-9.28	low. Line Pressure same	
CC, CE, CK, CL, HD, HM, HP				as intermediate or low at	
HS, HV, OP, PJ	2/Low @ 1000	130-150	9.14-10.55	minimum.	
BF, BL	2/Low @ 1000	160-183	11.25-12.87		
EP	2/Low @ 1000	130-150	9.14-10.55		

LINE PRESSURE TESTS

CAUTION: Parking and service brakes must be applied at all times during test. Total duration for portion of test with selector in driving ranges should not exceed 2 minutes.

1) Before making line pressure tests, check ATF for proper fluid level and condition. Check T.V. (throttle valve) and manual control linkages for proper adjustment and ensure engine is in good state of tune. Correct conditions and components as necessary.
2) Connect a tachometer to engine and an oil pressure gauge to line pressure take-off point on transaxle case. Line pressure tap is on bell housing side of transmission, above valve body cover.

NOTE: The line pressure is basically controlled by pump output and the pressure regulator valve. In addition, line pressure is boosted in Reverse, "2" Range and "1" Range by the reverse boost valve. In Neutral, "D" Range and Reverse positions, line pressure should increase with throttle opening.

Minimum T.V. Pressure Check
With T.V. cable properly adjusted to specifications, check line pressure in ranges and at RPM indicated on chart.

Maximum T.V. Pressure Check
With T.V. cable supported at full extent of its travel, check line pressure in ranges and at RPM indicated in chart.

Automatic Transmissions
GENERAL MOTORS TURBO HYDRA-MATIC 125C TRANSAXLE (Cont.)

LINE PRESSURE TEST RESULTS

Line Pressure Too Low
1) Check for low fluid level. Check oil strainer "O" ring seal for leakage or damage and plugged oil strainer. If pressure is low in Neutral and Drive and low to normal in "2" and Reverse, the T.V. cable may be incorrect or out of adjustment. Inspect T.V. linkage for binding.
2) Inspect control valve and pump assembly for loose bolts or internal leaks. Check T.V. valve and plunger, shift T.V. valve, pressure regulator valve, T.V. boost valve and pressure relief valve for sticking in bore or damaged valves. Check for missing or off location No. 5 or 6 check ball.
3) Check 1-2 accumulator piston and/or seal for leaking or missing. Check low blow-off valve and for damaged low blow-off valve and missing or off location No. 4 check ball. For Reverse only, inspect Low-Reverse clutch housing-to-case cup plug assembly for leaking.
4) Inspect oil pump for loose bolts and damaged or missing pump valve seals. Check intermediate oil passages to pressure regulator for blockage. Check driven sprocket support-to-case cover for leaks.

Line Pressure Too High
1) With pressure high in Neutral and Drive and normal to high in "2" and Reverse, check for broken, sticking or out of adjustment T.V. cable.
2) Inspect T.V. linkage for binding or incorrect cable. Check throttle valve or shift T.V. valve for sticking. Inspect T.V. lifter for bend, damage or too short condition.
3) Inspect components of control valve and pump assembly for sticking or damaged T.V. valve and plunger, shift T.V. valve, pressure regulator valve, T.V. boost valve and/or pump slide.
4) Check for worn or missing pressure regulator valve retaining pin. For Low only, check Low blow-off valve for sticking closed. Inspect internal pump or case cover for leaks.

SERVICE (IN VEHICLE)

The following components may be removed from transaxle without removing transaxle from vehicle: Throttle valve control cable with "O" ring, governor assembly, filler pipe with "O" ring, intermediate servo assembly with direct clutch accumulator check valve, Low-Reverse oil pipe/seal assembly and speedometer drive gear assembly.

The following may also be removed without removing transaxle: Oil pan with gasket/strainer assembly, control valve body assembly with cover, throttle lever with bracket, oil pump drive shaft, parking pawl and axle shafts.

For removal and installation procedures of components other than drive axles, see TRANSAXLE DISASSEMBLY and TRANSAXLE REASSEMBLY procedures in this article.

DRIVE AXLE SHAFTS

NOTE: Removal, Inspection and Installation procedures apply to either side drive axle assembly.

CAUTION: When either or both drive shaft ends are detached, DO NOT over-extend assembly or separation of internal components will result.

Description
There are two types of drive axle designs. The two designs both use the same type outer Constant Velocity (CV) joint. One design, for "X" model vehicles, uses a Double Offset inner joint. The other design, for "A", "J" and "P" models, uses a Tripod inner joint.

The drive axles are completely flexible assemblies consisting of an inner and outer joints connected by an axle shaft. The inner joint is completely flexible and has the capability of in and out movement. The outer joint is also flexible but cannot move in or out.

The right-hand inboard joint of the automatic transaxle incorporate a male spline and interlocks with the transaxle gear through the use of a barrel type snap ring. The left-hand inboard shaft attachment utilizes a female spline which installs over a stub shaft protruding from the transaxle. The drive shaft spline end which mates with the steering knuckle/hub assembly incorporates a slight helical spline to assure a tight press-type fit.

Removal (Except Fiero)
1) Remove hub nut with washer. Raise and support front of vehicle. Remove wheels and tires. Install Boot Seal Protectors (J-28712) for all outer CV joints. Boot

CLUTCH AND BAND APPLICATION CHART (ELEMENTS IN USE)

Selector Lever Position	Direct Clutch	Forward Clutch	Low & Reverse Clutch	Intermediate Band	Low Roller Clutch
D – Drive					
First Gear		X			X
Second Gear		X		X	
Third Gear	X	X			
2 – Intermediate					
First Gear		X			X
Second Gear		X		X	
1 – Low					
First Gear		X	X		X
R – Reverse	X		X		

NEUTRAL OR PARK – All clutches and bands released and/or ineffective.

FIGURE 16-6   Summary tables of test values and diagnostic information.

TRADE TERMS

Foreword
Glossary
Heading
Illustrations
Index
Paragraph
Preface

Section
Sequence
Structure
Survey
Table of
  contents

Tabular
Technical
  bulletin
Text
Topic

Automatic Transmissions
GENERAL MOTORS TURBO HYDRA-MATIC 125C TRANSAXLE (Cont.)

Fig. 1: Exploded View of Transaxle Case and Related Components

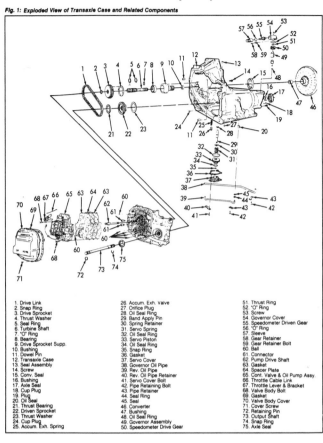

1. Drive Link	26. Accum. Exh. Valve	51. Thrust Ring
2. Snap Ring	27. Orifice Plug	52. "O" Ring
3. Drive Sprocket	28. Oil Seal Ring	53. Screw
4. Thrust Washer	29. Band Apply Pin	54. Governor Cover
5. Seal Ring	30. Spring Retainer	55. Speedometer Driven Gear
6. Turbine Shaft	31. Servo Spring	56. "O" Ring
7. "O" Ring	32. Oil Seal Ring	57. Sleeve
8. Bearing	33. Servo Piston	58. Gear Retainer
9. Drive Sprocket Supp.	34. Oil Seal Ring	59. Gear Retainer Bolt
10. Bushing	35. Snap Ring	60. Ball
11. Dowel Pin	36. Gasket	61. Connector
12. Transaxle Case	37. Servo Cover	62. Pump Drive Shaft
13. Seal Assembly	38. Governor Oil Pipe	63. Gasket
14. Screw	39. Rev. Oil Pipe	64. Spacer Plate
15. Conv. Seal	40. Rev. Oil Pipe Retainer	65. Cont. Valve & Oil Pump Assy.
16. Bushing	41. Servo Cover Bolt	66. Throttle Cable Link
17. Axle Seal	42. Pipe Retaining Bolt	67. Throttle Lever & Bracket
18. Cup Plug	43. Pipe Retainer	68. Valve Body Bolt
19. Plug	44. Seal Ring	69. Gasket
20. Oil Seal	45. Seal	70. Valve Body Cover
21. Thrust Bearing	46. Converter	71. Cover Screw
22. Driven Sprocket	47. Bushing	72. Retaining Pin
23. Thrust Washer	48. Oil Seal Ring	73. Output Shaft
24. Cup Plug	49. Governor Assembly	74. Snap Ring
25. Accum. Exh. Spring	50. Speedometer Drive Gear	75. Axle Seal

Automatic Transmissions
GENERAL MOTORS TURBO HYDRA-MATIC 125C TRANSAXLE (Cont.)

Fig. 37: Thrust Bearing, Thrust Washer & Bushing Locations

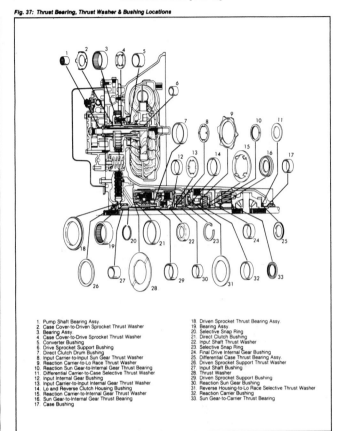

1. Pump Shaft Bearing Assy.	18. Driven Sprocket Thrust Bearing Assy.
2. Case Cover-to-Driven Sprocket Thrust Washer	19. Bearing Assy.
3. Bearing Assy.	20. Selective Snap Ring
4. Case Cover-to-Drive Sprocket Thrust Washer	21. Direct Clutch Bushing
5. Converter Bushing	22. Input Shaft Thrust Washer
6. Drive Sprocket Support Bushing	23. Selective Snap Ring
7. Direct Clutch Drum Bushing	24. Final Drive Internal Gear Bushing
8. Input Carrier-to-Input Sun Gear Thrust Washer	25. Differential Case Thrust Bearing Assy.
9. Reaction Carrier-to-Lo Race Thrust Washer	26. Driven Sprocket Support Thrust Washer
10. Reaction Sun Gear-to-Internal Gear Thrust Bearing	27. Input Shaft Bushing
11. Differential Carrier-to-Case Selective Thrust Washer	28. Thrust Washer
12. Input Internal Gear Bushing	29. Driven Sprocket Support Bushing
13. Input Carrier-to-Input Internal Gear Thrust Washer	30. Reaction Sun Gear Bushing
14. Lo and Reverse Clutch Housing Bushing	31. Reverse Housing-to-Lo Race Selective Thrust Washer
15. Reaction Carrier-to-Internal Gear Thrust Washer	32. Reaction Carrier Bushing
16. Sun Gear-to-Internal Gear Thrust Bearing	33. Sun Gear-to-Carrier Thrust Washer
17. Case Bushing	

FIGURE 16-7 Exploded and sectional views are guides for parts ordering and reassembly.

REVIEW QUESTIONS

16-1. Match the type of publication in the first column with the kind of information it is most noted for in the second column.

   (a) How-to and single-topic.   **(1)** Most complete information.

   (b) Manufacturer-published.   **(2)** Best selected information.

   (c) Independent-published.   **(3)** Specialized information.

16-2. To keep up to date with developments in automotive technology, including improved parts and procedures, three of the best sources are consumer _____, trade _____, and technical _____.

16-3. We can become familiar with a book and its parts in much the same way as we become familiar with a transmission and its parts.
  T   F

16-4. Most paragraphs present one _____ _____.

16-5. Chapters usually begin with titles, and sections often begin with _____.

16-6. Sometimes chapters and sections are identified only by numerals.   T   F

16-7. It is just as important to know a book's ____ or _____ as it is to know how a particular transmission is put together.

16-8. Portions of some manuals are organized by _____ and others are organized by _____.

16-9. The main line of information in a bulletin, magazine, or book is called the _____; it is supplemented by tables and illustrations.

Automatic Transmissions
GENERAL MOTORS TURBO HYDRA-MATIC 125C
TRANSAXLE (Cont.)

Fig. 21: Removing Low-Reverse Clutch Housing

Reverse Clutch
Housing Remover/
Installer (J-28542)

Use lifter to lift out Low-Reverse Clutch housing.

reaction carrier-to-reaction internal gear thrust washers off end of reaction carrier (or inside reaction internal gear).

8) Remove Low-Reverse clutch plates off final drive sun gear shaft. Remove reaction internal gear-to-reaction sun gear thrust bearing assembly off reaction gear. Remove reaction internal gear off final drive sun gear shaft.

FINAL DRIVE UNIT

NOTE: Before proceeding with transaxle disassembly, final drive-to-case end play should be checked to determine proper final drive differential-to-case selective thrust washer for install during reassembly. Also, case bushing should be inspected for wear and replaced if necessary.

Final Drive-to-Case End Play

1) Rotate transaxle so right hand axle end is up. With Output Shaft Aligner/Loader Adapter Plug (J-26958-10) in place, press down on adapter to fully seat final drive onto final drive internal gear-to-case snap ring.

2) Install dial indicator onto post and install post into one of the motor mount bolt holes. Ensure indicator plunger rests on top of adapter. Zero dial indicator while pressing down on adapter.

3) Insert large screwdriver into transaxle governor bore. Lift final drive by prying up on governor drive gear. Read end play at dial indicator. End play should be .005-.032" (.12-.82 mm).

4) Selective washer controlling end play is located between differential carrier and differential carrier case thrust bearing assembly. Select correct thrust washer. See FINAL DRIVE-TO-CASE END PLAY table.

5) Remove dial indicator, indicator post and loader/aligner adapter. Remove final drive internal gear spacer-to-case snap ring. The snap ring is .092" (2.36 mm) thick. Remove final drive internal gear spacer. DO NOT deform or bend spacer when removing.

6) Using Final Drive Unit Remover/Installer (J-28545), lift final drive unit from case. Remove final drive differential-to-case selective thrust washer. Remove differential carrier-to-case thrust roller bearing assembly from final drive assembly. The thrust washer and thrust bearing may be located in case.

FINAL DRIVE-TO-CASE END PLAY

Thickness In. (mm)	Identification Code
.055-.059 (1.40-1.50)	0
.059-.062 (1.50-1.60)	1
.062-.066 (1.60-1.70)	2
.066-.070 (1.70-1.80)	3
.070-.074 (1.80-1.90)	4
.074-.078 (1.90-2.00)	5
.078-.082 (2.00-2.10)	6
.082-.086 (2.10-2.20)	7
.086-.091 (2.20-2.30)	8
.091-.095 (2.30-2.40)	9

COMPONENT DISASSEMBLY & REASSEMBLY

NOTE: During disassembly, note component locations for reassembly reference. When reassembling transaxle unit, lubricate all bushings, seals, thrust bearings and internal mating surfaces with transmission fluid. Use petroleum jelly to lubricate and retain all thrust washers.

TRANSAXLE CASE

NOTE: Disassembly procedures include drive sprocket support, drive sprocket roller bearing, third oil cup plug, parking pawl and governor oil pipe removal. It is not necessary to remove and service these components unless they are damaged or worn.

Disassembly

1) Rotate transaxle case until case cover side is up. Using slide hammer and Adapter (J-26941), remove drive sprocket support roller bearing assembly. Inspect bearing bore and roller bearing race on drive sprocket for wear or damage. Replace components as needed.

2) Inspect drive sprocket support for damaged journals or splines. If removal is needed, turn transaxle case so right axle side is up. Remove converter oil seal. From inside torque converter housing, unbolt and remove drive sprocket support.

3) Inspect parking pawl shaft cup plug for damage. If replacement is needed, turn transaxle case so oil pan side is up. Using a 3/8" drift, remove parking pawl shaft cup plug from oil pan side of case. Inspect parking pawl for damage.

4) If replacement is needed, remove parking pawl shaft retainer, parking pawl shaft, parking pawl and return spring from case. Check governor pipe for damage, cracks or possible leak points. If replacement is necessary, remove governor oil pipe clamp screw and clamp.

CAUTION: If governor pipe needs replacement, remove right hand axle end first. The pipe is sealed strongly in place and may require a high effort to break loose. DO NOT damage machined case surface if pipe must be pryed out.

FIGURE 16-8 Special tools are often shown with part numbers.

16-10. The only purpose of a table of contents is to show what pages chapters start on.   T   F

16-11. The index shows how a book is organized.   T   F

16-12. A glossary is like a _____; it lists words and phrases alphabetically and tells something about them.

16-13. The only thing in the front of a manual that tells anything about the book itself is the table of contents.   T   F

16-14. A lot of information can be shown in a very efficient and organized form by arranging it in a _____.

16-15. Soon all technical manuals and bulletins will be replaced by video.   T   F

NOTE: Before proceeding with disassembly of reaction unit parts, reaction sun gear-to-input drum selective snap ring and Reverse clutch housing-to-Low race selective thrust washer end play measurements should be taken to determine correct snap ring and thrust washer to install during reassembly.

Automatic Transmissions
GENERAL MOTORS TURBO HYDRA-MATIC 125C TRANSAXLE (Cont.)

7) While lifting up on input shaft, remove direct and forward clutch assemblies. Separate direct and forward clutch assemblies. Remove input internal gear-to-input shaft thrust washer. Remove input internal gear.

8) Remove input carrier assembly, input carrier-to-input internal gear thrust washer and input carrier-to-input sun gear thrust washer. Remove input sun gear and input drum.

REACTION UNIT

NOTE: Before proceeding with disassembly of reaction unit parts, reaction sun gear-to-input drum selective snap ring and Reverse clutch housing-to-Low race selective thrust washer end play measurements should be taken to determine correct snap ring and thrust washer to install during reassembly.

Reaction Sun Gear-to-Input Drum End Play

1) Install Output Shaft Aligner/Loader (J-26958) in fully loaded position. Install Reaction Sun Gear Snap Ring Gauge (J-28588) to case using 2 case cover bolts. Position gauge extension between open ends of selective snap ring.

2) Press reaction sun gear down to make sure it is seated. Install a dial indicator onto Extension Post (J-25025-7). Position feeler gauge beneath shoulder of gauge extension. Zero dial indicator.

3) Rotate selective snap ring under gauge extension. Swing feeler gauge from beneath extension while checking full range of indicator needle movement. Reading should be +.013 to -.005" (+.33 to -.13 mm) when measured from zero reference point.

4) The selective snap ring controlling this end play is located on reaction sun gear shaft. Measure thickness of snap ring for proper identification. To select proper snap ring to be installed, see REACTION SUN GEAR-TO-INPUT DRUM SNAP RING SELECTION table.

Low-Reverse Clutch Housing-to-Low Roller Clutch Race Thrust Washer End Play

1) With dial indicator and output shaft aligner/loader installed as it was for measurement of reaction sun gear-to-input drum snap ring, press down reaction sun gear to ensure it is seated. Zero dial indicator.

2) Insert screwdriver through parking pawl case opening next to parking pawl. Lift reaction internal gear to check Low-Reverse clutch selective end play. Read resulting end play. DO NOT rest screwdriver on spacer in parking pawl case opening when prying reaction internal gear. Spacer damage will result. See Fig. 20.

Fig. 20: Checking Low-Reverse Clutch Housing-to-Low Roller Clutch Race Thrust Washer End Play

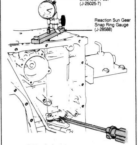

DO NOT rest screwdriver on spacer in parking pawl case opening when prying reaction internal gear.

3) End play should be .003-.046" (.08-1.17 mm). The selective washer controlling this end play is located between Low-Reverse clutch housing and low roller clutch assembly. Select proper thrust washer. See REVERSE CLUTCH HOUSING-TO-LOW RACE WASHER table.

4) Remove dial indicator, gauge and output shaft loading/aligning tool. Leave output shaft loader adapter in place for use when final drive-to-case end play is measured.

5) Remove reaction sun gear. Sun gear will lift straight out. Remove Low-Reverse clutch housing-to-case snap ring. Snap ring is .092" (2.36 mm) thick. Using Low-Reverse Clutch Housing Remover/Installer (J-28542), lift out Low-Reverse Clutch housing. See Fig. 21.

6) Remove Low-Reverse clutch housing-to-case spacer ring from groove in case. Spacer ring is .042" (1.07 mm) thick. Lift out final drive sun gear shaft and reaction gear set as an assembly.

7) Remove roller clutch and reaction carrier assembly off final drive sun gear shaft. Remove 4 tanged

REACTION SUN GEAR-TO-INPUT DRUM SNAP RING SELECTION

Thickness In. (mm)	Color Code
.089-.093 (2.27-2.36)	Pink
.096-.100 (2.44-2.54)	Brown
.103-.107 (2.61-2.71)	Lt. Blue
.109-.113 (2.78-2.88)	White
.116-.120 (2.95-3.05)	Yellow
.123-.127 (3.12-3.22)	Lt. Green
.129-.133 (3.29-3.39)	Orange
.136-.140 (3.46-3.56)	No Color

REVERSE CLUTCH HOUSING-TO-LOW RACE WASHER

Thickness In. (mm)	Identification Code
.039-.043 (1.00-2.20)	1
.056-.060 (1.42-1.52)	2
.072-.076 (1.84-1.94)	3
.089-.093 (2.26-2.36)	4
.105-.109 (2.68-2.78)	5
.122-.126 (3.10-3.20)	6

REACTION SUN GEAR-TO-INPUT DRUM SNAP RING SELECTION

Thickness In. (mm)	Color Code
.089-.093 (2.27-2.36)	Pink
.096-.100 (2.44-2.54)	Brown
.103-.107 (2.61-2.71)	Lt. Blue
.109-.113 (2.78-2.88)	White
.116-.120 (2.95-3.05)	Yellow
.123-.127 (3.12-3.22)	Lt. Green
.129-.133 (3.29-3.39)	Orange
.136-.140 (3.46-3.56)	No Color

REVERSE CLUTCH HOUSING-TO-LOW RACE WASHER

Thickness In. (mm)	Identification Code
.039-.043 (1.00-2.20)	1
.056-.060 (1.42-1.52)	2
.072-.076 (1.84-1.94)	3
.089-.093 (2.26-2.36)	4
.105-.109 (2.68-2.78)	5
.122-.126 (3.10-3.20)	6

FIGURE 16-9 Look for helpful guidelines, such as wear measurements during disassembly, as well as critical information, such as selective parts tables during reassembly.

and apply pin. Remove and discard all "O" ring seals. *See Fig. 35.*

Fig. 35: Exploded View of Intermediate Servo Assembly

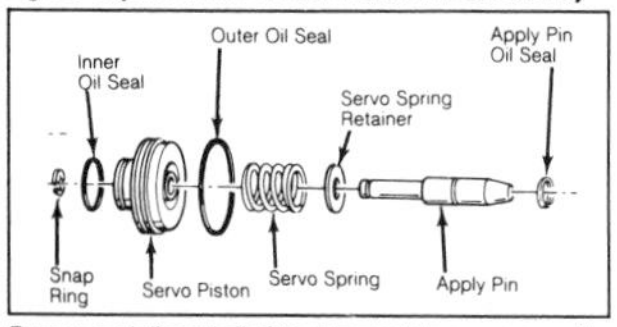
Outer Oil Seal
Apply Pin Oil Seal
Inner Oil Seal
Servo Spring Retainer
Snap Ring
Servo Piston
Servo Spring
Apply Pin

Remove and discard all of the intermediate servo assembly "O" ring seals whenever assembly is removed.

NOTE: If THM 125C transaxle (code BL, CE, CT or OP) is being serviced for 3-2 coast-down clunk condition, check for broken, cracked or damaged intermediate servo spring. If spring (White) needes replacement, be sure to use spring (Violet) with part No. 8652057.

2) Inspect all parts for damage, cracks, scoring and distortion. Check apply pin for free fit in bore. Check servo cover and piston assembly for porosity.

3) Reassemble servo using new inner and outer oil seals on piston and new seal on apply pin (proper apply pin size determined during disassembly).

GOVERNOR/SPEEDOMETER GEAR ASSEMBLY

Inspection

1) Check for plugged oil passage, wash in solvent and blow out oil passage. If necessary, remove speedometer drive gear from governor shaft and inspect gear for nicks or damage. Check governor cover for damage or distortion of mating surface. Remove and discard cover "O" ring.

2) Inspect governor driven gear for nicks or damage. Check governor shaft seal rings for cuts, damage and free fit in groove. Check for free operation of governor weights. The weights must operate freely and independent of each other. Check for damaged, mispositioned or tilted springs. *See Fig. 36.*

3) Inspect for presence of 2 check balls. Inspect governor shaft and thrust washer for damage. If seal ring is being replaced, ensure cut ends of seal are assembled in the same relationship as cut. *See Fig. 28.*

4) Install speedometer drive gear and thrust bearing assembly onto governor assembly. Install governor assembly into transaxle. Install governor cover with new "O" ring. Ensure governor shaft is piloted in cover before tightening retaining bolts. Install speedometer drive gear and retainer.

TRANSAXLE REASSEMBLY

NOTE: All selective snap ring and thrust washer measurements taken during disassembly should be rechecked at appropriate stage of reassembly. Follow procedures given in TRANSAXLE DISASSEMBLY.

Fig. 36: Sectional View of Governor Assembly

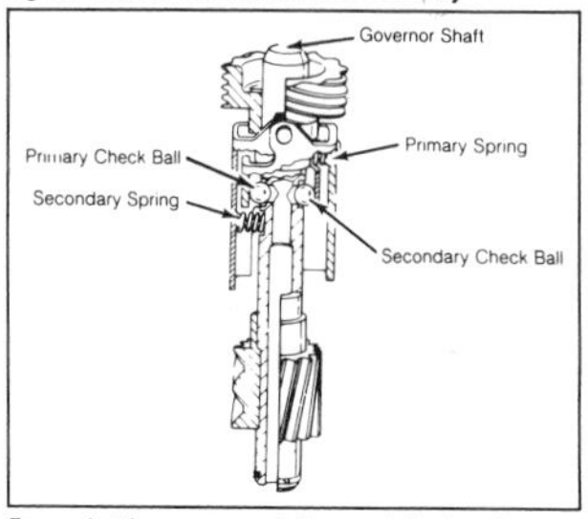
Governor Shaft
Primary Check Ball
Primary Spring
Secondary Spring
Secondary Check Ball

Ensure that the governor weights operate freely and are independent of each other.

1) Turn transaxle so case cover end is up. Install proper final drive-to-case thrust washer and thrust bearing assembly to final drive unit (inner race of bearing against selective washer). Install differential and final drive assembly into case.

2) Install final drive internal gear spacer (cupped side against final drive internal gear). Ensure opening in spacer aligns with parking pawl opening in case. Check to see that parking pawl passes through spacer freely.

3) Install final drive spacer-to-case snap ring with ring gap away from parking pawl opening in case. Install reaction sun gear set into case.

4) Install Low-Reverse clutch backing plate (stepped side down) into case, then install clutch plates, starting with a composition plate and alternating steel and composition plates until all plates are installed. See LOW-REVERSE CLUTCH PLATE USAGE table.

LOW-REVERSE CLUTCH PLATE USAGE

Application	Flat Steel	Composition
All Models	4	5

5) Install Low-Reverse clutch housing-to-case spacer ring. This case spacer ring is .042" (1.07 mm) thick. Install Low-Reverse clutch housing into transaxle case. Ensure clutch feed hole in case lines up with clutch feed hole.

6) Install proper selective snap ring onto reaction sun gear. Install reaction sun gear onto final drive sun gear shaft in transaxle. Rotate reaction sun gear while pushing down on the Low-Reverse clutch housing until clutch housing drops below snap ring groove in case.

7) Install Low-Reverse clutch housing-to-case snap ring. This snap ring is .092" (2.36 mm) thick. Install input drum onto reaction sun gear. Install input sun gear into input drum. Install input carrier-to-input sun gear tanged thrust washer to pinion side of carrier.

8) Install input carrier-to-input internal gear tanged thrust washer to internal gear side of carrier (input carrier-to-input internal gear thrust washer is larger of 2). Install input pinion carrier onto input sun gear.

9) Install input internal gear over input carrier. Place forward clutch assembly on bench with input shaft up. Install direct clutch assembly over input shaft onto the forward clutch housing.

10) When clutch housings are fully seated together, it should be about 1 7/32" (31 mm) from tang end of direct clutch housing to end of forward clutch housing drum. *See Fig. 38.*

Fig. 38: Measuring Forward Clutch-to-Direct Clutch Assembled Height

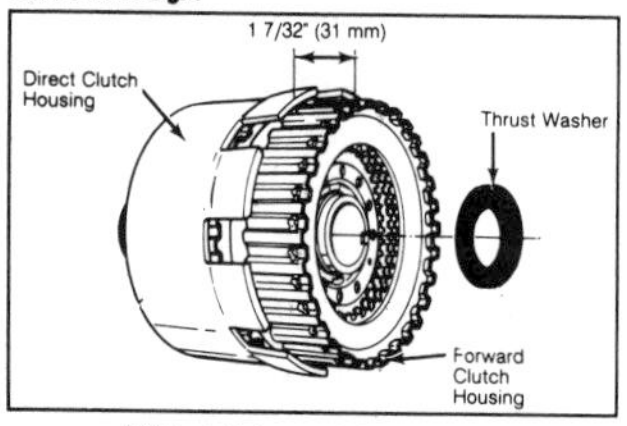
1 7/32" (31 mm)
Direct Clutch Housing
Thrust Washer
Forward Clutch Housing

11) Install input shaft-to-input internal gear thrust washer, with rounded side against input shaft and stepped side facing outward, onto forward and direct clutch assembly.

12) Install direct and forward clutch assemblies into case. Rotate clutch assemblies, without pushing down, until they drop into fully seated position in case. When correctly installed, case face-to-direct clutch housing measurement should be 1.688" (42 mm). *See Fig. 39.*

Fig. 39: Checking Installed Position of Direct & Forward Clutch Assemblies

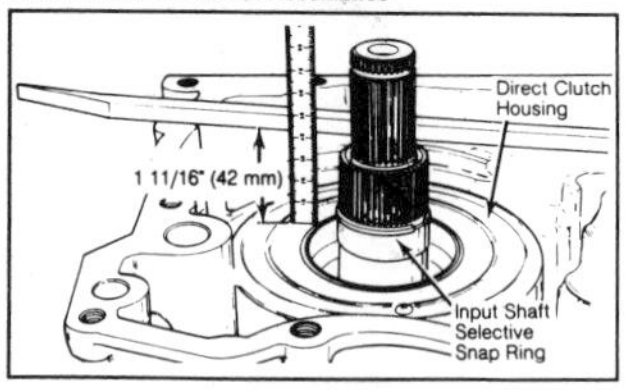
Direct Clutch Housing
1 11/16" (42 mm)
Input Shaft Selective Snap Ring

13) Install intermediate band, locating eye of band into case and aligning lugged end with apply pin bore. Install band anchor hole plug (use new design hole plug with securing tab attached).

14) Install driven sprocket support-to-direct clutch housing thrust washer. Install driven sprocket support. *See Fig. 19.*

NOTE: Manual shaft and detent lever assemblies are made as a matched set. Replacement of complete set is required if either part is damaged.

15) Install manual shaft and parking lock actuator rod into case through driven sprocket support. Install detent lever on manual shaft (hub side away from driven sprocket support) and push manual shaft in place.

16) Install detent lever-to-manual shaft retaining nail. Install manual shaft-to-case retaining pin. *See Fig. 19.*

Fig. 40: Case Cover Bolt Locations

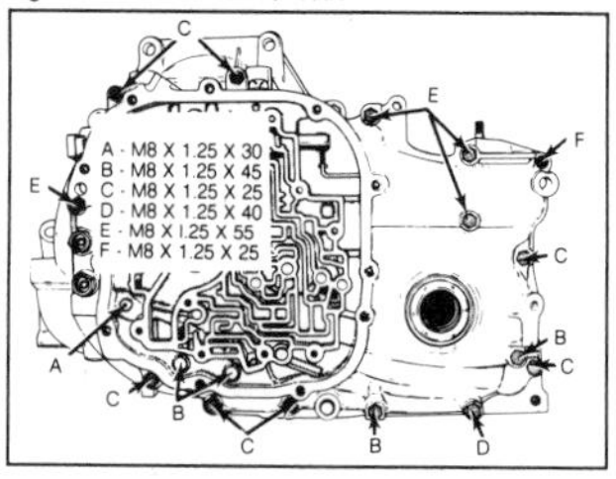
A - M8 X 1.25 X 30
B - M8 X 1.25 X 45
C - M8 X 1.25 X 25
D - M8 X 1.25 X 40
E - M8 X 1.25 X 55
F - M8 X 1.25 X 25

Fig. 41: View of Spacer Plate Showing Passage Location

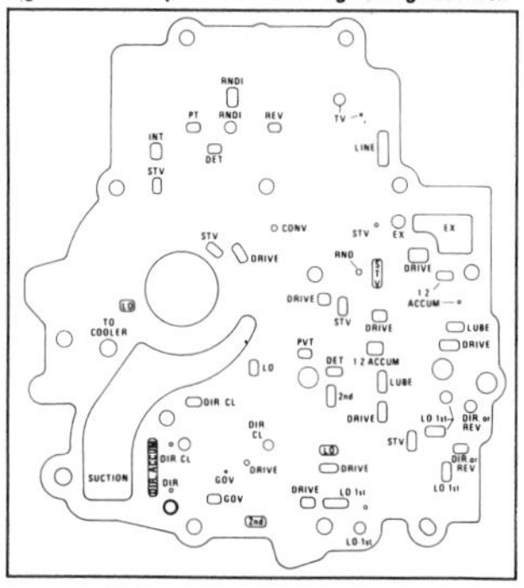

17) Assemble drive and driven sprockets with link assembly and install drive and driven thrust washers to sprockets. Install drive link assembly onto transaxle. The colored guide link, which has numerals, must face the case cover.

18) Install case cover-to-driven sprocket roller bearing thrust washer (outer race against sprocket). Install 1-2 accumulator piston. Install thermostatic spring if removed.

19) Install 1-2 accumulator spring in its bore in case. Install inner and outer case-to-cover gaskets and case cover. Install 2 case cover bolts from inside torque converter housing (M8 X 1.25 X 14 mm). Install remaining case cover bolts using *Fig. 40* as a guide.

20) Connect manual valve rod to manual valve. Using *Fig 16* as a guide, install No. 2 check ball into direct clutch accumulator passage, No. 3 check ball in circular Low-First passage, No. 4 check ball in Low-Reverse slot and No. 5 check ball in direct clutch passage in case cover.

21) Install case cover-to-spacer plate gasket and spacer plate. Install spacer plate-to-control valve gasket. Install No. 1 check ball on direct clutch passage on spacer plate. Install oil pump shaft into its bore in case cover.

22) Install two 6 mm guide pins (M6 X 1.0 X 75 mm) in case cover-to-valve body bolt holes. These will aid in positioning valve body down onto case cover.

23) Install control valve body with bolts and tighten. Install valve body wiring harness as shown in *Figs. 43 and 44*. Connect lever link to T.V. bracket. Install T.V. bracket onto valve body.

Fig. 42: Control Valve Body Bolt Locations

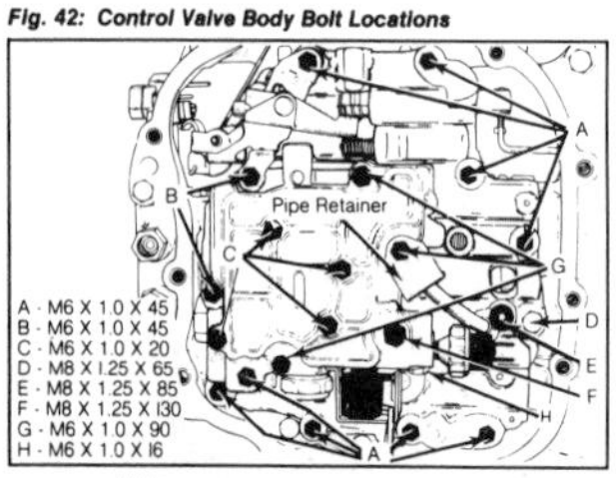
Pipe Retainer
A - M6 X 1.0 X 45
B - M6 X 1.0 X 45
C - M6 X 1.0 X 20
D - M8 X 1.25 X 65
E - M8 X 1.25 X 85
F - M8 X 1.25 X 130
G - M6 X 1.0 X 90
H - M6 X 1.0 X 16

24) Remove guide bolts used to install valve body and install remaining 2 valve body bolts. Thoroughly clean valve body cover and install using new gasket.

25) Turn transaxle so oil pan side is up. Install output shaft into transaxle. Rotate final drive so retaining ring groove is visible through access window in case. Install new retaining ring onto shaft groove.

26) Install parking lock bracket and dipstick stop. Using a 3/8" drift, install new Low-Reverse oil pipe seal assembly. Install "O" ring back-up washer and "O" ring seal onto end of Low-Reverse pipe. Install pipe, plain end in first, then "O" ring end. Install retainer bracket.

27) Install intermediate servo piston assembly. Install third accumulator check valve and spring into check valve bore next to servo piston. Install intermediate servo cover and 3 bolts.

28) Install reverse oil pipe bracket to oil pipe and servo cover. Install remaining servo cover bolt through bracket and cover. Tighten servo cover bolts.

Fig. 43: Wiring Harness Connections For Vehicles Equipped With Gasoline Engine

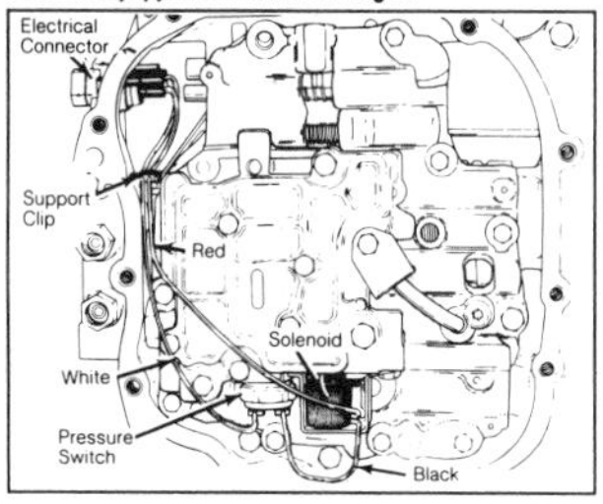
Electrical Connector
Support Clip
Red
Solenoid
White
Pressure Switch
Black

Fig. 44: Wiring Harness Connections For Vehicles Equipped With Diesel Engine

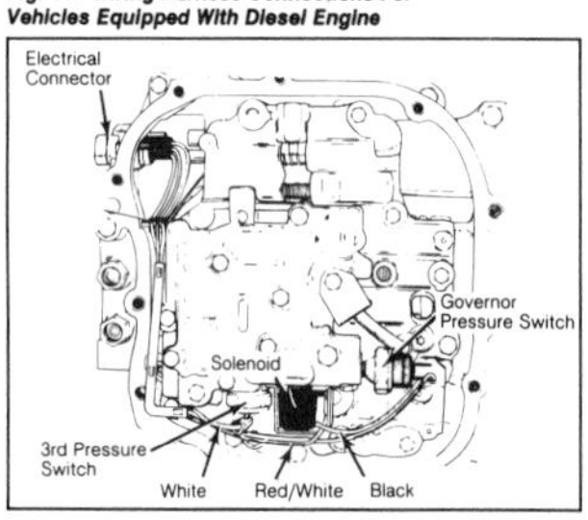
Electrical Connector
Governor Pressure Switch
Solenoid
3rd Pressure Switch
White
Red/White
Black

NOTE: If transaxle was equipped with a third accumulator check valve cup plug, and plug was removed, DO NOT install a new plug or old servo cover. Replace servo cover and gasket with replacement version. Replacement version has cast lug to take place of cup plug.

29) Install new oil strainer and "O" ring. Install oil pan gasket and oil pan. Rotate transaxle so oil pan side is down. Install governor assembly. Install new "O" ring to governor cover and install cover onto case. Install speedometer driven gear assembly into governor cover.

NOTE: Ensure governor shaft is piloted in governor cover before tightening cover bolts.

30) Install torque converter. Converter is properly installed if the distance is .50" (13 mm) minimum between engine mount face of case and front face of converter cover lugs.

TIGHTENING SPECIFICATIONS

Application	Ft. Lbs. (N.m.)
Case Cover-to-Case	18 (24)
Case-to-Drive Sprocket Support	18 (24)
Drive Axle Hub Nut [1]	
Initial Tightening Torque	70 (100)
Final Tightening Torque	185-225 (250-305)
Flywheel-to-Torque Converter Bolt	41-52 (55-70)
Oil Pan & Valve Body Cover	12 (16)
Parking Lock Bracket-to-Case	18 (24)
Pipe Retainer-to-Case	18 (24)
Pump Cover-to-Case Cover	18 (24)
Valve Body-to-Case	18 (24)
Valve Body-to-Driven	
Sprocket Support	18 (24)
	INCH Lbs.
Auxiliary Valve Body	96 (11)
Cooler Connector	96 (11)
Governor Cover-to-Case	96 (11)
Intermediate Servo Cover	96 (11)
Line Pressure Take-Off	96 (11)
Manual Detent	
Spring-to-Case	96 (11)
Pressure Switch	96 (11)
Pump Cover-to-Valve Body	96 (11)
Solenoid-to-Valve Body	96 (11)
T.V. Cable-to-Case	72 (9)
Valve Body-to-Case Cover	96 (11)

[1] – Discard hub nut whenever it is removed and use only a new hub nut during installation.

FIGURE 16-10 Reassembly sequence and torque specifications.

Latest Changes & Corrections

FOR 1985 & EARLIER DOMESTIC MODELS

NOTE: The Latest Changes and Corrections represent a collection of the last minute 1985 information which arrived too late to be included into the regular data pages. In addition, we have included information on prior year models which we have received since last year's edition.

This information is numbered to assist you in relating them to the regular data pages. To correctly use them, simply write the corresponding number within the small box and the year of the edition on the appropriate page(s) of the text.

AUTOMATIC TRANSMISSIONS

AMC/RENAULT

[1] *1984 MB1 AUTOMATIC TRANSAXLE: INCORRECT TESTING PROCEDURE* – In the 1984 edition of Mitchell's TRANSMISSION SERVICE & REPAIR MANUAL, the MB1 automatic transaxle testing procedure should be corrected. Under ELECTRONIC CONTROL COMPONENT TESTING (6-Way Connector), step **2)** should read:

2) Connect voltmeter between terminal "A" and ground. With ignition "ON", voltage should be 10-14 volts. If not, check back-up light fuse and accessory plate wiring. Repair as needed.

CHRYSLER CORP.

[2] *1984 ARIES, E-CLASS, LEBARON, NEW YORKER, RELIANT AND 600 MODELS WITH 2.6L ENGINE AND A-470 TRANSAXLE: GRINDING NOISE AND/OR FAILURE OF FRONT PUMP AND TORQUE CONVERTER* – Some Chrysler products with 2.6L engine and A-470 transaxle may exhibit a grinding noise and/or failure of the front pump and torque converter. This condition may be caused by an undersized torque converter-to-crankshaft adapter. A new adapter (MD024893) is available to correct this condition. To diagnose and repair this problem, proceed as follows:

1) Remove the transaxle and torque converter. Measure the inside diameter of torque converter-to-crankshaft adapter. The inside diameter should not be smaller than 1.34" (34 mm). Inspect the torque converter pilot for wear. Disassemble the front pump and inspect for worn pump gears.

2) Replace the adapter with a new adapter if less than the minimum size. Replace the torque converter or front pump if necessary.

[3] *1983-84 ARIES, CARAVAN, "E" CLASS, LEBARON, MINI RAM VAN, NEW YORKER, RELIANT, VOYAGER, 400 AND 600 WITH AUTOMATIC TRANSAXLE: NO MANUAL 1ST GEAR OPERATION* – These Chrysler products with a column shift may not have 1st gear operation due to a misadjusted gear selector cable. Condition may diagnosed and repaired as follows:

1) Place gear selector in "DRIVE 1" position. Accelerate vehicle to about 45 MPH. If transaxle shifts from 1st to 2nd gear, readjust selector cable.

2) Loosen the cable housing clamp. Grasp the cable housing and move it to rear 1/8". Retighten cable housing clamp.

FORD MOTOR CO.

[4] *1980-84 FORD AOD TRANSMISSIONS: 2-3 MODULATOR VALVE ASSEMBLY* – Due to an error in the factory service manual, the exploded view of the valve body in the 1980 through 1984 editions of Mitchell's TRANSMISSION SERVICE & REPAIR manual are incor-

rect. The 2-3 modulator valve and spring positions are reversed. The modulator spring should be installed in the valve body BEFORE the modulator valve. The illustration has been corrected for the 1985 edition.

[5] *1981-83 ESCORT, EXP, LYNX AND LN7 WITH ATX TRANSAXLES: REVISED CLUTCH SNAP RING* – Selective retainer snap rings are no longer required for the reverse clutch assembly. During overhaul or other service procedures, use the revised retainer snap ring (E1FFZ-7D483-G). When assembling the clutch pack, install the reverse clutch return spring and holder assembly. Install the clutch wave spring, clutch pack, pressure plate and REVISED retaining snap ring.

[6] *1981-84 ESCORT, EXP, LYNX, LN7, TEMPO AND TOPAZ WITH ATX TRANSAXLES: NEW FINAL GEAR HOUSING BOLTS* – When servicing 1981-84 Ford products with the ATX transaxle, always use new revised final gear housing bolts. The new design bolts (E4FZ-7A291-A) are now available. These bolts are coated with a high strength thread adhesive. Always use new bolts when servicing the final gear housing.

[7] *1981-84 ESCORT, LINX, EXP, LYNX, LN7, TEMPO AND TOPAZ WITH ATX TRANSAXLE: REVISED DIRECT CLUTCH SEALS* – Revised direct clutch seals are available for 1981-84 ATX automatic transaxles. The new design inner seal (E55FZ-7A548-A) and outer seal (E55FZ-7C099-A) may be identified by a short lip as shown in illustration.

1981-84 Ford ATX Transaxle Direct Clutch Seals

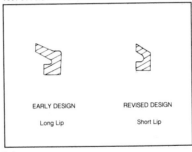

EARLY DESIGN   REVISED DESIGN

Long Lip   Short Lip

[8] *1983-84 FORD CAPRI, COUGAR, LTD, MARQUIS, MUSTANG AND THUNDERBIRD WITH C-5 TRANSMISSION: SENSITIVE 3-2 DOWNSHIFT* – Some Ford C-5 transmissions in 1983-84 may exhibit a sensitive 3-2 downshift. This condition may be caused by the throttle

FIGURE 16-11 Special section showing recent modifications and specification changes.

ESSAY QUESTIONS

16-1. Describe an automotive trade magazine or consumer magazine that you would like to subscribe to, or read regularly, and why.

16-2. Discuss the major elements of written material (e.g., books and manuals) and how you use them.

CHAPTER ACTIVITIES

16-1. Go to your school or public library and look at the shelves containing books with library reference numbers in the 629.2 group. A great deal of valuable and interesting information on specific motor vehicles and automotive technology is located there.

16-2. Familiarize yourself with the manuals available to you in your shop class by surveying the tables of contents and other elements in the fronts of the books.

Glossary

Accumulator A hydraulic device similar to a servo, but whose function is to cushion the application of pressure by acting against a spring or restricted flow or both.

Aftermarket A term referring to any product, service, process, etc., produced and marketed by manufacturers independent of vehicle manufacturers (OEMs).

Altitude compensating vacuum valve A vacuum operated valve equipped with a vacuum sealed bellows that expands as ambient pressure decreases with increasing altitude.

Analog A device that has a continuous physical output in direct proportion to input (typically, voltage, resistance, rotation, etc.), that is, one that measures. *See also* digital.

Annulus gear A gear with internal teeth; the largest gear in a planetary gearset (ring gear).

Apply pressure Jargon identifying hydraulic pressure that activates rather than deactivates, or releases.

ATF Automatic transmission fluid.

Atmosphere *See* One atmosphere.

Automatic Acting without manual assistance; self-acting.

Axial Of or pertaining to anything extending perpendicular to the plane of rotation.

Axis A point or line locating the center of a rotating element.

Backlash The amount of clearance between meshing gear teeth.

Balanced valve One in which control is achieved by opposing hydraulic pressures.

Ball and trunnion A universal joint configuration.

Bellcrank A lever whose ends form an angle to its fulcrum point, causing the direction of mechanical force to be modified.

Bevel gears Gears cut so their axes are at an angle to each other.

Black light Ultraviolet or infrared.

Branching diagram A number of instructions or descriptions (usually boxed) arranged in logical or natural sequence, each resulting in a conclusion, some of which offer alternative ensuing steps (branching).

Brinelled Archaic jargon for a condition of metal heat damage (hardening). (Coined from the Brinnel scale, which establishes a numerical system for indicating the relative hardness of metals, alloys, and other solids.) *Damage* is just as good a term.

Bushing A one-piece replaceable cylinder that provides a bearing surface for rotating parts.

Cage The part of a bearing that helps to position rollers or balls.

Cam A mechanical configuration whose interior or exterior surface perimeter varies in distance from the center of rotation. When made to bear against a rod, or cam follower, it can create reciprocating motion characterized by the particular design of the cam itself.

CCC Computer Command Control (developed by General Motors and introduced in mid-1980s).

CCW Counterclockwise.

CEC Computerized Engine Control.

Centrifugal clutch One that is designed to be applied by centrifugal force.

Circumference The distance around a circle.

Closed loop Computer operating under programmed instructions coupled with variable input from feedback devices (sensors). *See also* open loop.

Compound planetary gearset Two planetary gearsets sharing a common member, or with one member of one connected to one member of the other (e.g., Simpson: common sun gear; Ravigneaux: common ring gear).

Compression strength A material's resistance to crushing or collapsing under equal and opposite forces.

Conservation of energy A term summarizing the fact that energy cannot be created or destroyed.

Constant mesh Gears that are permanently meshed and cannot be disengaged by sliding apart (e.g., planetary gears).

Continuity test Applying current with a meter or a battery and test light to determine whether a circuit or conductor is broken (discontinuous) or intact (continuous).

Counterbalance An equal but opposing force to one that tends to cause rotation about an axis.

Counter gears What some foreign manufacturers call transfer gears.

Coupling phase When input speed (impeller) and output speed (turbine) of a fluid coupling are equal, or very nearly so.

Crocus cloth An extremely fine abrasive cloth coated with iron oxide and used for polishing machine-finished metal, such as bearing journals, cams, etc.

Cross and yoke A universal joint configuration.

Cup The external race of a tapered roller or ball bearing.

CW Clockwise.

Damper A device that tends to absorb vibrations caused by rotary or reciprocal motion.

Detent valve Spool valve in the "kickdown" or "passing gear" circuit.

Dexron IID A brand of ATF made primarily for transmissions used in some General Motors vehicles.

DFI Digital fuel injection.

Diagnosis The process of examining a problem (symptoms, evidence, etc.) and reaching a conclusion.

Differential A gearset that permits power to be transferred to two axle shafts independent of their relative speed.

Digital A Device that has a discrete (discontinuous) output in direct proportion to input (typically frequency, amplitude, polarity, etc.) that is, one that counts and displays in numbers, signs, symbols. *See also* Analog.

Diode An electronic resistor (allows current to pass more easily in one direction than the other).

Direct drive The path of power flow through a transmission that produces no reduction or overdrive (input = output).

Double cardan A universal joint configuration.

Dynamic A state of motion.

Dynamic torque Force applied to or produced by a rotating element.

ECA Electronic Control Assembly (same as ECU).

Eccentric A device that turns off-center, *See also* Cam.

ECM Engine Control Module.

ECT Electronically Controlled Transmission (or Transaxle).

EEC Electronic Engine Control.

EFI Electronic fuel injection.

Electrolysis Metallic displacement or etching from electrical current.

Electromechanical A process or device that utilizes both electric and mechanical forms of energy.

Element (1) In physics and chemistry: any of a number of fundamental substances composed of one or more identical atoms; (2) a general term used to describe a whole or part thereof.

Final Drive The last gear reduction in an automotive power train.

Flare-up Jargon identifying sudden increasing engine rpm because of slipping friction elements in the drive train; usually occurs between shifts.

Flex plate A thin (approximately 1/8in.) metal plate connecting crank-shaft to torque converter.

Fluid Coupling A term used to describe the principle of driving one rotating element with another using a fluid medium.

Foot-pound (1)An expression of a unit of work; (2) an expression of a unit of torque as might be applied with a torque wrench; another is inch-pound.

Force Directed energy.

Free wheeling A condition by design or malfunction that allows the driven element (e.g., rear wheels) to overrun the drive element (e.g., engine); the absence of "engine braking" on deceleration.

Fulcrum A support between the ends of a lever around which the lever will rotate if the force on one side of the support is greater than on the other.

FWD Front-wheel drive.

Full-time 4WD Operable on any surface, hence *full-time*, by incorporating a coupling of clutches in a silicone-fluid-filled housing to prevent wind-up between front and rear drive axles.

Gearset Two or more gears that mesh.

Governor A regulating device that makes use of centrifugal force.

Grounding Locking a rotating element to its case or housing, rather than to another rotating device, so that it cannot rotate.

Helical gears Gears with teeth cut at an angle to the gear's axis.

Hotchkiss drive An exposed, hollow tube drive shaft with universal joints at both ends.

Hypoid A bevel gearset with teeth cut to allow both gears to turn on perpendicular but nonintersecting axes.

Idler gear A gear whose primary purpose is to change direction.

Impeller The driving element of a fluid coupling.

Integrated circuit One or more semiconductor chips, each of which contain all the active and passive elements of an electronic circuit, packaged with pronged terminals permitting connection to an electronic device.

ISC Idle speed control.

Limited slip differential One containing differential clutches to provide some power to both axles during traction loss.

Master cylinder An input mechanism for a hydraulic circuit.

Matter A general term for anything that occupies space and has mass (weight).

MCU Micro Computer Unit (AM); Microprocessor Control Unit (Ford).

Mechanical advantage A term used to describe the gain in effective force when active input is less than output.

Mesh The meeting of teeth on two matching gears.

Mopar 7176 A brand of ATF made primarily for transmissions used in some Chrysler vehicles.

Needle A roller in a small roller bearing (needle bearing).

Neutral switch Controlled by the transmission selector lever to allow the engine to be started only in neutral.

Nomenclature A method or system of naming.

OEM Original equipment manufacturer.

One atmosphere Pressure exerted by the mass (weight) of air at sea level (14.7 lb/in.^{2} or 29.6 in. Hg).

One-way clutch A device that allows rotation in one direction only; overrunning clutch; roller clutch.

Open loop Computer operating under totally preprogrammed instruction only (no external variables). *See also* Closed loop.

Orifice A restriction to fluid flow on one side of which pressure will be higher than on the other (as long as fluid is flowing).

Overdrive The condition produced by a gearset in which input speed is less than output speed.

Overrunning clutch *See* One-way clutch.

Part-time 4WD Because of a rigid coupling between front and rear drive axles, it is operable only on surfaces permitting slippage to prevent wind-up.

PCV Positive crankcase ventilation.

Perpendicular A position described by one line meeting or crossing another at a right (90°) angle.

Pinion The smaller, usually significantly smaller, gear in a gearset.

Planet carrier The framelike element of a planetary gearset that holds two, three, or four pinion gears turning on their own axes and meshing simultaneously with the sun and annulus gears.

Planetary gears An assembly of gears consisting of an external gear (sun gear) concentric with an internal gear (ring or annulus gear) both of which mesh with two, three, or four pinion gears (planetary gears) mounted on individual, but parallel axes positioned by a frame (carrier).

Ported vacuum Vacuum tapped from *between* the carburetor venturi and the throttle valve. It is not available at closed throttle (idle).

Potentiometer A variable resistor that varies voltage in proportion to mechanical input.

Preload The adjustment of tightness applied to the installation of a tapered roller or ball bearing.

Press fit A general term indicating that more than manual pressure is required to fit one part inside another.

Pressure Fluid force.

Pressure line That point of contact between meshing gear teeth.

Pressure test Applying pressure to a hydraulic system and (1) visually checking for leaks, (2) observing any drop in pressure gauge reading, indicating leakage, and (3) measuring specified pressure with a pressure gauge.

Pulse relay An electronically controlled device that causes a locked-up torque converter to release during gear changes.

Race The internal or external ring of a bearing between which are located rollers or balls.

Rack A straight bar containing gear teeth over which a matching pinion runs (rack and pinion gearset).

Radial Of or pertaining to anything extending between the center and perimeter of a circle.

Radius Distance from the center to the circumference of a circle.

RAM Random access memory.

Reaction member Specifically that member of a planetary gearset that is being held.

Reduction The condition produced by a gearset in which input speed exceeds output speed.

Ring and pinion Usually the gearset associated with a bevel-gear final drive.

Ring seal A precisely made ring similar to a piston ring, used to seal between two rotating parts (usually cast iron, but also nylon or Teflon).

R.N.D. Reverse–neutral–drive. Abbreviation used to identify part of the hydraulic circuit in the valve body used in each of those selector positions.

Roller clutch *See* One-way clutch.

ROM Read-only memory.

Rotary flow Circular flow characterized by a torque converter operating in coupling phase.

Rotary pump A general term describing gear, rotor, and vane, or turbine pump as opposed to reciprocating pumps.

RTV rubber Room-temperature vulcanizing rubber.

RWD Rear-wheel drive.

S.A.E. Society of Automotive Engineers.

Select pattern switch Permits one or more alternate shift speed patterns to be used.

Self-energizing band A brake band designed so that the application force is in the direction of rotation rather than against it.

Semiconductor A solid, crystalline substance (e.g., germanium or silicon) having an electrical conducting capability lying somewhere between the capability of a good conductor and a good insulator. The basic element in electronics.

Separator plate A thin sheet of steel having orifices and other openings to direct the flow of hydraulic fluid between the two halves of the valve body.

Servo A hydromechanical device that converts hydraulic force to mechanical force.

Shear strength A material's resistance to dividing from adjacent forces applied in opposite directions.

Shift recalibration A change in shift timing and quality through hydromechanical modifications.

Side gears Beveled gears splined to the axle shafts and meshing with the spider gears in a differential.

Single-wrap band A simple brake band design that wraps once around a rotating element.

Slave cylinder An output mechanism for a hydraulic circuit (e.g., wheel cylinder).

Solenoid An electromechanical device that converts electrical energy into mechanical force.

Spider gears A beveled form of idler gear turning on a shaft mounted in the differential housing and which meshes with the side (axle) gears.

Spline Long external teeth on a shaft or long internal teeth on a receiving element that make a strong, positive connection when the two are mated.

Split torque Two input (or output) paths. *See also* Splitter gear.

Splitter gear A term applied to a planetary gearset used in conjunction with a torque converter to share or split torque mechanically and hydraulically.

Spool valve A valve design used in automatic transmission hydraulic circuits so named because of its spool-like appearance.

Sprag clutch A one-way clutch incorporating dogbone-shaped elements (sprags), instead of a roller/cam design, to allow rotation in one direction only.

Spur gear Gears with teeth cut parallel to the gear's axis.

Standard pressure One atmosphere (14.7 lb/in.^{2} or 1 N/M^2).

Standard temperature Melting point of ice (32°F or 0°C).

Static A state of rest.

Static torque Force applied to or produced by a grounded rotatable element.

Stator The element of a torque converter that serves to redirect vortex flow for torque multiplication.

Step-down gears What some foreign manufacturers call transfer gears.

Sump An unpressurized chamber at the lowest point in a hydraulic system serving as a reservoir from which oil is drawn and pumped through a closed system and back into which oil is exhausted.

Symptom The result of a cause; a secondary problem resulting from a primary failure or malfunction.

TCC Torque Converter Clutch.

Tensile strength A material's resistance to stretching.

Thermactor Ford's name for its air injection system.

Thermistor An electronic sensor whose resistance changes with temperature.

Third member A somewhat outdated term to identify the final drive/differential assembly in RWD vehicles. (The engine and transmission being the "first" and "second" members—although never referred to as such.)

Throttle position sensor *See* Potentiometer.

Thrust washer Acts as a bearing surface for axial loads (sometimes of selective thickness).

TIG weld Tungsten inert gas welding; used to join highly alloyed materials.

Tooth flank The tooth surfaces that bear against each other when meshing.

Torque A term used to describe a twisting force; it is a product of radial distance and tangent force.

Torque Converter A fluid coupling designed with a stator between the impeller and turbine to redirect vortex flow for torque multiplication.

Torque tube A drive shaft housing between transmission and final drive.

Torsional strength A material's resistance to twisting.

Torus A doughnut-shaped configuration. A cross section cut perpendicular to the axis shows two concentric circles; one cut parallel to and directly through the axis shows two circles connected by two straight, parallel tangent lines.

Transaxle An automotive mechanism that includes both the transmission and final drive in the same housing and whose rotating axes are parallel to those of engine and wheels.

Transducer A device that converts the form of power going from one system to another.

Transfer case A housing between transmission and front and rear final drive containing a gearset for front drive axle engagement and disengagement and often augmenting the transmission by including low and high range gearing as well.

Transistor An electronic switch or amplifier having three terminals—one common to both input and output; the current between one pair of terminals controls the current between the other pair.

Transmission A mechanism that can change speed and direction of rotation; one of four major assemblies in an automotive drive train; the others being engine, final drive and drive wheels.

Trunnion A short pin or peg which serves as a center or bearing for rotation.

Turbine The driven element of a fluid coupling.

Turbulent flow Rough fluid flow.

T.V. Throttle valve.

Type H ATF made primarily for transmissions used in some Ford vehicles.

Vacuum modulator A mechanical device that responds to engine vacuum, controlling the automatic transmission throttle valve accordingly.

Viscous silicone fluid Used in differential couplings, or limited slip applications because its properties are such that it does not thin out when subjected to heat or high shear forces.

VMV Vacuum modulator valve.

Vortex flow   A circular flow of fluid from impeller through turbine and back as might be observed through a torus cross section.

VOTM   Vacuum-operated throttle modulator.

VSS   Vehicle Speed Sensor.

"Wet" clutch   One designed to operate in fluid such as ATF, rather than dry as in most manual transmission applications.

Windup   Jargon expressing the torsional strain set up in a shaft or power train due to metal elasticity.

Work   The amount of force multiplied by the distance over which the force is applied.

W.O.T.   Wide-open throttle.

Index